ABY-8287

REFRIGERATION

REFRIGERATION

INCLUDING HOUSEHOLD AUTOMATIC REFRIGERATING MACHINES

BY

JAMES A. MOYER, S.B., A.M., Mem. A.S.M.E.

*State Director of University Extension in Massachusetts, Member of Federal
Commission on Radio Education; formerly Junior Professor of Mechanical
Engineering, University of Michigan, Professor in charge of the
Mechanical Engineering Department, Pennsylvania State College,
and Director of Pennsylvania Engineering Experiment
Station*

AND

RAYMOND U. FITTZ, S.B., Mem. A.S.R.E.

Assistant Professor of Mechanical Engineering, Tufts College

FIRST EDITION
FOURTH IMPRESSION

McGRAW-HILL BOOK COMPANY, INC.

NEW YORK AND LONDON

1928

THE MAPLE PRESS COMPANY, YORK, PA.

PREFACE

Refrigeration has come to be an industry of large proportions, and there is a constantly increasing demand for adequate refrigerated storage facilities. The subject is now of great importance not only to operating and designing engineers who have to do with refrigerating plants but also to those who have made a business of the installation and servicing of household refrigerating equipment.

There is an increasing demand for mechanical refrigerating devices which are suitably applicable and safe for producing refrigeration on a small scale in private houses, single apartments, small hotels, restaurants, and stores.

The sphere of usefulness of refrigeration by mechanical means is constantly expanding, and the number of refrigerating machines manufactured is every year larger than in the preceding one. Doubtless, in the near future, practically every house in suburban and urban districts either will be supplied with artificial ice manufactured in large refrigerating plants or will depend for food preservation on refrigerating equipment which is all but completely self-servicing.

Modern refrigeration, which includes practical methods of ice making in a refrigerating plant and of direct cooling without ice, is a comparatively recent development. In the last three-quarters of a century, this industry has expanded to such an extent and our dependence on it has become so complete that our present-day system of freight transportation and of ocean commerce in perishable foods could not exist without it. The feeding of cities, even the avoidance of famine, depends on the facilities for shipping over long distance and for storing in good condition the products of one season for consumption at other times of the year.

Refrigeration is a field which is far from being overcrowded by competent men, and, unquestionably, there are now more new applications of the principles of refrigeration than at any time in the past. There is a new application of the absorption system, for example, in the recently developed gas-heated household refrigerating units.

Unusual features of this book are the data and complete calculations of a commercial test of 15-ton compression refrigerating plant. The index has been prepared carefully and completely so that it may be useful for reference, and that this text-book may also be valuable as an engineers' handbook of information on refrigeration.

To facilitate the rapid correction of problems, the complete solution of those in the Appendix may be obtained from the authors upon application.

Representatives of the refrigeration industry have cooperated in many ways in the preparation of this volume by supplying data and by giving valuable suggestions. In this connection, the authors want to mention especially Messrs. Thomas and Raymond T. Shipley, York Manufacturing Company; Mr. G. E. Wallis, Creamery Package Manufacturing Company; Mr. N. H. Hiller, Carbondale Machine Company; Mr W. H. Carrier, Carrier Engineering Corporation, and Mr. M. J. Nusin, Ingersoll-Rand Company. Mr. John F. Wostrel, Massachusetts Division of University Extension, has contributed many valuable services.

THE AUTHORS.

BOSTON, MASS.
November, 1928.

CONTENTS

REFRIGERATION

CHAPTER I

REFRIGERATION METHODS

Refrigeration, in engineering practice, is a process of removing heat from an enclosed space which is to be maintained at a colder temperature than its surroundings. The idea that refrigeration is a heat-removing process may be more easily understood when one perceives that coldness is really a relative term and that things are hot or cold only as they differ from our everyday experiences. Some degree of heat is, of course, present in all substances at ordinary temperatures.

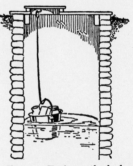

Fig. 1.—Early method of refrigeration.

The earliest method of refrigeration was the cooling of water in *porous* earthenware vessels. By this device, the temperature of the water in the vessel is lowered by the rapid evaporation of the "sweat" which gathers on the surface of the container. In countries where the air is unusually warm and dry, this method can be used with some success. Another mode of cooling which is probably just as old as the evaporative method is to put food and water into a cave or into a stream of flowing water in a place sheltered from the sun. In nearly all countries, there are natural or artificial caves, cellars, and wells (Fig. 1) in which a temperature between 50 and 60° F. may be maintained even in warm weather.

Ice-box Refrigeration.—The ice box did not come into genera use until early in the nineteenth century. Refrigeration is produced in an ice box by the melting of ice in the compartment *A*, as shown in Fig. 2. When the ice melts, a circulation of cold air, as indicated by arrows, is produced in the enclosure, which

1

keeps foods and liquids cool.   For many years, ice-box refrigerators were supplied exclusively with natural ice, that is, with ice
which is cut during the winter from the surface of ponds, lakes, or
rivers and stored for summer use in buildings called *ice houses.*
Natural ice for refrigeration was probably first used in an American home in 1802.   A few years later, a shipload of natural ice
was sent from Boston to the West Indies.   At present, the
annual harvest of natural ice in the United States amounts to
about 15,000,000 tons which, added to 45,000,000 tons of manu-

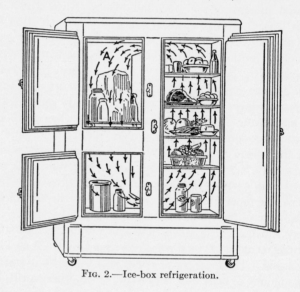

Fig. 2.—Ice-box refrigeration.

factured ice, makes the total yearly consumption of ice about
60,000,000 tons.

Heat at Refrigerating Temperatures.—Heat in some amount is
present in all substances at ordinary temperatures.   It is obvious,
of course, that as the temperature of a substance is reduced, there
is less heat in it and that with a progressive lowering of temperature, there is always a reduction in the amount of heat down to
the absolute zero of temperature, which on the Fahrenheit
thermometer is 460° below zero.   It has been the experience of
those in charge of refrigerating plants that for the proper preservation of food the temperature in the refrigerator should, as a
rule, be not much higher than 40° F. that is, 460 + 40 or 500° F.
above absolute zero.   Thus, there is necessarily a great deal of

heat in the walls, the shelves, the air, and the stored foods in a refrigerator with reference to the absolute zero of temperature; this amount of heat is, in fact, so large that it is possible to boil inside the refrigerator some liquids which have low boiling points, as, for example, liquified gases and vapors such as liquid air, liquid carbon dioxide, liquid sulphur dioxide, and liquid methyl chloride.

Solids, Liquids, Vapors, and Gases.—It was stated in the preceding paragraph that refrigeration is a method of taking away heat from substances and enclosed spaces. In a study of this subject, it is, therefore, necessary to give some attention to the nature of heat. The accepted theory is that heat springs from the energy of motion of the molecules of which all forms of matter are supposed to be composed. The molecules are in constant motion but are attracted and held together by a force similar to magnetism, which is, however, effective at only short distances. Thus, a substance is said to be *hot*, or *heated*, when its molecules are stirred by some force into violent motion and tend to be driven apart from one another and to be cold when the molecules are relatively inactive and close together. When all heat is removed from a substance so that its temperature is at the absolute zero, the molecules are stationary so that there is, of course, no possibility of the further removal of heat.[1]

Every substance at a given time exists in one of four states or conditions, that is, (1) as a solid, (2) as a liquid, (3) as a vapor, (4) as a gas. These states or conditions differ from each other by the amount of heat that is present, or, in other words, by the amount of movement of the molecules and by the distance between them. In a solid, for example, the molecules are relatively close together, and their movement is consequently so restricted that the substance preserves a definite shape. In a liquid, the molecules are farther apart and have freer movement than in a solid. In a vapor or a gas, the molecular distances and rates of movement are still more increased. In a solid and in a liquid, the molecules tend to hang together, while in a vapor or gas, the molecules tend to get as far apart as possible. Briefly,

[1] By the use of a very carefully constructed refrigerating machine, the investigators at the U. S. Bureau of Standards were able to remove practically all the heat from liquified hydrogen so that a small portion of it was actually frozen, indicating that the absolute zero of temperature had been nearly reached.

then, it may be stated that all forms of matter exist as solid, liquid, vapor, or gas, according to the amount of heat contained.

Refrigerating Processes.—All refrigerating *processes* depend upon the use of a substance which is readily convertible from a liquid into a vapor, or gas, and also from the vapor or gas into the liquid; and further, these changes must be accomplished within a reasonably narrow range of pressures.

A liquid which boils at a lower temperature than usually prevails inside a refrigerator has the principal requisite for a *refrigerant*, namely, the fluid used as a cooling agent in refrigeration. A small quantity of a liquid refrigerant in a refrigerator, when it boils,[1] will absorb a large amount of heat, which is, of course, its *latent heat* of evaporation.

There is no liquid which in its "natural state" boils at the temperature usual in refrigerators; and, since no such liquids exist in nature, it is necessary to manufacture them. Refrigerating machines are really devices which are used to "manufacture" liquids which will boil at temperatures slightly above those usually required for refrigeration. Such "manufactured" liquids are made from gases or vapors which are *compressed* and then *cooled*. The compression and cooling causes the gas or vapor to liquify. These "manufactured" gases are expensive, so that it is not economical in the operation of the process of refrigeration to allow them to escape. Nearly all these fluids are, furthermore, objectionable, for various reasons, when discharged into the air. It is, therefore, a part of the process to collect the gases or vapors of refrigerants and bring them back to their liquid state so that they can be used over and over.[2]

----

[1] The liquid which is ordinarily associated with boiling is water, but water is obviously not suitable for use as a refrigerant, as its boiling point at atmospheric pressure is 212° F. It can be made to boil, however, at a lower temperature than 212° F. by lowering the vapor pressure at its surface as, for example, with a vacuum pump; in fact, one system of refrigeration is based on the boiling of a liquid in a vacuum chamber.

[2] One type of mechanical refrigeration that will be explained later is based on the use of a compressed gas or vapor which is allowed to expand in an engine cylinder and gives up some energy by the loss of heat in proportion to the amount of energy which is converted into work. The refrigerant, in this case, gives up some of its energy in the form of work, as done by the steam engine. The complete process of this kind of refrigeration is not very different from the generation of steam in a boiler and its use in a steam engine, when the steam which is discharged from the engine is condensed and used again.

Natural Ice.—The size of the natural-ice harvest is always uncertain, so that there is a strong incentive for inventors to perfect a mechanical means of refrigeration, in order to make ice from water at any time of the year. From 1830 to 1890, there was relatively little progress in mechanical refrigeration. In 1890, however, when there was an unusually small harvest of natural ice in the United States, the shortage forced an interest in methods and devices for producing ice by mechanical means. In the years immediately following 1890, there was very rapid and successful development of refrigerating machines.

Early History of Refrigerating Machines.—The present systems of mechanical refrigeration depend on the fundamental principle that some vapors or gases which do not ordinarily exist in the liquid state may be liquified upon being subjected to high pressure. Although this fundamental principle was discovered about 1820, it was not until 1834 that a satisfactory mechanical device was invented to apply this principle to the refrigerating process. The inventor of this device was Jacob Perkins, a Massachusetts mechanician and engineer. This first compression refrigerating machine used ether as a refrigerant. In 1855, the first absorption refrigerating machine (see p. 18), using ammonia as a refrigerant, was produced in Germany.

Refrigeration by Compression.—One of the methods of "manufacturing" a liquid refrigerant which will boil in refrigerators below the usual temperatures requires the use of a compressor which has the effect of increasing both the temperature and the pressure of the vapor or gas of the refrigerant which is used. In other words, in this compression, the vapor or gas of the refrigerant is used as the raw material. The vapor or gas of the refrigerant becomes hot by this compression, and the next step in the process is to cool it in a condenser by the use of a stream of cold water or, in some cases, by cool air. In this part of the process, the molecules of vapor or gas are pushed together so closely by compression and their movement reduced by cooling to such an extent that the attractive force between them becomes effective, and, as the cooling continues, the vapor or gas gradually condenses and becomes liquid. A condenser as used for this purpose consists usually of a metal coil containing the compressed vapor or gas, and the coil is surrounded by cold water or cool air.

As the process is continued, the cool liquid refrigerant, which has been condensed from the vapor or gas, is forced through a small orifice, usually in the form of an expansion or throttling valve. In this valve, the pressure of the liquid refrigerant is reduced to such an extent that it will boil in the cooling coil of the *evaporator* at a sufficiently low temperature to maintain satisfactory refrigeration. After the liquid refrigerant goes through the expansion valve, it passes on into the cooling coils of the evaporator, consisting usually of a coil of pipes which is connected to the low-pressure or "suction" side of the compressor.

It may be interesting to explain here why the compression of the refrigerant and its subsequent expansion are necessary. The reason for the compression is that when the pressure of the vapor of a refrigerant is increased, the temperature of its boiling point is raised in proportion to the increase of pressure; and, similarly, the reason for the expansion is that when the pressure is reduced, the temperature of the boiling point is lowered.

Applications of Refrigeration.—The compression type of refrigerating system which was invented by Perkins, after further development by other inventors, became a practical machine, and, about 1855, commercial quantities of ice were produced. The first shipments of refrigerated fruit were made in 1866. These shipments were in large boxes containing 200 quarts of strawberries which were packed with 100 pounds of ice.

In 1872, the first successful shipments of beef and fish were made in railway cars which were heavily insulated on all sides and were refrigerated with natural ice. This was the beginning of the refrigerator-car industry.

Mechanical refrigeration has found application in a number of other industries, as, for example, in the refining of oil, where a refrigerating apparatus is used for the removal of paraffin; also, in the ventilation of buildings in warm weather when a cold liquid is circulated to reduce the temperature of the air used for ventilating. Refrigeration is applied in metallurgical operations, as, for example, in removing the moisture from the air which enters the blast furnaces. Other applications are in the manufacture of textiles, in the curing of tobacco, in the manufacture of cigars, in the making of candy, in the making of photographic films and similar celluloid products, and likewise in surgical operations and in excavating; this last process is accomplished by freezing a ring of quicksand so that tunneling can be done in the difficult material.

"Dry-ice" Refrigeration.—Carbon dioxide is now being made and distributed as a solid, and in this form it enters into competition with ice and small-scale refrigeration. Solid carbon dioxide is made by passing the liquified gas through a coil with provision for cooling to a low temperature. When the cold liquid is permitted to expand suddenly through a series of small spray nozzles, the carbon dioxide takes the form of snowflakes. The discharge from the nozzles is very much like a snowstorm of solid carbon dioxide. In this expansion, not all of the liquid carbon dioxide is solidified, and that part which remains in the liquid state goes back into the refrigerating system. The solid carbon dioxide is scraped into molds and then pressed into blocks which are known in the trade as *dry ice.*

The principal use for solid carbon dioxide will probably be as a refrigerant for long-distance transportation and for any purposes where the water resulting from ordinary ice refrigeration is objectionable. This method of refrigeration is especially valuable for the transportation of medicinal antitoxins and biological preparations for which a low temperature must be constantly maintained, and which are to be delivered by the ordinary mail or express service.

CHAPTER II

SYSTEMS OF REFRIGERATION

Simple Refrigeration Devices.—In an ice-box refrigerator, foods are kept cool by the melting of ice. The ice is, of course, the refrigerating medium and serves to remove heat from the foods as well as also to absorb the large amount of heat which enters through the insulation. It must always be kept in mind that the fundamental principle underlying the operation of any refrigerating device is the transfer of heat from one body to another by the method of temperature equalization.[1]

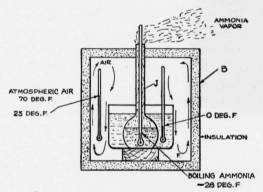

Fig. 3.—Elementary refrigerating apparatus.

Figure 3 shows the application of an elementary evaporating apparatus for producing refrigeration. A jar *J* which is partly filled with liquid ammonia is shown inside a suitable box *B*. The principle of operation is, however, the same if some other refrigerating medium such as sulphur dioxide were used. If the jar is *open at the top*, the temperature of the ammonia vapor which is given off by the liquid will be $-28°$ F., and the insulated

[1] If two bodies have different temperatures and are placed near together, the heat in the hotter body has a tendency to flow into the colder body until the temperatures are the same. By this method, the hotter body is refrigerated, and the colder one is heated. Heat always flows from a hot body into a colder body just as water flows from a high to a lower level.

bodies surrounding the ammonia jar *J* may easily be maintained at a temperature of 0° F. when the temperature outside the box *B* is about 70° F. In the operation of this device, the heat of the air inside the box is absorbed by the ammonia when it evaporates vigorously and boils in the jar. During this evaporating process, it is possible to maintain in the ammonia jar a uniform temperature. In the apparatus shown in Fig. 3, the vapor from the evaporation of the refrigerant escapes to the atmosphere from the top of jar *J*.

Ice-freezing System.—A modification of the last figure is shown in Fig. 4, which is an application of the circulation of cold brine for use in a box or tank in which artificial or manufactured ice is made. In this figure, there is a jar containing liquid

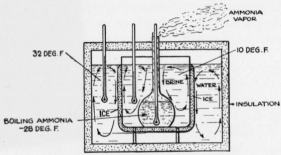

Fig. 4.—Elementary ice-making apparatus.

ammonia which is immersed in brine. The brine tank is supported in a larger tank containing the water from which ice is to be made. The jar containing the liquid ammonia has a long, narrow neck which passes up through the top of the larger tank. The pressure in the ammonia jar is, therefore, atmospheric, and the temperature of the ammonia is, consequently, −28° F., which is sufficiently low to maintain a temperature of from 10 to 15° F. in the brine tank. This low temperature of the brine will cause the water surrounding the brine tank to freeze on the surface of the tank. In this freezing process, the ammonia absorbs a quantity of heat from the brine; and the brine, in turn, absorbs, when freezing the water to ice, approximately the same quantity of heat from the water in the outside tank.[1] The brine is made of

[1] In addition to this amount of heat exchange in the actual process of freezing, the brine absorbs also the heat required to cool the water to the freezing point as well as any heat which enters the water through the walls of the tank.

such a concentration that it does not freeze at the temperatures usually maintained in the brine tank, so that there may be always a circulation of brine.

Systems of Mechanical Refrigeration.—The standard systems of mechanical refrigeration are

a. The air system, in which air is used as the refrigerant and this air is first compressed and is then expanded in very much the same way as the steam in a steam engine, giving up energy to the moving system and, in this way, losing heat.

b. The compression system, using ammonia, carbon dioxide, sulphur dioxide, or some refrigerant with similar properties, is so called to distinguish it from a third system (which is mentioned below), because a *compressor* is used to raise the pressure of the vapor of the refrigerant and deliver it to the condenser after removing it from the cooling coils or the evaporator.

c. The absorption ammonia system, is so called because a weak ammonia solution removes ammonia vapor from the cooling coils of the evaporator by *absorption* and the richer aqua ammonia so formed is then pumped into a high-pressure chamber called a *generator*. By heating the generator, the ammonia vapor is driven off from the liquid and passes through suitable piping into the condenser.

No matter what system is used, a circulating fluid, usually water or air, is employed to carry away the heat, so that the temperature of the cooling fluid limits the liquefying temperature in the system and indirectly limits also the maximum permissible pressure.

Refrigerating Machines Using Air.—The air system has two essential parts: (1) the air compressor and (2) the air engine or expansion motor which operates by the expansion of the high-pressure air which comes from the air compressor. Usually, the air engine or expansion motor is connected mechanically to the shaft driving the compressor so that the work done by the air motor assists in compressing the air which is used in the system. In the operation of this system, the compressor takes in and compresses air to a high pressure. The compression of the air produces heat just as in any other compression system. The compressed air is discharged from the compressor into the coils of the cooler in which heat is removed by cool water which circulates through the coils. The cooled compressed air which is at high pressure is then used to drive the air engine or motor.

In the *expansion of the compressed air* in the air engine or motor, the air becomes very cold and is carried off in pipes to the refrigerating rooms, where it absorbs heat and can finally pass off into the outside air.

The air machines intended for refrigeration purposes have not been applied to any considerable extent in small units, because of the very high cost of equipment, which consists, of course, of two machines, that is, the compressor and the air engine or motor. In comparison, the ammonia compression system of refrigeration has only one machine—the ammonia compressor. From this comparison, it will be seen that the air refrigerating system is likely to cost about twice as much as the ammonia compression system and may probably cost twice as much for repairs because of the multiplicity of moving parts, all of which must operate at high pressures. There is also likely to be considerable trouble caused by the freezing of moisture carried into the compressor with the atmospheric air. This difficulty may, however, be eliminated by the use of a *dense air refrigerating system*[1] in which the same air is used over and over again without discharging any into the outside air. The dense air machine for refrigeration is explained on page 217.

Compression System of Refrigeration.—Figure 5 shows a simple form of the compression system of refrigeration. In the operation of this system, there is alternating compression and expansion of the refrigerant. The object of compressing the vapor of the refrigerant is to increase its boiling point, because, as the pressure of a vapor is increased, the temperature of its boiling point is also raised. Similarly, the reason for expanding the refrigerant is that when the pressure is reduced, the temperature of the boiling point is also lowered.[2] In the figure, the essential parts of a compression refrigerating system are shown,

---

[1] This system is so called because in order to reduce the size of the cylinders and pipes through which the air circulates, its pressure is never permitted to get so low as atmospheric.

[2] If a refrigerant in the liquid state is brought into a room where the temperature is higher than the boiling point of the refrigerant, its temperature will rise until the boiling point is reached, when it will evaporate or boil at a constant temperature depending on the pressure. Similarly, if a refrigerant in the vapor state is brought into a room where the temperature is lower than the condensing point of the vapor of the refrigerant, its temperature will be lowered until the condensing point is reached, and at this temperature, which will remain constant, all the vapor will be condensed.

and the typical temperatures are given for refrigeration *with ammonia*. The working cylinder *C* of the compressor as shown at the top of the figure has two valves, one *S* for the suction, and the other *D* for the discharge of the compressed vapor. In the operation of the compressor, the piston first reduces the pressure in the cylinder *C* somewhat below the pressure in the *evaporator*, which is shown at the right-hand side of the figure. This reduction of pressure in the evaporator causes the vapor of the refrigerant to flow through the suction valve into the cylinder of the compressor. The pressure in the evaporator is determined largely by the temperature which is required for the refrigerating

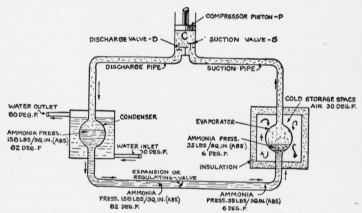

FIG. 5.—Elementary compression system.

purposes. Thus, if the temperature in the refrigerator is to be 25° F., the temperature of the vapor in the evaporator must be a few degrees lower in order to cause heat to be removed from the refrigerator by the evaporation of liquid refrigerant. The description of this compression system so far has explained only the low-pressure part of the process, that is, the right-hand side of the apparatus as shown in the figure. On the left-hand side is the *condenser*, which receives the compressed vapor of the refrigerant at high pressure. The temperature of the refrigerant in the condenser must be a few degrees above the temperature of the cooling water circulating through the condenser, in order that heat may pass from the vapor in the condenser into the circulation water used for cooling. The effect of this cooling by water is to condense the vapor of the refrigerant. After the vapor has been condensed or, in other words, has become liquid, it passes through a regulating valve, generally called an *expansion valve*, which is really a reducing or throttling valve intended to reduce the pressure of the liquid refrigerant from the *high pressure in the condenser* to the *lower pressure in the evaporator*. After the refrigerant has passed through the expansion or regulating valve, where its pressure is reduced, and through the evaporator, it flows again into the suction pipe of the compressor.

Briefly, in the compression system, refrigeration is produced by the repeated process of compression, condensation, expansion, and evaporation.

The refrigerants which are most suitable for use in this system are *"manufactured"* vapors or gases. It would be too expensive and otherwise objectionable to discharge into the atmosphere the vapor or gas of the refrigerant after it has been used. For this reason, the refrigerant is used over and over again. If there are no appreciable leaks in the system, there will be very little loss of the refrigerant in long periods of time.

In the compression system, the action of the refrigerant in transferring heat from a *low* temperature to a higher temperature and then discarding the heat at the *higher* temperature may be compared to the action of a sponge which is used to lift water from a bucket. First, the sponge is compressed by the hand; it is then immersed in the water in the bucket. As the pressure of the hand is released, the sponge expands and absorbs water which may then be lifted out of the bucket with the former. If the sponge is now compressed somewhere other than over the bucket, the water in the sponge may be discarded, and when the sponge is again compressed and allowed to expand in the bucket it will absorb water as before. The repetition of this process with the sponge is like the repetition of events in the compression system of refrigeration.

The necessary parts of a compression system—the compressor, the condenser, the expansion valve, the liquid receiver, and the cooling coils of the evaporator—are shown in an outline drawing in Fig. 6. Arrows show the direction of flow of the refrigerant through the system. The compressor C may be operated by any suitable source of power A. Compressors may be operated by direct connection to electric motors, oil engines, or steam engines, or they may be driven indirectly by belts receiving their

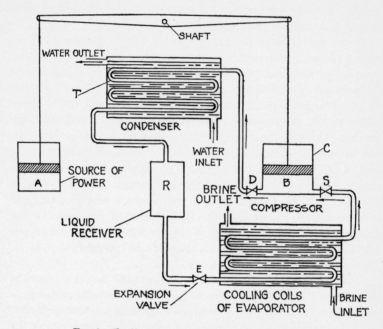

FIG. 6.—Outline of compression refrigerating system.

FIG. 7.—Modern compression refrigerating plant.

power from electric motors. As shown in Fig. 7, the electric motor E drives the compressor C.[1]

In the operation of the compressor in Fig. 6, the low-pressure vapor of the refrigerant is taken from the cooling coils of the evaporator in which the liquid refrigerant has previously been evaporated, and this vapor is compressed to a higher pressure in order to raise the temperature at which it will boil. After compression, the vapor of the refrigerant is discharged at a high pressure through the discharge valve D into the condenser. In the apparatus shown in the figure, the condenser consists of a coil of pipe submerged in a tank T of running water for cooling and condensing the vapor of the refrigerant. For the proper operation of the condenser, the temperature of the water for cooling must be lower than the temperature of the vapor of the refrigerant in any of the coils of the condenser. The water will then remove heat, and the vapor of the refrigerant will be changed to a liquid.

Liquid Receiver.—From the condenser, the liquid refrigerant flows into the liquid receiver R (Fig. 6), where the pressure is nearly the same as in the condenser, although its temperature may be somewhat lower than that of the vapor which enters the condenser. The liquid receiver is a storage space for the liquid refrigerant which would accumulate otherwise in the condenser. By the application of this receiver, there is no accumulation of liquid refrigerant in the condenser to reduce the effectiveness of its cooling surface.

From the liquid receiver, the refrigerant passes on into the expansion valve at E. This valve consists of a "needle-pointed" stem which makes possible a sensitive adjustment of the flow of the liquid refrigerant through the valve and into the coils of the evaporator. It is generally adjusted so that all the liquid refrigerant will be vaporized in the coils of the evaporator. *Needle-pointed expansion valves* are shown in Figs. 8 and 9; and a slightly different type, in Fig. 10.

The refrigerating effect of the system is produced in the cooling coils of the evaporator when the liquid refrigerant evaporates. As shown in Fig. 6, the cooling coils of the evaporator consist of a

[1] The heavy flywheel effect of the electric motor E is needed to make the rotary drive of the electric motor adaptable to the reciprocating motion of the compressor. The motor M is used only for starting. When the compressor is started, the synchronous motor E is used to drive it.

coiled pipe which may be placed where the cooling effect is desired.
The liquid refrigerant, after passing slowly through the expansion

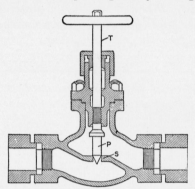

Fig. 8.—Needle-pointed expansion valve with screwed ends.

valve, enters the cooling coils of the evaporator in which a comparatively low pressure is maintained by the suction of the com-

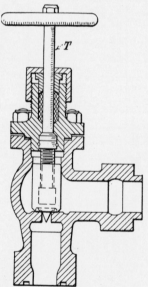

Fig. 9.—Angle type of needle-
pointed expansion valve.

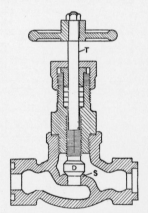

Fig. 10.—Expansion valve with
flanged ends.

pressor. In becoming a vapor, the refrigerant absorbs heat from
the surrounding substances in contact with the coils and thus
cools them.

In places where electric current is obtainable at a reasonable cost, the compressor in modern refrigerating plants is driven by an electric motor. When electricity for power is not available, Diesel oil engines are frequently used as a source of cheap power.

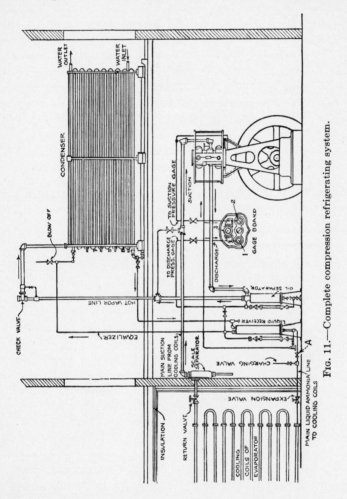

Fig. 11.—Complete compression refrigerating system.

Formerly, steam engines were used almost exclusively for power in refrigerating plants. Figure 11 shows a compression refrigerating plant.

Refrigerant a Carrier of Heat.—In the compression system, the circulation of the refrigerant is from the compressor to the condenser, to the liquid receiver, through the expansion valve to the cooling coils of the evaporator, and then back again to the compressor. Thus, the refrigerant is actually a *carrier of heat*. The action of the compressor is similar to that of a pump, as it *lifts heat* at a low temperature from the cooling coils of the evaporator and delivers it to the condenser at a much higher temperature. When the vapor of the refrigerant is subjected to a high pressure by the mechanical action of the compressor, a certain amount of heat is added to the vapor, which raises its temperature. The heat added in this way is carried along in the refrigerant to the condenser, where it is removed.

Absorption System of Refrigeration.—Refrigeration by the absorption system differs only slightly from the compression system, the principal difference being that a coil supplied *alternately with steam and water* and fitted into a *closed pressure tank* filled with a mixture of refrigerant and water is used in place of a compressor. The evaporator, condenser, and the expansion or regulating valve are the same in the two systems. Briefly, the difference in the two systems is in the method of increasing the pressure between the evaporator and the condenser. In the compression system, the increase of pressure is brought about by mechanical means, that is, by the use of a compressor. In the absorption system, the increase in pressure is produced by heat supplied by means of steam which circulates through a coil of pipe.

At some temperatures, water has the property of absorbing many times its volume of ammonia vapor. For example, when water is at the temperature of 55° F., it will absorb about one thousand times its volume of ammonia vapor, but if the temperature of an aqua-ammonia solution is raised to, say, 80° F., ammonia vapor will escape freely from the liquid solution.

The absorption system of refrigeration is based on the principle of the *absorption of ammonia vapor by water at relatively low temperatures and the giving up of ammonia vapor when the mixture is heated.* Ammonia is the most suitable refrigerant for use in absorption systems. Mixtures of ammonia and water are called *aqua ammonia.*

In the operation of the absorption system in its simplest form, as shown in Fig. 12, the liquid ammonia which comes from the condenser flows through a short length of piping to the expansion or regulating valve, where its pressure is reduced in the same way as in the compression system. After expansion, the refrigerant passes on through other piping to the evaporator. From the evaporator, the low-pressure ammonia vapor passes upward into a *closed* pressure tank *T*, entering through the inlet or *suction valve*. The low-pressure ammonia vapor is absorbed by the "weak" aqua ammonia already in the tank. The absorption of ammonia vapor is accelerated by the method of cooling the aqua ammonia by passing cold water through the coil shown in the tank *T*.

When water is circulated through the coil in this tank, the ammonia gives up heat to the water, which is heated, for example, from 75 to 90° F. When the *aqua ammonia* in the pressure tank has absorbed all the ammonia which it can hold, the valve on the

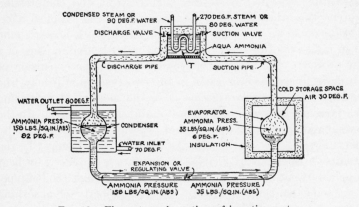

FIG. 12.—Elementary absorption refrigerating system.

water supply is shut off, and the valve on the steam supply is opened so that steam can pass through the coil. In the apparatus in the figure, the temperature of the steam is 270° F. By giving up heat, the steam raises the temperature of the aqua ammonia in this tank from about 150 to 250° F. At the higher temperature, the aqua ammonia is reduced as the result of this rapid evaporation to a concentration of about 25 per cent of ammonia by weight. The steam supply is then shut off, and water is again passed through the coil.

The ammonia which boils off the surface of the aqua ammonia passes out through the discharge valve and the pipe leading to the condenser, where it becomes liquid by being cooled with the water which circulates through the condenser. This set of operations is repeated over and over again with the continuous circulation of the same supply of ammonia which is successively *evaporated, absorbed, distilled, liquefied,* and *expanded.*

In order to make more vivid the similarity of the absorption system to the compression system, the closed pressure tank *may be regarded as a compressor operated by heat* rather than by mechanical means. The absorption period in the pressure tank corresponds to the suction stroke of the compressor, while the period of increasing pressure in this tank takes the place of the compression stroke.

The closed pressure tank T, in Fig. 12, performs a double duty; in the first place, it absorbs the low-pressure ammonia vapor, and by this absorption its concentration of ammonia is increased. The tank T serves also as a pressure generator when, by the application of heat from the steam coil, high-pressure ammonia vapor is driven off. In a more practical device for the absorption system, there is one vessel, called the *absorber*, for absorbing the ammonia vapor, and another, called the *generator*, for increasing the temperature to the boiling point and driving off ammonia vapor at a high pressure. The absorber and generator will be described in detail in the following paragraphs.

When the amount of ammonia in an aqua-ammonia solution is relatively small, as, for example, after considerable vapor has been driven off, the aqua ammonia is called *weak liquor*. When, on the other hand, the concentration of ammonia is large, it is called *strong liquor*.

A *diagrammatic drawing* of a practical absorption system of refrigeration is shown in Fig. 13. The condenser C consists simply of a coil, submerged in water. The cooling water entering the condenser at A_1 and leaving at B_1 serves to condense the ammonia vapor which comes to the condenser from the *generator*, entering the condenser at D. The liquid ammonia formed by condensation is drawn off at F into the liquid receiver L, from which it flows through the expansion valve E into the coils of the *evaporator*. The condenser, expansion valve, and evaporator are exactly like those of the compression system. All of the remaining parts of the absorption system are different.

The ammonia vapor leaves the coils of the evaporator at J and passes into the a*bsorber* through a perforated pipe K. The purpose of this perforated pipe is to cause the ammonia vapor to rise through the weak ammonia liquor in the form of bubbles.

The *comparatively cool* weak liquor absorbs the ammonia vapor so that it becomes strong liquor. The strong liquor is continuously removed from the bottom of the absorber by the pump

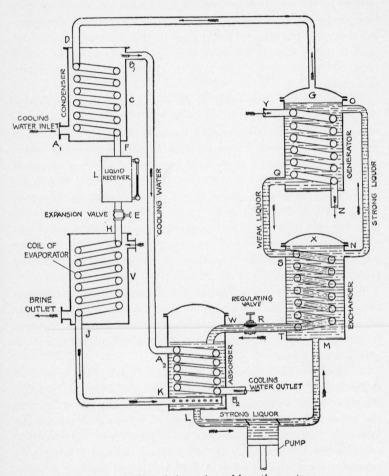

Fig. 13.—Outline of absorption refrigerating system.

P, which forces it into the exchanger, entering at M, leaving at N, and then flowing back into the *generator* at O.

The strong liquor entering at the top of the generator is heated by the steam coils YZ, the steam entering at Y. In these coils, the steam condenses, and the condensed steam is drawn off at Z. In condensing, the steam gives up heat to the strong liquor, thus raising its temperature.   This increase in temperature drives off ammonia vapor from the strong liquor.

Strong liquor is lighter than weak liquor, or, in other words, the specific gravity of strong liquor is less than the specific gravity of weak liquor.   Hence, the weak liquor formed in the generator settles to the bottom and flows out at Q into the exchanger at S. The weak liquor flows out of the exchanger at T through a regulating valve R into the upper part of the absorber at W.

The purpose of the regulating valve R is to reduce the pressure of the weak liquor.   The weak liquor leaving the exchanger is at the high pressure in the generator, and its pressure is reduced by this valve to the lower pressure in the absorber.   The pressure in the absorber is about the same as that of the *ammonia vapor* entering the absorber from the coil of the evaporator.

Although not essential to the operation of the absorption system, the exchanger is a heat-saving device and is useful in reducing the operating costs.   The strong liquor leaving the absorber is comparatively cool and is heated later in the generator. On the other hand, the weak liquor *leaving the generator* is at a high temperature.   This liquor must be cooled either before reaching the absorber or in the absorber.   The purpose of the exchanger is to *transfer heat* from the hot weak liquor coming from the generator to the cool strong liquor going back to the generator.   In doing this, the weak liquor is somewhat cooled, while the strong liquor going to the generator has its temperature raised.   By the use of this device, there is then a saving in the amount of cooling water required by the absorber.   There is also a saving in the amount of steam required to raise the temperature of the strong liquor in the generator.

Although there is a saving of a large amount of heat by the use of the exchanger, there is only an "equalling" of temperature. This means that the heat in the weak liquor cannot raise the temperature of the strong liquor to that of the generator.   On the other hand, the strong liquor cannot cool the weak liquor to the temperature of the weak liquor in the absorber.   Because of this, some heat must then be added to the strong liquor in the generator, and some heat must be removed from the weak liquor in the absorber.

The weak liquor, in passing through the exchanger, is cooled a few degrees more than the temperature of the strong liquor is raised.   This is because the weight of strong liquor passing through the exchanger in a given time is greater than the weight of the weak liquor passing through the exchanger in the same time. For example, if the weight of strong liquor entering the generator is 10 pounds and the weight of the weak liquid returning to the absorber is 9 pounds, the 9 pounds of weak liquor will be cooled through a greater range of temperature than the number of degrees the 10 pounds of strong liquor will be heated.

The exchanger consists of either a vertical or a horizontal steel drum, capable of carrying the generator pressure. This drum contains a coil of pipe. The weak liquor flows from the generator through the coil of pipe to the absorber. The strong liquor surrounds the coil and is pumped through the exchanger X into the generator.

The weak liquor flowing out of the exchanger will have a higher temperature than that of the absorber. This means that there is considerable heat in the weak liquor when it enters the absorber; besides this heat, there is also the heat generated by the absorption of the ammonia vapor by the liquor in the absorber. In order that the liquor in the absorber may absorb ammonia vapor, the heat brought in by the weak liquor and the heat generated by absorption must be removed. Because of this, it is necessary to cool the absorber. This can be accomplished by circulating the cooling water, which is discharged from the condenser at B_2, through the submerged coil of the absorber. The temperature of cooling water leaving the condenser at B_2 will be about 85 or 90° F. This temperature is sufficiently low for cooling the liquor in the absorber to a temperature that will give the desired absorption. Sometimes the weak liquor is cooled by a separate cooler which is entirely separate from the absorber. This separate cooler receives a part or all of the cooling water from the condenser, thus permitting the absorber to be cooled by an independent water supply.

The amount of liquor which must be circulated to absorb one pound of liquid ammonia containing no water (*anhydrous ammonia*) depends on the strengths of the strong and the weak liquor. Because of this, it is necessary to have the strong liquor entering the generator as strong as possible and the weak liquor going to the absorber as weak as possible. When this is accomplished, a comparatively large amount of ammonia vapor can be driven out of the liquor in the generator. It is necessary then only to circulate a comparatively small amount of liquor, to produce a given refrigerating effect. A high temperature in the generator means a large amount of ammonia vapor driven off, while the liquor returning to the absorber will be very weak. On the other hand, a low temperature in the absorber will result in a large quantity of ammonia vapor being condensed and absorbed, and the strong liquor going to the generator will have a large percentage of ammonia. It is essential, then, to have a high temperature in the generator and also to have a large amount of cooling in the absorber.

An actual layout of an absorption refrigerating system is shown in Fig. 14. Taking the condenser as the starting point in this description, the liquid ammonia flows from the bottom of the condenser, by gravity, first into the liquid receiver and then through an expansion valve (not shown) into the coil of the evaporator, which is located, in this case, in a brine cooler. Then, after absorbing heat by cooling the brine during its evaporation, the ammonia passes as a cool vapor to the bottom of the absorber.

In the absorber, the ammonia vapor coming from the evaporator coil is absorbed by the liquor already in it and gives up heat to the cooling water. The strong liquor resulting from the absorption of the ammonia vapor is then transferred from the absorber by the ammonia pump.

The absorption system is usually provided with a *rectifier* for the purpose of thoroughly drying the ammonia vapor before it enters the condenser. This is a device which is used to condense the water vapor from the mixture discharged by the generator. This condensed water vapor, of course, absorbs some ammonia, making a strong liquor which must be returned to the generator to be used over again. As shown in the figure, this liquid is removed from the piping system at the bottom of the separator and is carried to the generator through the "drip" pipe.

After passing through the rectifier, the strong liquor enters the top of the exchanger, and, after passing downward through this apparatus, it is discharged into the generator, near the top.

In the generator, steam is used to heat the ammonia liquor in order to distill the ammonia vapor and steam, which pass out and upward to the rectifier from a connection shown at the top of the generator. As the result of removing ammonia vapor, weak liquor settles to the bottom of the generator, and passes because of pressure difference into the exchanger. After passing

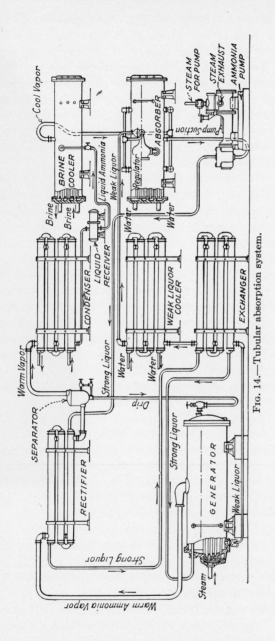

Fig. 14.—Tubular absorption system.

upward through the exchanger, the weak liquor leaves at the top and then enters the bottom of the weak-liquor cooler. Cooling water circulates through this apparatus by entering at the inlet at the top and leaving at the outlet at the bottom. This cooling water reduces the temperature of the weak liquor so that when it reaches the absorber it will be at the best temperature for the most efficient operation. From the weak-liquor cooler, the weak liquor discharges through a liquor regulating valve into the absorber, where it reabsorbs ammonia vapor which comes into the absorber from the coil of the evaporator.

In the meantime, the *ammonia vapor and steam*, which discharged upward from the top of the generator, have gone to the top of the rectifier, where the strong liquor from the ammonia pump flows in countercurrent direction to the direction of flow of the ammonia vapor and steam, and the strong liquor takes up in the rectifier some heat from the ammonia vapor and steam, thereby condensing the steam. The rectifier has a use here somewhat similar to that of a regular steam condenser. The moisture resulting from this condensation collects in the separator shown at the right of the rectifier. The drain or drip pipe of the separator carries the moisture back to the right-hand end of the generator.

The warm ammonia vapor passes from the bottom of the rectifier through the separator into the top of the condenser. Here the heat taken up from the ammonia vapor by the cooling water condenses the ammonia vapor. The ammonia in the liquid state then passes on again through the expansion valve and the coil of the evaporator in the brine cooler, thus completing its circuit.

Absorption refrigerating systems will vary somewhat in the arrangement and methods of connecting the various parts. In some plants, a "drying" apparatus, called an *analyzer*, is recommended to be inserted in the system between the generator and the rectifier. The analyzer is used as a companion device to the rectifier to bring about a large transfer of heat between the hot vapors coming from the generator and the strong liquor which circulates through these two devices.

A typical layout of an absorption system in which an analyzer is used to supplement the rectifier is shown in Fig. 15. As shown here, the analyzer consists of a vertical cylinder, containing a stack of shallow pans, one placed above the other. A different

arrangement of the analyzer with respect to the generator is
shown in Fig. 16. The different cycles or paths of the liquids and

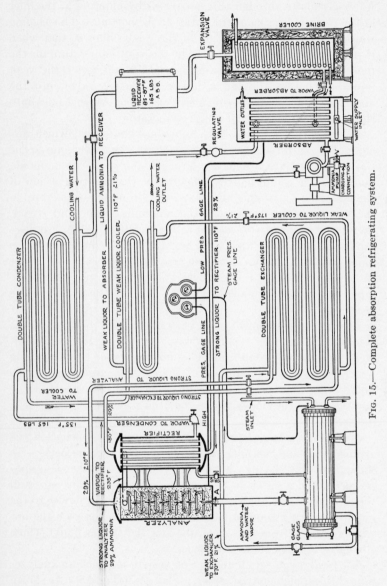

Fig. 15.—Complete absorption refrigerating system.

vapors are shown by arrows in Fig. 15. The cycle of interest
now is that of the strong liquor from the absorber, through the

ammonia pump, and into, first, the exchanger and then the analyzer. The discharge of liquor from the analyzer is downward by gravity into the generator. Another cycle of importance as showing the use of the analyzer is that of the anhydrous ammonia, which, after leaving the generator at A, passes first, through the "rain" of strong liquor in the analyzer and then through the rectifier on its way to the condenser. From the condenser, the liquid refrigerant flows through the liquid receiver and the expansion valve into the coil of the evaporator, where the liquid ammonia again becomes a vapor. This ammonia vapor then passes into the absorber, where it is absorbed by the weak liquor, and is pumped as strong liquor through the rectifier,

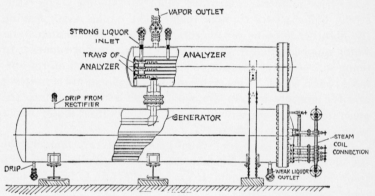

FIG. 16.—Typical generator and analyzer for absorption system.

exchanger, and analyzer. From the analyzer, the strong liquor falls by gravity back into the generator. There is also the cycle of the brine, which passes through the brine cooler, where it gives up heat to the cooling coil of the evaporator and then passes through the refrigerating coils, where it takes up heat on its way back to the brine cooler.

Analyzers and Rectifiers.—In driving off the ammonia vapor in the generator, some water will also be driven off; hence, a mixture of ammonia and water vapor will result. If this mixture is permitted to pass over into the condenser (where it will be condensed) and then passes on into the liquid receiver and into the coil of the evaporator, the liquid ammonia in the evaporator coil will, of course, evaporate, leaving the water, which will eventually fill the coil. Such an accumulation of water in the evaporator coil will obviously lower its efficiency. On the other hand, if the water vapor passes along with the ammonia vapor and enters the condenser, settling in the bottom, the water will accumulate and also reduce its efficiency. It is very necessary, therefore, to remove this water vapor from the ammonia vapor, and this is accomplished very successfully by the use of the *analyzer* and *rectifier* in combination.

The purpose of a rectifier when used in conjunction with an analyzer is to remove about 7 per cent of water vapor, which remains mixed with the ammonia vapor, thus bringing only pure anhydrous ammonia vapor to the condenser. The rectifier shown in Fig. 15 consists of a cylindrical drum containing tubes. The tubes have ammonia and water vapor surrounding them, while strong liquor passes through them. The strong liquor leaving the absorber is quite cool, as compared to the hot ammonia and water vapors, so that it will absorb heat from the hot vapors. In doing so, the water vapor is cooled and is condensed on the surfaces of the tubes. This water absorbs ammonia in the rectifier and the mixture is then drained through a drip pipe into the generator. The ammonia vapor now freed from water vapor passes on into the condenser.

Present Use of Analyzers.—Some manufacturers recommend the use of the analyzer, while some do not. Analyzers were used frequently in the past, but, at present, they are to be used only under special conditions.

Field of Application of Absorption System.—The absorption refrigerating system has its own particular field of application. It operates quite economically at low evaporator pressures. At evaporator pressures below 8 to 10 pounds suction-gage pressure, the absorption system will show more economical results, in most cases, than the ammonia compression system when operated by electric motors or compound condensing steam engines.

The application of the compound (two-stage) ammonia compression system (p. 54) is restricting somewhat the further application of the absorption system. *In plants, however, where there is available a quantity of low-pressure steam, it is advantageous, in some cases, to install the absorption system.* As previously stated, *when very low temperatures are needed*, the absorption system will produce these low temperatures very economically.

The inefficiency of the absorption system results from the fact that the amount of heat which is contributed by the steam in the pressure tank and then removed by the cooling water in the condenser is very much larger than the heat which is absorbed by the expansion and boiling of the cool liquid in the evaporator. This fact accounts for the relatively low thermodynamic[1] efficiency of the absorption system when compared with the compression system. This system uses more cooling water than a compression system.[2]

The cost of an absorption refrigerating plant is about 65 per cent more than the cost of a compression plant, exclusive of piping, insulation, and buildings.

The experts of the National Electric Light Association state that, until some absorbent is found which will not heat so much as water in absorbing the ammonia vapor, there is little hope for the commercial success of the absorption system in small plants which must be *heated by electricity*.

Vacuum System of Refrigeration.—Water is sometimes used as a refrigerant in refrigerating systems by causing it to boil by merely reducing the pressure in the container with a vacuum pump. In this case, the refrigerant (water) is liquid at ordinary temperatures and pressures and is always conveniently obtained. In this respect, it has important advantages over the so-called *gas* refrigerants. On the other hand, when a very low pressure is obtained in a container, there is likely to be trouble from air leaks.

Vacuum systems using water for the refrigerant have not been used very much, but, recently, an apparatus of this type has been developed for use in air-conditioning work. A centrifugal type of high-vacuum pump is preferably used, and considerable capacity is obtained in this type in small dimensions; likewise, very low pressures (vacuum of 28 inches of mercury or about 1 pound per square inch absolute) are obtained. In this process,

---

[1] The thermodynamic efficiency of the absorption system of refrigeration is explained on p. 236.

[2] The absorption systems of refrigeration are often equipped with electric heating devices which require, when operating, from 1 to 2 kilowatts and are in use for only an hour or two a day. This type of machine if installed in large numbers is an undesirable load for an electric lighting system. It would be a desirable improvement to reduce the kilowatt capacity of heat elements to, say, 500 watts, so that the maximum load on the electric lighting system would not be so large.

the water evaporates quite freely at ordinary atmospheric temperatures and a vacuum of 29 inches of mercury and is condensed on the high-pressure side of the system at a vacuum of about 18 inches. It will be noted, therefore, that all pressures throughout the system are less than atmospheric and that none of the refrigerant can, therefore, leak out. The air which leaks into the system is, from time to time, sucked out by the operation of a very efficient air ejector. The principal advantage of this system is that it can be installed in much smaller space than would be required for an ammonia compression system. The experts of the National Electric Light Association make the following comment as to the possible future application of this type of machine: "The vacuum machine gives some promise because with proper machine design and the right refrigerant only moderate volumes of vapor need be pumped, and the machine may be small."

Vap-air System of Refrigeration.—A combination system of refrigeration has been worked out which is based partly on the vacuum system and partly on the air-machine system. In this combination system, a vacuum pump reduces the pressure in the container for the liquid refrigerant and, at the same time, compresses the residual air in the system and allows it to expand through the liquid. When the air is expanded or is being blown through the liquid, it gives up some energy, because some work is being done in greatly extending the surface. The extension of the surface of the liquid proportionately increases the amount of evaporation. The process is then further aided through the evaporation's becoming more effective as a result of reducing the total pressure at the surface of the liquid by rapidly removing the vapor and air mixture (vap-air) with a vacuum pump. Briefly, the vap-air system consists of two of the simpler systems combined into one. In the first place, compressed air expands against the resistance of a body of liquid, and in this expansion it becomes cold. In the other part of the system, a violently boiling liquid causes heat to be absorbed as latent heat.

In further explanation of this system, it may be stated that it is not subject to some of the limitations of the air machine, in that an expansion engine or motor is not required. As regards the vacuum machine itself, furthermore, not so high a vacuum is necessary as with the vacuum system, so that there is not so much difficulty in preventing air leaks in the system. There is, also, the further advantage that the pressure throughout the system is about atmospheric. The pressure in the evaporator is the sum of the vapor pressure of the refrigerant and the air pressure,[1] but the temperature is limited only by the pressure of the vapor.

There are several fundamentally new thermodynamic principles applied in the vap-air system, and in this respect it is of more ordinary interest. In the commercial development of the device, there is commendable conservatism, so as to avoid, if possible, the disastrous results of premature commercialism.

Absorbers.—The various kinds of absorbers can be classified in three groups: (1) the wet absorber, (2) the wet-and-dry absorber, and (3) the dry absorber. The absorbers shown in Figs. 13 and 15 are both of the wet type. In the wet absorber, the drum is nearly full of liquor. The ammonia vapor enters at the bottom of the absorber and passes up through the liquor, by which the vapor is absorbed before it reaches the surface.

It is necessary to cool the absorbers, and, for this purpose, coils of pipe or straight tubes are provided to carry the cooling water. If the cooling is done by coils of pipe, there are generally several concentric coils. This permits a large cooling surface in a small space. The ends of these coils are each connected to common headers. Owing to the fact that straight tubes are easy to clean, they are more often used than coils.

The *dry absorber* shown in Fig. 17 is somewhat different from a wet absorber. In this absorber, the ammonia vapor enters at the left of the top below the perforated plate, and the weak liquor enters at the top of this plate. The weak liquor then passes through the perforated plate, which causes it to fall in the form of rain. This perforated plate also distributes the weak liquor evenly over the entire cross-section of the drum. The mixing of the ammonia vapor and the weak liquor in this manner causes the vapor to be quickly absorbed, as there is a large liquor surface exposed to the ammonia vapor. The strong liquor thus formed is collected at the bottom of the drum and is removed by the liquor pump. The cooling water enters at the bottom, passes through the coils, and leaves near the top. This arrangement makes the absorber work efficiently, as it operates on the

---

[1] For an explanation of combined vapor pressures (Dalton's law), see pp. 159 and 233 and Moyer, Calderwood, and Potter, "Elements of Engineering Thermodynamics," 4th Ed.

counter-current principle. Thus, this arrangement requires the smallest amount of cooling surface. In Fig. 17, only one coil is shown, although, generally, there are several. This type of absorber may also be made horizontal, but, as the floor space required is greater, the vertical type is preferred.

The dry absorber is objectionable, as the cold ammonia vapor on entering may come into direct contact with the cooling-water tubes. This occurrence is likely to freeze the water in the tubes. It can be prevented, to some extent, by making the dry absorber so as to enter the vapor in such a way that it does not come

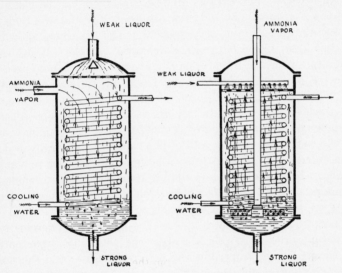

FIG. 17.—Dry absorber. FIG. 18.—Wet-and-dry absorber.

immediately into direct contact with the cooling tubes. The vapor will then be warmed before it comes itself into contact with the tubes or coils.

A *wet absorber* is filled with liquor, and the ammonia vapor passes upward in the form of bubbles. A *dry absorber* contains only a small quantity of liquor, and the vapor is absorbed by contact with the rain of liquor.

An absorber utilizing both of these systems is called a *wet-and-dry absorber* (see Fig. 18). The wet-and-dry absorber contains a small amount of liquor. The ammonia vapor enters at the top and passes down through a vertical pipe. This pipe extends to the bottom where it is connected to a perforated pipe. The ammonia vapor leaves this perforated pipe and passes up through the small quantity of liquor. That which is not absorbed by the liquor then rises and meets the rain of weak liquor which absorbs it. The weak liquor enters at the top and is sprayed upon a perforated plate, which causes it to fall over the cooling coils. This arrangement has the advantage that the ammonia vapor is effectively heated before coming into contact with the cooling coils. This eliminates the possibility of freezing the cooling water.

When using dry or wet-and-dry absorbers, the weak liquor is effectively cooled by the cooling coils, thus doing away with the weak-liquor cooler, saving the cost of a piece of apparatus, and reducing the expense for repairs.

In order to obtain the best results, the pressure in the absorber and in the coil of the evaporator should be nearly the same. By carrying a temperature as high as possible in the coil of the evaporator, there will be the smallest drop in temperature between the ammonia vapor in the coil of the evaporator and the brine, this condition being necessary for the best efficiency. As stated before, the strong liquor leaving the absorber should be as strong as possible, so that it will be necessary to raise its temperature through only a small range in the generator to obtain adequate vaporization. If, however, the temperature of the strong liquor is too high, the liquor pump will race and slip, as the vapor will be formed in the pump. This action is similar to that of a boiler feed pump when it handles very hot water.

Rectifiers.—The rectifier shown in Fig. 15 is cooled by the strong liquor pumped directly from the absorber. As this liquor is comparatively cool, it is relied upon to condense all the water vapor which may enter the rectifier with the ammonia vapor. Such an arrangement is somewhat objectionable, as the cooling action which takes place is nearly constant and cannot be easily controlled or adjusted. This cooling action is dependent on the quantity and temperature of the strong liquor pumped through the rectifier. It may happen that the quantity and temperature may not be just right to condense all the water vapor suspended in the ammonia vapor. If these conditions cannot be adjusted to condense all of the water vapor, part will pass into the condenser, where it will condense. If this occurs, watery ammonia will be supplied to the evaporating coils. On the other hand, the quantity and temperature of the strong liquor can be such that all of the water will be condensed, and if the quantity and temperature of the strong liquor cannot be adjusted, some of the ammonia vapor will also be condensed. When this occurs, the liquid ammonia formed is returned by the drip pipes to the generator. This liquid ammonia produces no refrigerating effect, and its evaporation in the generator and circulation in the system are a loss. The rectifier in Fig. 15 must be designed to meet the required operating conditions in order to work satisfactorily. If this is done, the rectifier will give satisfaction, but it has the disadvantage of not being flexible.

In some absorption systems, the rectifier is cooled by the water discharged from the condenser.

If the rectifier is cooled by water, it is constructed similar to a condenser but has several taps for draining the liquor collecting at the bottom. Such rectifiers may be of the double-tube type

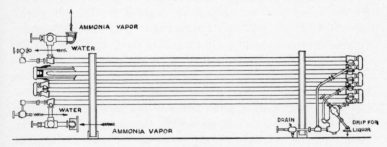

Fig. 19.—Double-tube rectifier.

or of the atmospheric type. Figure 19 shows a water-cooled *double-tube type of rectifier.* The method of draining off the liquor collected at the bottom is clearly shown. The only difference between this rectifier and the atmospheric rectifier is that the atmospheric rectifier has single tubes and water is sprayed on the top tubes and then falls over those below.

Because of the importance of the rectifier in the absorption system, it should receive particular attention and care. The economy and capacity of this system is controlled by the cooling substance. In case the cooling substance is water, it should be carefully regulated to give the proper cooling, following the conditions of cooling already stated. The refrigerating effect of all the ammonia which is returned by the drips to the generator is wasted, as it simply evaporates over and over in the generator. This reduces the amount of liquid anhydrous ammonia available for producing refrigeration.

In order to have the rectifier work at its best, the vapor leaving the rectifier should have a temperature of 20 to 40° F. above the temperature corresponding to the pressure. A thermometer is generally placed between the rectifier and the condenser. By observing this thermometer, the temperature of the vapor entering the condenser may be obtained. If the condenser pressure gage is also observed, the operator can determine if the amount of cooling in the rectifier is properly regulated. To do this, find the temperature corresponding to the absolute pressure in the ammonia tables and take the difference between the thermometer reading and the temperature found in the tables. It is also well to test the drip liquor occasionally to see if it contains too much ammonia; it should be hot and contain as little as possible. This testing should be done without raising the temperature of the vapor leaving the rectifier to such a value that it will be more than 40° F. above the temperature corresponding to the pressure in the condenser.

Condensers.—A water-cooled condenser should cool the refrigerant to nearly the same temperature as the entering cooling water. If the condenser is to be very efficient, it should operate on the *counter-flow* principle. When this principle is used, the *entering* warm *vapor* of the refrigerant is cooled by the surfaces in contact with the water *leaving* the condenser, and the liquid refrigerant on *leaving* comes into contact with the surfaces cooled by the *cold entering* water. This permits the liquid refrigerant to be cooled within a few degrees of the temperature of the cold cooling water. On the other hand, if the compressed vapor and the cooling water travel through the condenser in the same direction, called *parallel flow*, the warm vapor first comes into contact with the coldest surfaces, and the leaving liquid refrigerant comes into contact with surfaces having the highest temperature. In parallel-flow operation of a condenser, cooling water on leaving the condenser is only about 10 to 20° F. warmer than on entering, and, obviously, the liquid refrigerant is not cooled to a temperature so low as it would be by the counter-current principle. This reduces the available amount of refrigeration for cooling purposes, because there still remains considerable heat in the liquid refrigerant, thus reducing the cooling effect which would otherwise be available for producing refrigeration. Another disadvantage of parallel flow in a condenser is the possibility of re-evaporating some of the refrigerant. This is likely to take place when the liquid refrigerant formed by contact with the cooler surfaces comes later into contact with surfaces which are at a higher temperature.

Classification of Condensers.—Condensers may be divided into four distinct classes: (1) the submerged condenser, (2) the atmospheric condenser, (3) the double-pipe condenser, and (4) the shell-and-tube condenser.

Submerged Condenser.—The simplest condenser for a refrigerating system is the submerged type. It consists of coils of pipe

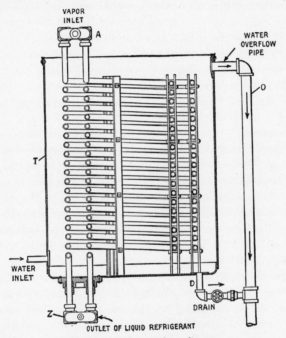

FIG. 20.—Submerged condenser.

containing the compressed vapor of the refrigerant which are submerged in a tank of water. The ends of the coils are brought out at the top and at the bottom of the tank, thus avoiding submerged pipe joints. If these coils are made with submerged joints which are not tight, the escaping refrigerant would not easily be detected, because it would be absorbed by the water and pass off. The high-pressure vapor from the compressor enters at the top of the tank, and the liquid refrigerant is drawn off at the bottom. The cooling water enters the tank through a pipe connected at the bottom. The water gradually rises as it is heated and passes off through an overflow pipe at the top. This condenser is operated on the *counter-flow* principle.

The submerged condenser has been found inefficient and is rapidly going out of use. The inefficiency is caused by the large amount of cooling water which passes through the condenser, much of which absorbs only a little heat. Furthermore, air bubbles collect on the coils of pipe and retard the transfer of heat. For these reasons, it is necessary to use 20 per cent more circulating water in submerged condensers than in some other types.

Figure 20 shows a typical submerged condenser suitable for small plants or where the mist from falling water of atmospheric condensers would be objectionable. The vapor of the refrigerant enters at the top and flows downward, and the cooling water enters near the bottom of the tank *T* which surrounds the condenser coil and discharges into the overflow pipe *O* at the top. A drain pipe *D* at the bottom is to be used occasionally to remove all the water with accumulated sediment and scale.

Atmospheric Condenser.—The atmospheric condenser has found favor in recent years. This type of condenser consists of several vertical rows of horizontal pipes. Each length of pipe is joined to the next by return bends, and several lengths make up a so-called *stand*. When several rows or coils are used, they are connected into a common header. The number of rows varies with the capacity of the plant. In this form of condenser, the vapor of the refrigerant is in the coils, and the cooling water is allowed to flow over their outside surfaces. At the top of each coil is a trough with small holes. This trough distributes cooling water as "rain" upon the upper pipes of each coil, and the water which is not evaporated falls in streams over the surfaces of the lower pipes to be collected in the condenser pan and drawn off.

Cooling water distributed in this way increases the transfer of heat and removes heat from the refrigerant with a comparatively small amount of water. The evaporation of a small amount of water, in this way, absorbs a large quantity of heat, because the latent heat of evaporation of the water is large.

In atmospheric condensers, it is impossible to utilize fully the counter-current principle, because the cooling water must flow from the top to the bottom. The compressed vapor of the refrigerant enters at the bottom and in rising through the coils is condensed. The liquid formed then flows toward the bottom, where it comes into contact with warm surfaces and vapor. This will cause a portion of the liquid refrigerant to reevaporate. This difficulty may be partly overcome by draining off the liquid through "bleeder" tubes which are tapped into the lower pipes of the coils.

The cooling effect produced by the evaporation of the water can be increased by locating the condenser on a roof, where it will receive a good circulation of air, thus removing the air which has

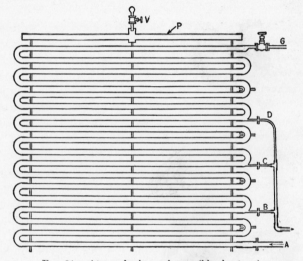

FIG. 21.—Atmospheric condenser (bleeder type).

become saturated with water vapor. If the condenser is to be placed on a roof, it should be shielded from the direct rays of the sun.

Some of the water spray may be blown away from the surfaces of the pipes by a strong wind. The cooling effect of atmospheric air blowing over the rack of pipes reduces the amount of cooling water required in cold weather.

A typical atmospheric condenser is shown in Fig. 21. The vapor of the refrigerant enters at A. Cooling water enters through the valve V and flows out through spray holes or narrow slots in the distributing pipe P, falling as a rain or spray over the surfaces of the rack of pipes below it. The vapor of the refrigerant when it condenses is drained off at the "bleeder" connec-

tions at *B, C,* and *D.*   These bleeders are provided to remove
the liquid refrigerant from the lower tubes of the condenser and
convey the liquid to the liquid receiver.   By constantly removing
the liquid which is formed in the pipe coil, a greater amount of
heat is transferred to the cooling water than if the liquid refrigerant is allowed to accumulate.   If the liquid is not drained from
the condenser, it will accumulate in the bottom pipes and reduce
the effectiveness of the condensing surfaces.

Double-pipe Condenser.—The double-pipe type of condenser
shown in Fig. 22 is ordinarily used in refrigerating plants where
the mist from falling water is objectionable and where there is
little tendency for the cooling water to form scale.   In this type
of condenser, one pipe is placed inside another, and heavy fittings

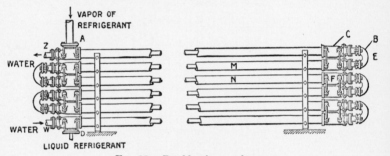

Fig. 22.—Double-pipe condenser.

are used at the ends of the pipes so that cooling water may be
passed through the inner pipe while the vapor of the refrigerant
flows into and is condensed in the annular space between the two
pipes.   The vapor enters the top of the condenser through a
special casting *A* which is provided with a stuffing box with a
metallic packing not corroded by the kind of refrigerant used.
At the right-hand ends of a pipe coil, as at *E,* the water pipes are
connected by a return bend *B,* while a casting *C* supporting the
two sets of pipes at the bend is connected so that the vapor of
the refrigerant passes through it to the next pipe level *M* and
then, flowing toward the left, passes on into the next lower level
N through a return bend and casting exactly like *B* and *C.*   The
water and vapor pipes are connected in this way until the drip
box *D* is reached, from which the liquid refrigerant passes to the
liquid receiver or other similar container.   The cooling water
enters at *W* and flows upward through the pipes, thus applying

the counter-current principle. A slightly different design of double-pipe condenser is shown in Fig. 23.

Figure 24 shows clearly a detailed design of one make of return bend and casting for the ends of a double-pipe ammonia con-

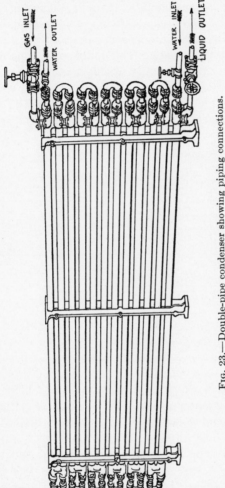

FIG. 23.—Double-pipe condenser showing piping connections.

denser. The directions of flow of ammonia vapor and cooling water are shown by arrows.

Attached to the top of a condenser is usually a blowoff or "purge" pipe, as shown at *G* in Fig. 21, which leads to a space provided for collecting the vapor of the refrigerant and is used to relieve the condenser of air and foreign gases which may accumulate. Air sometimes leaks into the system on the low-pressure side and is pumped around through the system into the condenser. This is apt to occur if low suction pressures are used. If air is allowed to remain in the condenser, its accumulation will prevent the vapor of the refrigerant from entering all of the tubes of the cooling coil of the evaporator, and will thus reduce the capacity. As shown in Fig. 11, there is a connection to the blowoff pipe which extends upward from the liquid receiver. This piping

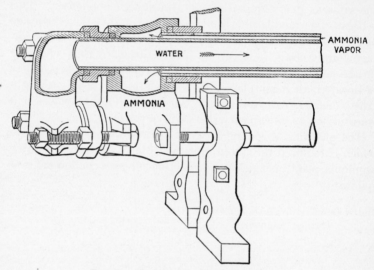

Fig. 24.—Details of double-pipe condenser.

provides for the removal of air or foreign gases which may accumulate in the liquid receiver. This connection is called the *equalizer line* and serves, also, to equalize the pressures in the liquid receiver and in the condenser, thus preventing any interruption in the flow of the liquid refrigerant from the condenser to the receiver.

The cooling surface of a double-pipe condenser is made only about one-third as large as the cooling surface of an atmospheric condenser. A double-pipe condenser with 1¼-inch inner pipes and 2-inch outer pipes, 19 feet long and 12 pipes high has a cooling surface of about 95 square feet and is suitable for an ammonia plant having a capacity of about 15 tons of refrigeration, allowing about 6.3 square feet of cooling surface per ton of refrigeration. The rate of flow of the cooling water should be about 275 feet per minute for the best results.

The most important advantages of the double-pipe condenser over some other types are that it makes full use of the counter-current principle, thus delivering the liquid refrigerant at the lowest possible temperature, and that it can be located nearly anywhere in the plant. It requires no condenser pan, with its possibility of wetting the surroundings.

The quantity of water required for a double-pipe condenser is the same as that required for an atmospheric condenser. This is because the double-pipe condenser does not have the advantage of the cooling effect produced by evaporation. This disadvantage is fully offset, however, by the operation of this condenser on the counter-flow principle. The double-pipe condenser may be located, in most plants, in the compressor room, where a trusty engineer can look after it, but it should not be placed in a warm room, as its capacity there will be reduced.

The quantity of cooling water at various initial temperatures which is required per minute for each ton of refrigeration in an ammonia plant, using *atmospheric* or *double-pipe* condensers is as follows:

Initial Temperature of Cooling Water, Degrees Fahrenheit	Gallons per Minute
50	½
55	⅝
60	¾
65	⅞
70	1
75	1¼
80	1½
85	2

The values given in the tables are based on water leaving the condenser at 95° F. and are the smallest sizes of pipe and amounts of water that should be allowed.

Shell-and-tube Condensers.—A kind of ammonia condenser which is coming into quite general use is the *shell-and-tube type*, which may be made in a number of different ways embodying, however, the same principles. The design most frequently found is shown in Fig. 25. It consists of a vertical cylindrical shell *A* to the top of which a heavy tube sheet is welded or riveted. A number of steel tubes are set and preferably welded into holes in this tube sheet. The ammonia vapor enters the shell of the condenser at *I*. Cooling water enters the condenser through the water inlet pipe shown at the top of Fig. 26, and discharges into a so-called *water box* where uniform distribution of water is obtained by the use of a perforated plate and slotted ring distributors. Water from the inlet pipe at the top enters the inner

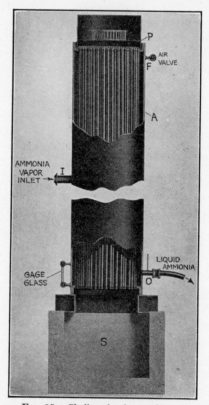

Fig. 25.—Shell-and-tube condenser.

slotted ring and is distributed by means of slots in the first and second of the concentric rings, so that it spreads out evenly over the entire surface of the perforated plate *P* without damming up or surging. Two slotted distributing rings are used, one of which fits closely inside the other, and are arranged to make it possible to adjust the size of the effective opening through the slots. The slots in the two rings coincide when set for the maximum size of the opening for the discharge of water, and the rings are adjustable in position so that they may be moved to secure a "shutter" effect, thus obtaining a fine regulation of the openings to correspond to the amount of water to be discharged through them. The cooling water which passes through the perforations in the plate P is evenly distributed around the tops of the water tubes which are in the body of the shell. The tops of these water tubes are provided with cast-iron deflectors intended to distribute a film of water over the surface of the inner walls of the tubes. The cast-iron deflector on each of the tubes has a handle so that it may be easily removed when the tube is to be cleaned. There are also handles on the perforated plate so that this plate together

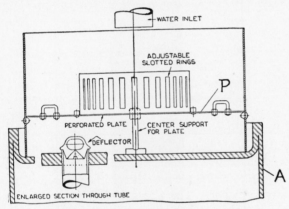

Fig. 26.—Details of shell-and-tube condenser.

with the slotted rings may be easily removed for cleaning. The water, after passing through the tubes, falls into the sump or pit S, (Fig. 25), from which it discharges into a drainpipe or sewer.

In the operation of this condenser, the ammonia vapor enters through the inlet pipe I and is condensed on the surfaces of the tubes. The liquid ammonia which is formed by condensation collects in the bottom part of the shell and is drained off through the liquid outlet pipe O. There is an air-purge valve F near the top of the shell.

The cast-iron deflectors which are set into the tops of the tubes are sometimes made with a cylindrical shape instead of conical as shown in Fig. 26, and have spiral grooves on the cylindrical surface. The object of providing these spiral grooves is to give the flow of water a corkscrew motion down through the tubes.

The condenser tubes may be cleaned by simply removing the perforated plate P and the cast-iron deflectors from the tops of the tubes and then working a tube cleaner up and down in the tubes. When installing a condenser of this type, headroom should be provided, so that the tube cleaner may be used without difficulty.

The shell-and-tube type of condenser has a practically parallel flow of water and ammonia vapor and does not, therefore, have the advantages of the counter-current principle. This kind of condenser, however, will usually cool the liquid ammonia to within 4 to 8° F. of the temperature of the cooling water, when it is discharged from the bottom of the condenser. It requires a comparatively small amount of tube surface per ton of refrigeration, due to the especially good heat transmission through the tubes in this design.

Flooded Condensers.—Both atmospheric and double-pipe condensers may be made so that there is some liquid ammonia on the bottom surface of one or more of its pipes. A condenser designed for this kind of operation is called a *flooded condenser*. It is the theory of this design that if the vapor of the refrigerant as it comes from the compressor into the condenser is mixed with a small amount of liquid ammonia, the mixture of vapor and liquid ammonia will be condensed by the cooling water supplied to the condenser at a higher rate than if the pipes were filled with only ammonia vapor. There is a lower rate of heat transfer from ammonia vapor to water, especially when the ammonia vapor is superheated, than from a *mixture* of ammonia vapor and liquid ammonia to water. The injection of liquid ammonia directly into the pipes of an ammonia condenser by means of an ejector nozzle, as shown at B in Fig. 27 and in detail at the right-hand side of the figure, has obviously the effect of removing, or at any rate reducing, the amount of superheat in the ammonia vapor as it comes from the compressor. Recent tests, however, have demonstrated conclusively that there is no merit in this somewhat expensive type of condenser construction, and that the best kind of condenser is the one which drains the condensed ammonia most promptly from *all* the piping in the condenser.

In the flooded type of atmospheric condenser, as shown in the figure, the lower pipes operate in practically the same way as those in an ordinary atmospheric condenser, and it is likely that after the liquid ammonia which discharges through the ejector is picked up by the ammonia vapor, it is carried more or less like slugs of liquid and vapor to the upper pipes where the liquid separates from the vapor.

It is difficult to operate several flooded condensers in parallel from a common header *H*, as shown in Fig. 27, as it is almost impossible to keep all the condensers operating under the same conditions. There is the further disadvantage that a flooded condenser cannot be operated with as low pressures in the condenser as the ordinary types. It is not unusual for the pressure in a flooded type of condenser to increase a considerable

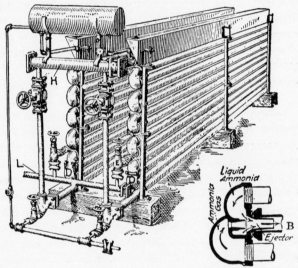

Fig. 27.—Ammonia condensers arranged for operation on "flooded" principle.

amount without any apparent reason. This type was formerly used to a considerable extent, but is now practically obsolete.

Selecting Ammonia Condensers.—Until recently, the atmospheric type of condenser was very much in favor, but a preference for the shell-and-tube type is observed in some of the recent installations. This is especially true where cooling towers are not to be used and water must be pumped from a low level. In that case, the shell type of condenser can be located in a place where the elevation to which water must be pumped is small, while, on the other hand, atmospheric condensers must usually be placed on the tops of buildings, where the additional pressure due to elevation is considerable.

The following table gives the surface and cooling water required by different types of *ammonia* condensers. It is based on a condenser-gage pressure of 200 pounds per square inch and on a cooling-water temperature of 70° F.

TABLE I

Type of condenser	Cooling surface per ton of refrigeration, square feet	Transmission, B.t.u. per square foot per minute per ton	Pipe, per ton of refrigeration. Size most used, inches	Lineal feet of pipe per ton of refrigeration	Water, gallons per minute per ton
Flooded double-pipe.............	5	40.0	1¼	14	1½–2
Flooded atmospheric...........	6	33.3	2	11	1½–2
Double pipe.......	8	25.0	1¼	22	1½–2
Shell and tube.....	18	11.0	1½	55	2 –3
Atmospheric.......	24	8.3	2	45	1½–3
Submerged........	35	5.7	2	65	3 –7

Condensers cannot be efficient unless clean. Oil, scale, and dirt gradually accumulate and tend not only to clog the pipes but also lower the heat conductivity.

Close attention to the refrigerant and the cooling-water temperatures will give an accurate indication of the condition of the condenser. Increased condenser pressure is another indication, although conditions will have become very bad before it is noticeable. High condenser pressure may indicate the accumulation of non-condensable gases, dirty tubes, too high condensing-water temperature for a given cooling surface, an excessive amount of ammonia in the system, or insufficient cooling water.

A high condenser pressure means an increase in power, greater wear and tear on apparatus, increased liability to leaks, and forced shutdowns. Because of this, the condenser pressure should be closely watched and should be kept as low as possible.

Water-cooling Systems.—It often happens that a plant is so situated that condenser cooling water must be purchased from the city. As ice plants require from 100 to 800 gallons per minute of cooling water, it is readily seen that the greatest economy should be attained. In order to save the water and to use it again for cooling purposes, several methods are in use to cool it; namely, cooling ponds, sprays, and cooling towers.

Cooling Ponds.—In this method, the water is partly cooled by radiation and conduction but chiefly by evaporation. The normal condition of the air is such that it can readily absorb more water vapor. Its capacity for absorbing water vapor is increased by contact with warm water and by radiation. Cooling ponds generally require considerable space, and their use is often impracticable. In such a case, cooling sprays are used to accomplish the same object.

Cooling Sprays.—With this method, the hot circulating or cooling water is distributed through pipes and discharged from nozzles into the air, falling like a heavy rain into a pond. The nozzles are so designed as to cause the discharged water to separate into drops. The water issuing from the nozzles induces a draft which, aided by the natural breeze, increases the evaporation. Sprays are often located on the roof of the plant. The loss of water carried off by the air seldom exceeds 4 per cent. In general, under ordinary conditions, the power required to operate the spray will average less than 1.5 per cent of the power required to operate the plant.

Cooling Towers.—A cooling tower is made up of a wooden or sheet-iron housing. This housing is open at the top and at the bottom and is arranged so that the hot water may be raised to the top of the tower. The water is then distributed in such a way as to cause it to fall in thin sheets or sprays into a reservoir at the bottom. Air at the same time is drawn in at the bottom by natural draft or forced in by a fan. The water in falling gives up its heat, chiefly to the rising air, by evaporation and convection.

Water-cooling towers are built in several different types as follows: (1) those with forced draft; (2) those with natural draft, open to the atmosphere; (3) those with natural draft closed to the atmosphere; and (4) those with combined natural and forced draft. Forced-draft towers are completely enclosed, except at the top and at the bottom, where space is left for the fan to open. In the natural-draft tower, the sides are lowered, and the necessary air is supplied through the open base and through the lowered sides by natural-air currents. The natural-draft closed type is like a chimney in its action. The combined forced and natural-draft tower may be used with natural draft for light loads and with forced draft for heavy loads.

Liquid Receiver.—A gage glass (Fig. 128) similar to those on oil separators is generally attached to the liquid receiver to indicate the amount of liquid, as it is important that the supply of liquid refrigerant should not be too large or too small. If a large quantity of liquid refrigerant should collect in the liquid receiver, the liquid will flow back into the condenser; on the other hand, if the quantity becomes small, there may not be enough liquid to supply the cooling coils of the evaporator. The liquid receiver in an ammonia refrigerating system serves, to some extent, as an oil separator, because the oil, being heavier than the liquid ammonia, sinks to the bottom of the receiver from which it can be drained.

In case the refrigerating plant is to be shut down and all of the liquid refrigerant in the system is to be stored in the liquid receiver, it should be about twice as large as the ones ordinarily used. Valves should be placed in the inlet and outlet connections of the liquid receiver. The liquid receiver of an ammonia refrigerating system is usually large enough to hold about ½ gallon of liquid ammonia for each ton of refrigeration capacity.

Scale Separator.—After the vapor of the refrigerant leaves the cooling coils of the evaporator, it should pass through a scale separator to remove scale which may have been freed from the inner walls of the coils and to prevent scale from finding its way to the compressor, where it would damage the valves.

Ammonia-vapor Precooler.—An ammonia vapor precooler consists usually of a metal shell containing a coil in which the liquid ammonia circulates. It is the practice of one designer to have the cold water enter at one end and pass out at the other. The ammonia vapor from the evaporator enters on one side and, after circulating through the space between the coil and the shell, passes out on the other side. At the bottom, there is an oil leg, so that this device serves as an oil separator as well as an ammonia-vapor precooler. Recent tests made of such a precooler show that one for a plant of 50-tons ice-making capacity operating at 25 pounds per square inch suction-gage pressure and 150 pounds per square inch discharge-gage pressure will heat 4.62 gallons of water per minute when the temperature of the discharged ammonia vapor is 217° F., the temperature of the water entering the precooler being 65° F., and the temperature of the water leaving the precooler 95.3° F. For this temperature range (30.3° F.), the heat transfer coefficient is 26.3 B.t.u. per hour per degree mean difference in temperature per square foot of surface. Ammonia-vapor precoolers are not extensively used, because it seems unwise to employ two pieces of apparatus to perform the same purpose. In other words, the condenser is depended on to remove heat from the ammonia vapor discharged from the compressor. The most useful application of precoolers, however, is in refrigerating plants in which ice is being made, the water for ice making being passed through a precooler to be heated for use in the hot-water tanks in which the ice cans are dipped, to facilitate the removal of the ice from the cans.

The more common method of precooling the liquid ammonia is by the use of the *accumulator* to be described in connection with Figs. 39 and 40, in which the liquid ammonia is cooled by the ammonia vapor in the suction line of the compressor. By this means the liquid ammonia is cooled to nearly the temperature in the evaporator.

Enclosed Compression Unit.—An unusual type of refrigerating machine in which the compressor, condenser, brine cooler, and pipe system are in a single unit is shown in Fig. 28. The Audiffren-Singrun refrigerating system, made for the H. W. Johns-Manville Company, is contained in two nearly spherical chambers A and V. There is a hollow shaft S, supporting a bowl-shaped casting B which is kept from turning by a heavy weight W. This casting carries the trunnions T, T of a cylinder C, the piston P of which is connected to a rod attached to the strap of an eccentric D on the shaft S. The shaft S is driven by means of a belt on the pulley Q. The circular chamber A and the oval chamber V are revolved by the shaft S. When the shaft rotates the chamber A, the cylinder C, which is a part of the large chamber B, remains nearly stationary, *oscillating* only a little under the influence of the heavy weight W, which causes it to hang down. The piston P in the cylinder C is drawn in and out of the cylinder by the eccentric D. The cylinder C oscillates between the "faces" of the suspended bowl-shaped casting B on the trunnions T, T. The right-hand face of the cylinder C is pressed by the spring X against the face of the lower part of the casting B which contains ports or holes marked N.

In this way, ports or holes in the two ends of the cylinder C are connected to the two suction ports N, N in the lower part of the casting B at the proper times in somewhat the same way that the distribution of steam is brought about in the cylinder of a reciprocating engine. Thus, the vapor of the refrigerant (sulphur dioxide) is admitted to the cylinder C at F, from the annular space E between the two hollow shafts. When the port or hole at G in the cylinder C and in the "face" at N come opposite, the vapor of the refrigerant is admitted into the cylinder and is compressed. When the proper pressure is reached, the cylinder discharge valves at H open and discharge the vapor into the casing A. Now, the casing A *revolves* (partly immersed) in a tank containing water for cooling, which condenses the refrigerant

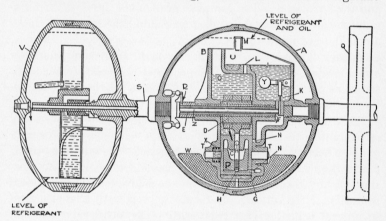

Fig. 28.—Audifferin-Singiun refrigerating apparatus.

and this liquid together with the oil supplied for lubrication collects by centrifugal force at the outer part of the revolving casing A, where some of it is caught up by a scoop M and is collected in the reservoir J. After the lubricating oil is removed, some of the liquid refrigerant passes through an expansion valve K which is regulated by a suitable float Y.

The oil floats in the reservoir J and overflows through the hole L into the chamber O, in the lower part of which the cylinder C oscillates, so that the eccentric D and the piston P are flooded with oil. The whole interior is under pressure, so that there is no leakage of refrigerant from the chambers. There is a tendency for the oil to enter around the piston rod and between the valve faces; but the spring X holds the lower part of the casting B against the sliding face containing the port or hole N. The liquid refrigerant which is at low pressure after passing the throttling expansion valve K passes along the inside of the inner shaft extending between the two chambers A and V and finally settles, by centrifugal force, at the circumference of the oval-shaped chamber V. In the low-pressure chamber V (evaporator), the liquid refrigerant is vaporized as it removes heat from brine in a tank in which it revolves.

The vapor of the refrigerant returns from the chamber V to the chamber A through a space (not shown) formed between the two hollow shafts which connect the chambers V and A and then passes again into the compressor through the annular space E and the opening F. The complete system is contained within a tight set of nearly spherical chambers and shafts, so that there are no moving joints to be kept tight, and, consequently, there is no danger of leakage. An extension on the right-hand chamber serves as one journal for the system, and the hollow shaft at S serves as the other. There is little weight on the journals, as the buoyancy due to the two chambers A and V being immersed, supports much of the weight. The pressure of the vapor of the refrigerant in the chamber A, in addition to the spring pressure, tends to keep tight the sliding joint between the oscillating piston P and the "face" of its cylinder. Should the cooling water be shut off and the temperature rise, the high pressure developed would finally be sufficient to cause the weight W to rotate and so prevent a further rise in pressure. The small valve at R is held down, when the apparatus is in operation, by centrifugal force of the ball weights, as shown, but upon stopping the machine, this valve is opened by the weight of the balls, thus equalizing the pressure.

This refrigerating unit is referred to again on page 156.

The cooling water in a tank below the chamber A *condenses* the vapor of the refrigerant while the *evaporation* of the liquid refrigerant in the chamber V cools the brine in another tank. When the brine in this tank is cooled to approximately the temperature of the vapor of the refrigerant, there will be no further evaporation of the liquid refrigerant, no vapor will be sent back to the compressor in the chamber A, and, consequently, no vapor will be liquefied in the chamber A. After a short time of operation of the apparatus, the level of the liquid in J will close the float valve K, and no more liquid refrigerant can pass over to the evaporator in the chamber V.

Compound Ammonia Compression System.—It has usually been considered good engineering practice to install an ammonia absorption refrigerating system when a low temperature was to be maintained in the cold-storage rooms or when the suction- or inlet-gage pressure was less than 10 pounds per square inch. There are, of course, many single-cylinder ammonia *compression* systems which are operating with a lower suction pressure than this value. It is generally admitted, however, that the single-cylinder ammonia compressor does not give satisfactorily economical operation with such low suction pressure, and the ultimate plan of operation for best economy is either to install an absorption refrigerating system or use a compression system which is equipped with a compound (two-stage) compressor. The compound ammonia compression system is, of course, more complicated than the system requiring only a single-cylinder compressor. The compound compression system requires, in addition to the usual equipment of the ordinary compression system, the following apparatus: (1) high-pressure compressor cylinder; (2) low-pressure compressor cylinder; (3) low-pressure discharge vapor cooler; and (4) intermediate receiver.

In the operation of the compound compression system, the low-pressure cylinder of the compressor takes in the ammonia vapor from the coil of the evaporator through its suction pipe. This vapor is compressed to an intermediate pressure in the low-pressure cylinder, from which it is discharged into the ammonia-vapor cooler. The vapor cooler is provided for the purpose of removing any superheat in the ammonia vapor. The cooling in this apparatus is usually done by circulating water. From the vapor cooler, the ammonia vapor passes on to the intermediate-pressure receiver. Part of the liquid ammonia which is obtained by the condensation of ammonia vapor in the condenser is also discharged into this intermediate-pressure receiver, and when thus discharging it immediately expands and vaporizes. The suction pipe of the high-pressure cylinder of the compressor opens at one end into this intermediate-pressure receiver, so that the ammonia vapor in the receiver is drawn into the high-pressure cylinder. The discharge of the high-pressure cylinder is into the condenser.

The liquid ammonia which accumulates in the bottom of the intermediate-pressure receiver or trap is transferred through a pipe into the coils of the evaporator where it expands. The expansion or regulating valve is provided in this pipe to control the pressure in the coil of the evaporator. Two principal advantages are claimed for the compound compression system, and these are: (1) less horsepower required for compression and (2) a lower discharge temperature in the condenser than with a system having a single-cylinder compressor.

Figure 29 shows the layout of a compound ammonia compression plant. The compressor as shown is driven by being directly connected to a synchronous electric motor which operates at 150 revolutions per minute. The stroke of the cylinder of the

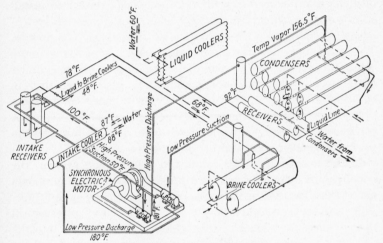

Fig. 29.—Compound ammonia compression plant.

compressor is 24 inches, and the diameter of the high-pressure cylinder is 13 inches, that of the low-pressure cylinder 22 inches.

A compound compressor, especially if of the *rotary* type, is sometimes called a *two-stage* compressor. There are also *multi-stage* compressors having a larger number of stages, as, for example, the compressor described on page 58.

Refrigerating System for Air Cooling.—When refrigeration is required for cooling the air in connection with air conditioning for halls and rooms in buildings, the refrigerating or cooling surfaces of the evaporator and the compressor are usually made very compact, to take up as little floor space as possible. Since nearly all air-cooling installations require the use of air at relatively high temperatures, it is possible, of course, to operate the compressor of the refrigerating system with a comparatively small difference between the discharge and the suction pressures. Because of this fact, the refrigerating capacity of a compressor in this kind of

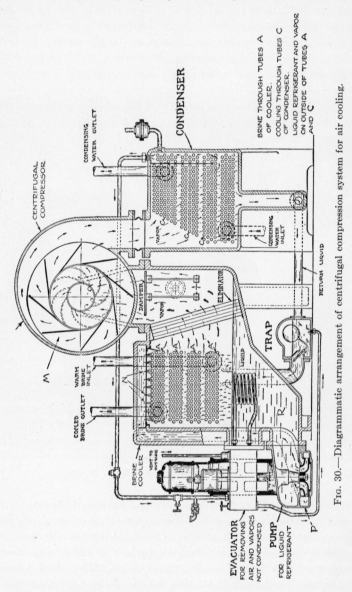

Fig. 30.—Diagrammatic arrangement of centrifugal compression system for air cooling.

service is usually about 100 per cent more than the standard rating.

A self-contained type of air-cooling system manufactured by the Carrier Engineering Corporation is shown in section in Fig. 30 and pictorially in Fig. 31. The nozzles N (Fig. 30) for spraying the re-circulated vapor of the refrigerant over the brine tubes A, which are to be cooled, are located in the left-hand chamber, while the tubes C for circulating the cooling water in the condenser are on the right-hand side. The compressor, which is of

Fig. 31.—Motor-driven centrifugal compression system.

the centrifugal type, is located above and between the brine tubes A and the condenser tubes C. The liquid refrigerant, after passing through the spray nozzles N, is vaporized and drawn into the suction or inlet of the centrifugal compressor M where, after being compressed to a high pressure, it passes into the condenser tubes C. In the condenser, the vapor of the refrigerant becomes a liquid and flows by gravity into the liquid reservoir R at the bottom of the apparatus from which it is re-circulated through the system by the motor-driven centrifugal pump *P* located at the side of the apparatus.

Compressor.—The centrifugal compressor used in the Carrier system is made with five pressure stages or compartments and operates, in most cases, at 3,600 revolutions per minute. At this speed, it is well adapted to be operated by direct drive by a steam turbine. When the compressor is driven by an electric motor, reduction gears are necessary to raise its speed to that of the compressor, because of the low speed of an electric motor. Figure 32 is a view of the centrifugal compressor with the top half removed to show the inlet passages and the impellers or rotors in

Fig. 32.—Five-stage centrifugal compressor.

each stage. The vapor to be compressed enters from the cooler, first, into the suction passages 1, 1 and then into the central portion of the first impeller which discharges into the second stage at 2, into the third stage at 3, and so on, to the high-pressure discharge at 6.

Figure 31 shows a plant of this kind which is operated by an electric motor and reduction gearing. The motor *M* drives the centrifugal five-stage compressor *C* through the gear box *G*. The vapor of the refrigerant is discharged at high pressure by the compressor into the condenser *O* from which the liquid refrigerant flows by gravity into the reservoir adjoining the pump *P* by which it is discharged through nozzles over the brine-cooling coils of the evaporator or "cooler" *E*, the pressure being reduced at the same time, so that nearly all the liquid is vaporized and cools (absorbs heat from) the brine. After evaporation, the vapor is drawn into the suction line leading to the compressor to be re-circulated in the system.

Data regarding several refrigerants which are especially suitable for use in air-cooling systems where small differences between discharge and suction pressures are permissible are given in the table on page 79.

Flooded System of Operation of Evaporator.—In Fig. 33, the cooling coil *C* of the evaporator of a refrigerating system is shown

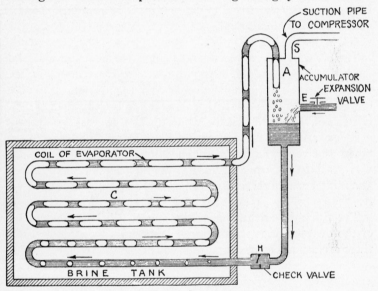

FIG. 33.—Diagram of "flooded" operation of evaporator.

immersed in a brine tank. Between the expansion valve *E* and the coil of the evaporator is an accumulator *A* into which the liquid refrigerant discharges after passing through the expansion valve. From the accumulator, the liquid refrigerant flows by *gravity*[1] into the bottom of the coil of the evaporator. The low-pressure end (top) of the coil *C* of the evaporator is connected up by piping so that the vapor of the refrigerant discharges into the

[1] Because the flow of liquid refrigerant from the accumulator into the coil of the evaporator is due to gravity, this system is sometimes called a *gravity-feed system*.

top of the accumulator A where it loses any entrained drops of liquid refrigerant, and only perfectly dry vapor passes out into the suction pipe S to the compressor. The pressure in the accumulator is nearly the same as the suction pressure at the compressor. The warm liquid refrigerant entering the accumulator from the expansion valve is cooled in the accumulator to the saturation temperature corresponding to the suction pressure. A check valve H is in the liquid line to prevent any vapor of the refrigerant which may be formed in the lower part of the coil of the evaporator from passing back through the liquid into the accumulator. In the application of this apparatus, the refrigerant does not become entirely vaporized in the coil C of the evaporator but is distinctly a *mixture* of the liquid and the vapor of the refrigerant, which is discharged into the top of the accumulator.

The use of the descriptive term *flooded* in connection with this method of operating the evaporator is to express, in a way, the condition of the refrigerant in the coils of the evaporator, which, however, are not, strictly speaking entirely "flooded." The mixture of the liquid and the vapor of the refrigerant in the coil of the evaporator may be represented by relative amounts of liquid and vapor, as shown roughly in Fig. 33. The expansion valve E must be regulated so that the liquid level is maintained at a fairly constant elevation in the lower part of the accumulator A.

The principal advantage of the flooded system of operation of the evaporator is its simplicity, especially in a plant where there are a number of evaporator coils which may be connected to a single liquid and suction headers connected into a single accumulator, thus reducing considerably the number of valves requiring adjustment. This system, further, regulates automatically the flow of refrigerant to each coil of a large evaporator, supplying the refrigerant in proportion to the amount required.

The system is effective in eliminating the drops of entrained liquid refrigerant which may be mixed with the vapor when it leaves the coil of the evaporator, so that, as a rule, the vapor of the refrigerant enters the suction valves of the compressor very nearly saturated or only slightly superheated. This condition of the vapor permits the compressors in a compression refrigerating plant to operate under the most favorable conditions. Also, because the interior surfaces of the evaporator are partly covered with liquid, there is unusually good heat transmission, for the reason that heat transmission from liquid to liquid is much better than from vapor to liquid. Better heat transmission in an evaporator makes possible the use of a smaller amount of coil surface than would otherwise be needed; or, without a change of the amount of coil surface, the compressor can be operated at a higher suction pressure. The important *disadvantage* of this system of operation of the evaporator is that a larger

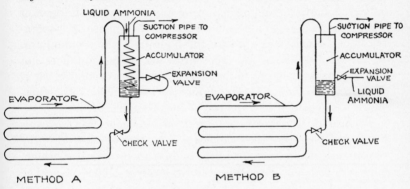

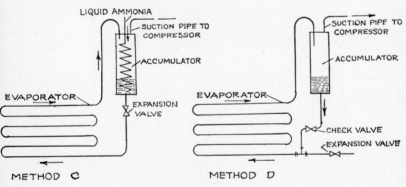

FIGS. 34–37.—Piping arrangements for flooded systems of operation of evaporator.

amount of refrigerant is needed to charge the system than when the liquid refrigerant passes directly from the expansion valve into the coil of the evaporator.

Four different methods of connecting the accumulator to the coil of the evaporator are shown in Figs. 34, 35, 36, and 37. These different methods are marked with the letters *A*, *B*, *C*, and *D*. In method *A*, the warm liquid refrigerant enters the top of

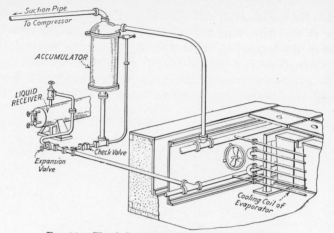

Fig. 38.—Flooded system using method D (Fig. 37).

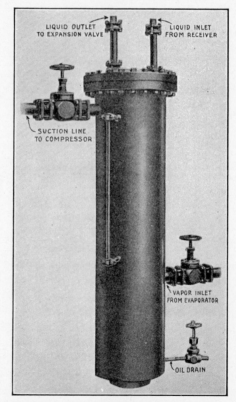

Fig. 39.—Accumulator for "flooded" system.

a coil in the accumulator and, after passing through the expansion valve at the right-hand side of the figure, discharges into the liquid in the bottom of the accumulator. By this method, the liquid refrigerant flows by gravity into the coil of the evaporator. If the expansion valve is not properly regulated, the vapor leaving the accumulator may be slightly superheated. The

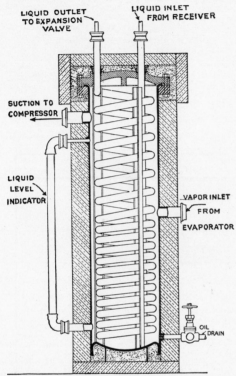

LIQUID OUTLET
TO EXPANSION
VALVE

LIQUID INLET
FROM RECEIVER

SUCTION TO
COMPRESSOR

LIQUID
LEVEL
INDICATOR

VAPOR INLET
FROM
EVAPORATOR

OIL
DRAIN

FIG. 40.—Cross-section of accumulator for "flooded" system using method C.

transfer of heat to the liquid refrigerant in the bottom of the accumulator may cause violent boiling of the refrigerant.

Method *B* is the same as described in Fig. 33. In method *C*, the warm liquid refrigerant passes, first, through the coil shown in the figure, after which it flows on through the expansion valve and the coil of the evaporator. It is important to note that by this method the liquid refrigerant does *not* flow by gravity into the coil of the evaporator. If the expansion valve is not properly adjusted, the vapor going into the suction pipe may be considerably superheated. In method *D*, the warm liquid refrigerant passes directly from the expansion valve into the coil of the evaporator without first entering the accumulator. The liquid refrigerant which is separated out of the return vapor in the accumulator falls into the accumulated liquid in the bottom of the accumulator and passes by gravity flow back into the coil of the evaporator. A check valve is placed in this "gravity-flow" line to prevent any possible flow of the low-pressure liquid from the expansion valve into the bottom of the accumulator.

The flooded system of refrigeration is especially advantageous for use where low temperatures are constantly required. For quick or "*sharp*" *freezing*, a direct-expansion arrangement of *flooded* cooling coils (without the use of brine) has found many important applications. Such quick or sharp freezing is desirable for hardening ice cream, making ice, and other low-temperature work. Figure 38 shows pictorially the Frick flooded system, which is an application of method *D*. The York accumulator for a flooded system of operation of the coils of the evaporator is shown in Figs. 39 and 40. This device operates by a variation of method *C*.

Direct and Indirect (or Brine) Systems Compared.—In the *direct system* of refrigeration, the coil of the evaporator is placed in the storage rooms of the refrigerator, and liquid refrigerant is allowed to expand into them. In the *indirect* (or *brine*) *system*, the storage rooms are cooled by means of pipes filled with cold brine which has been previously cooled. Both systems have advantages and disadvantages. The indirect (or brine) system is more frequently used than the direct.

Indirect (or Brine) System.—A brine tank or a double-pipe *brine cooler* is required in the indirect system, and a pump must be used to keep the brine in circulation. The tank and the pump add to the *first cost* of the indirect system, making it greater than the cost of the direct system.

In small plants, the *operating cost* of the indirect system is less than of the direct system; while, in very large plants, the direct system has the advantage. In order to maintain a fairly even temperature in the cold-storage compartments, the direct system must be operated night and day, as shutting down the plant means stopping the refrigeration process. On the other hand, if the quantity of the brine in the system is large, it may be kept in circulation by operating the brine pump during the night, while the rest of the plant is shut down. The pump is generally a small one of the centrifugal type. This type of pump requires little attention other than that which a night watchman can give. In large plants, this method of plant operation is not satisfactory, because the quantity of brine is usually relatively small compared to the size of the plant.

In the indirect system, there are two transfers of heat. In the direct system, heat is removed directly from the substances to be refrigerated, and there is only one transfer of heat. In order to produce the same cooling effect with both systems, the liquid refrigerant must be evaporated at a lower temperature in the indirect system than in the direct system. This puts additional work upon the compressor, for an increase in the range of temperature and, consequently, also, in the range of pressure requires greater pressure limits for the operation of the compressor.

In general, a more even temperature of the compartments of the refrigerator may be obtained by the indirect than by the direct system. All systems are subjected to variations in temperature by (1) irregular flow of liquid refrigerant through the expansion valve and (2) variations of speed of the compressor. The temperature variations are readily taken up by the brine in the indirect system, as the brine has a high specific heat, and a large quantity of brine is affected. The direct system has the disadvantage that if a leak should occur, the vapor of nearly all refrigerants would injure many kinds of foods in the compartments of the refrigerator.

A larger quantity of refrigerant is necessary for charging a direct than an indirect system, and the refrigerant is expensive. On the other hand, the direct system requires, usually, a greater number of expansion valves than the indirect, as each bank of cooling coils in the direct system has an expansion valve.

In the indirect system, the brine-cooling coils, the brine pump, and the expansion valve can be located near the engine room, so that the parts which require frequent attention may be conveniently taken care of by the engineer. If the brine cooler is located in the engine room, it must be well insulated, or it will absorb large quantities of heat. This heat must then be removed, and considerably more work will be placed upon the refrigeration system. Neither system can be operated at the maximum efficiency when the compartments of the refrigerator are to be cooled to different temperatures.

Brine Cooler.—In the indirect or brine system of refrigeration, the brine after passing through the brine cooler is pumped through pipes or coils in the storage compartments where refrigeration is needed. A brine cooler is often made like a double-pipe condenser, although larger pipes are used, the inner one being usually 2 inches in diameter, and the outer one 3 inches in diameter. The refrigerant passes between the pipes while the brine circulates in the smaller pipe. The countercurrent principle is utilized. In some brine coolers, the liquid refrigerant enters at the top, and the warm brine at the bottom, while, in others, the directions of flow are reversed. The advantages of a double-pipe brine cooler are the same as those of a double-pipe condenser.

CHAPTER III

PROPERTIES OF REFRIGERANTS

Properties of Refrigerants.—A substance which removes heat is called a *refrigerant*. The refrigerants most suitable for use in refrigerating systems are of two distinct kinds.

a. The first kind produces the refrigerating effect by removing heat from the substances to be cooled, using the method of absorbing heat during evaporation of the refrigerant. Refrigerants of this kind are vapors or gases at ordinary temperatures and pressures but are easily liquefied when compressed and then cooled. Examples are

1. Ammonia.
2. Sulphur dioxide.
3. Carbon dioxide.
4. Methyl chloride.
5. Ethyl chloride.
6. Ether, etc.

Nearly all the large refrigerating plants use ammonia as the refrigerant. Sulphur dioxide and methyl chloride are used extensively for small refrigerating machines intended for service in hotels, apartment houses, stores, and general household services. Carbon dioxide is not so much used as formerly, when it was employed almost exclusively in refrigerating plants on ships.

b. The second kind of refrigerant is used in the form of a solution made, usually, by the absorption in water of the vapor of a refrigerant which is readily liquefied (a refrigerant of the first kind). The water used to form the solution is really a carrier of the easily liquefied vapors which produce refrigeration by the method of absorbing heat during the evaporation of the refrigerant. An example of the second kind of refrigerant is *aqua ammonia*, a solution of ammonia vapor in water.

Temperature Range.—The temperature in the refrigerator must necessarily be a few degrees above the temperature of the boiling refrigerant in the cooling coils of the evaporator. The boiling points at the same pressure of the refrigerants in common use are not the same, so that a refrigerant should be used which will produce during evaporation and boiling a sufficiently low temperature. It is obvious, of course, that a refrigerant must be selected of which the vapor will liquefy at a temperature slightly above the usual temperatures of the cooling water when it leaves the condenser.

Approximate boiling temperatures at atmospheric pressure of the commonly used refrigerants are given in the following table:

	Degrees Fahrenheit
Ammonia	− 28
Sulphur dioxide	+ 14
Methyl chloride	− 10
Ethyl chloride	+ 55
Carbon dioxide	−110

Pressure Range.—The pressure in the cooling coils of the evaporator should preferably be somewhat higher than atmospheric, because, if the pressure is lower than atmospheric, air and moisture may enter the system through loose joints. Such air and moisture which enter by leakage are likely to cause trouble in the operation of the refrigerating device.

High pressures in a refrigerating system, and especially in the condenser, add greatly to the expense of construction, as extra-heavy pipes, fittings, stuffing boxes, etc., are required.

Cost of Replenishing Charge of Refrigerant.—Refrigerating systems might be made very simple if a suitable refrigerant were cheap enough to be discharged into the air after being used, in the same way that the exhaust gases from an automobile engine are discharged after combustion. All the refrigerants suitable for commercial purposes are too expensive to be discharged into the air after use and must, therefore, be converted to service over and over again. There is always some loss of refrigerant because of leakage through joints and stuffing boxes, and, after a time, impurities enter into it, making it unsuitable for further use, so that a new supply becomes necessary. For this reason, the cost of the refrigerant has some bearing on commercial applications.

Shipping Refrigerants under Pressure.—Refrigerants may be kept in the liquid state if the temperature is below the boiling temperature corresponding to the pressure to which they are subjected. This principle is applied in shipping refrigerants in steel drums under high pressures. Sufficiently high pressures are used to keep the temperature during transportation sufficiently low to prevent boiling. A greater weight of refrigerant can be shipped in the liquid state than if the drums were filled with its vapor.

Corrosive Action of Refrigerants.—Several refrigerants have a corrosive action upon some metals. For example, ammonia has a corrosive action on alloys of zinc and copper, especially brass. For this reason, brass or gun-metal fittings cannot be used in any part of a refrigerating system in which ammonia is the refrigerant. On the other hand, there are some refrigerants which do not attack metals appreciably when the refrigerant is in a pure state, but when it becomes mixed with foreign matter, such as oil, grease, or water, and especially if an emulsion is formed, there is likely to be considerable corrosion in spite of the fact that the pure refrigerant has no destructive effect.

Chemical Disintegration of Refrigerants.—A refrigerant which is to be circulated continuously in a refrigerating system must have a strong chemical bond to withstand repeated evaporations, condensations, and absorptions. In the compression system, some refrigerants have a tendency to disintegrate into their respective elementary substances, especially when working temperatures after compression are high. It should be noted here, however, that all the important refrigerants used in commercial refrigerating plants have chemical properties that permit them to be used without disintegration at the usual working pressures or temperatures.

Properties of Refrigerants as They Affect the Design of Refrigerating Systems.—The property of a refrigerant which has the most effect on the design of a refrigerating system is the pressure necessary to liquefy the vapor of the refrigerant in a condenser when using cooling water at ordinary temperatures. The volume of the gas or vapor of the refrigerant per pound at its pressure in the cooling coils of the evaporator is a determining factor in the size of the cylinder of the compressor in a compression system. Obviously, if this volume of the gas or vapor per pound is relatively small, the refrigerant is more suitable for commercial use than a refrigerant with a larger volume. On the other hand, the latent heat of evaporation of one pound of a really satisfactory refrigerant should be large, so that the minimum weight of the refrigerant may be circulated for a given refrigerating effect.[1]

Ammonia.—The refrigerant which is most commonly used in large refrigerating plants is ammonia. It is not suitable, however, for use in the types of small refrigerating systems frequently used in apartment houses and dwellings. It has an offensive and penetrating odor which is very irritating to any of the membranes of the body and especially to the eyes. The chemical symbol for ammonia is NH_3. In its natural state, it is a vapor which is very soluble in water. At atmospheric pressure, it boils at $-28°$ F. and has a critical temperature of $271°$ F.[2]

For reasons that will be explained later, only ammonia which is entirely free from water (*anhydrous*) can be used in a compression system of refrigeration.

It is desirable to use a refrigerant of which a small quantity can produce a large cooling effect. In order to have a small power requirement to keep the refrigerant in circulation through the system and to permit the use of a small cylinder in the compressor, the vapor of the refrigerant should have a small volume per pound; or, in other words, the weight of 1 cubic foot of the *vapor* should be large. This makes it possible to produce a given amount of refrigeration with a small compressor, as the size of the compressor and its power requirement depend on the volume of refrigerant circulating through the system. Ammonia possesses both of these desirable properties, and it is for this reason that it is so generally used in the large refrigerating plants.

Solubility and Purity.—Ammonia is very soluble in water, and at ordinary "room" temperatures, water will absorb about nine hundred times its own volume of ammonia vapor. At ordinary temperatures, it is also extremely volatile. It sometimes contains impurities that reduce its effectiveness as a refrigerant. To test liquid ammonia for purity, pour a little into a test tube and allow it to evaporate; impurities will be left in the test tube.

[1] The *critical temperature* of the vapor of a refrigerant is the temperature above which the vapor cannot be condensed by the application of any pressure. It is obvious, of course, that the temperature of the gas or vapor in the condenser must be several degrees higher than that of the cooling water circulating through the condenser. The critical temperature of the vapor, therefore, must be considered with respect to the maximum probable temperature of the cooling water.

[2] The temperature after compression in a compression type of refrigerating machine should not exceed about $300°$ F. because of the unstable condition of ammonia above this temperature.

Inflammability.—Ammonia gas or vapor at ordinary atmospheric temperatures does not burn readily in air, but when heated, it burns readily with a greenish-yellow flame. When it is heated to a higher temperature than 1600° F., it breaks up into its constituent gases (nitrogen and hydrogen), and, under some conditions, these gases form an explosive mixture,[1] especially when some oil vapor is present in a mixture of nitrogen, hydrogen, and ammonia vapor. An explosive mixture of this kind has been known to cause explosions of considerable violence in ammonia refrigerating plants. Ammonia should not be allowed to come into contact with a red-hot metal or an ordinary flame, for these will decompose the vapor of ammonia and ignite the resulting gases, thus causing an explosion.

Effect on Metals.—Either as a liquid or as a vapor, ammonia produces an active chemical effect on brass and similar alloys, especially when water vapor is present. On the other hand, it has no chemical or corrosive effect on iron or steel, at least under the conditions found in ammonia refrigerating systems.

Testing for Leaks.—Ammonia vapor is very light and readily finds its way through pipe joints. Special care should be taken in making all pipe connections. As ammonia has a disagreeable and pungent odor, a small leak is readily noticed, but its location is not so easily found. A water hose should always be in readiness to be used in case a large leak occurs. Water from the hose should be discharged upon the leak to absorb the ammonia and prevent serious damage. Sulphur candles[2] have proved very

[1] Explosive mixtures of ammonia vapor and air range from 13 per cent of ammonia and 87 per cent of air to 27 per cent of ammonia and 73 per cent of air.

[2] Sulphur sticks may easily be made by melting ordinary sulphur or brimstone in a tin can or ladle. The mixture should not get too hot, or it may burn. As an additional precaution to prevent burning, the tin can or ladle should be covered to exclude the air. Thin sticks of wood, about ¼ inch thick and 6 to 9 inches long, or strips of cardboard of the same size, may be dipped into the melted sulphur, the dipping being repeated until the coating on the sticks or strips is about ¹⁄₁₆ inch thick.

In order to use the sulphur sticks for testing, the end of the sulphur coating should be lighted with a match, and the sulphur sticks should then be moved at a distance of about 1 inch, along all pipes, around all fittings, joints, valves, and stuffing boxes. As long as no gray smoke is noticeable, there is no leak, but as soon as smoke is observed while moving along some part of the piping, the place from which the smoke comes should be carefully investigated. The ammonia leak, no matter how small it is, will be found by this method.

helpful in discovering leaks. The fumes given off by them when burning combine with the ammonia. If a burning sulphur candle is held near the nose, one may approach an ammonia leak without much danger. By using sulphur candles, a person who is caught in a compartment filled with ammonia gas can make his escape without serious injury. (For methods of testing water for ammonia leakage, see p. 183.)

Effect on Lubricants.—In the compression system of refrigeration, a considerable amount of lubricant is required in the compressor. The oil used for this lubrication obviously comes into

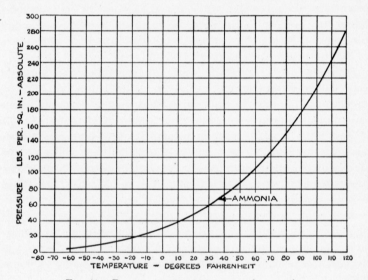

Fig. 41.—Pressure-temperature curves of ammonia.

contact with the ammonia. Anhydrous ammonia has little or no effect on petroleum lubricating oil. In the presence of moisture, however, at the usual temperatures in compressors, ammonia has the tendency to make an oil emulsion.[1]

Charts and Physical Properties.—A comparison of the physical properties of ammonia and some other refrigerants is shown in Table IX (p. 409). A pressure-temperature curve of ammonia is shown in Fig. 41. When ammonia is used as the refrigerant

[1] Osborn, W. F. "The Physical Characteristics of Lubricating Oils as Applied to Refrigerating Machinery" in *Jour. Amer. Soc. Refrigerating Eng.*, Vol. 7, p. 166.

in a refrigerating system, only moderate pressures and temperatures are required.

Sulphur Dioxide.—When sulphur is burned, it combines with the oxygen in the air to form a vapor called *sulphur dioxide* (chemical symbol SO_2). Even in small concentrations in air, sulphur dioxide is very unpleasant to breathe, but it is not considered poisonous because its very presence is so suffocating that one will immediately seek fresh air. It is a colorless vapor, with the aforementioned pungent and suffocating odor. This vapor is very stable, and because it will easily withstand the temperature conditions of ordinary household refrigeration, it is used as a refrigerant in many of the small refrigerating machines intended for household use. Its boiling point at atmospheric pressure is 14° F., and its critical temperature is 311° F.

Inflammability.—Sulphur dioxide is not combustible, so there is no danger of explosion.

Effect on Metals.—Pure sulphur dioxide has no corrosive effect on copper, copper alloys, zinc, iron, or steel unless water is in contact with the vapor, when sulphurous acid is formed which has some corrosive effect on copper, zinc, and iron. Because of this tendency of sulphur dioxide to form sulphurous acid, the presence of water vapor is detrimental and should not exceed 0.3 per cent by volume.

Testing for Leaks.—An easily applied method of locating leaks of sulphur dioxide is to apply ammonia water (aqua ammonia) to pipes and joints in which leaks are suspected. Sulphur dioxide in the presence of ammonia in any form becomes a dense white vapor.

Effect on Lubricants.—Sulphur dioxide has an objectionable effect on some kinds of petroleum oils commonly used for lubrication. To a certain extent, this refrigerant is self-lubricating; but, on the other hand, it has a tendency to absorb oils. The kinds of oil that have a light color are not so readily absorbed by sulphur dioxide as are dark oils.

Because of the tendency of sulphur dioxide to form sulphurous acid in the presence of even small quantities of water, it is necessary to be extremely careful in selecting oils that they contain no water.

Relative Displacement Compared with Ammonia.—A refrigerating machine using sulphur dioxide for the refrigerant requires about three times as much displacement in the cylinder of the compressor as a machine using ammonia for equal amounts of refrigeration.

Charts.—Figure 42 shows a pressure-temperature curve of sulphur dioxide, also similar curves for a number of other refrigerants.

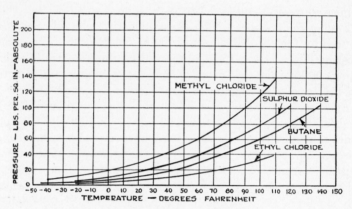

Fig. 42.—Pressure-temperature curves of sulphur dioxide, methyl chloride, butane and ethyl chloride.

Methyl Chloride.—By the chemical action of hydrochloric acid on methyl alcohol, a colorless, sweet-smelling vapor is obtained called *methyl chloride* (chemical symbol CH_3Cl). This vapor is easily liquefied when compressed and then cooled. Its odor resembles that of chloroform. Small quantities of methyl chloride when mixed with air have very little effect upon the lungs and eyes. When more than 10 per cent by volume is in the air, it acts as an anæsthetic, and larger concentrations of the vapor may produce death by suffocation. Because of this tendency to produce unconsciousness, it is not so safe as sulphur dioxide which is more irritating and consequently produces a constant urge to obtain pure air.

The color of methyl chloride as well as its effects are somewhat like chloroform. It is very stable at the usual temperatures of household refrigeration and is now being used as a refrigerant in a number of household refrigerating systems. Its boiling point at atmospheric pressure is $-10°$ F.

Inflammability.—Methyl chloride is inflammable but does not burn readily. It is explosive under certain conditions, as, for example, when a mixture of from 10 to 15 per cent of methyl-chloride vapor and from 85 to 90 per cent of air is exposed to a spark or to a wire which is at a white heat. Mixtures of smaller concentrations will not explode. The flashpoint is about $-10°$ F.

Effect on Metals.—Methyl chloride does not affect copper, copper alloys, iron, or steel.

Testing for Leaks.—A large leak of methyl chloride may be noticed by the peculiar odor resembling chloroform. The exact location of the leak can be determined by the use of an alcohol flame and knowing that methyl chloride gives a greenish tinge to the nearly colorless flame of an alcohol lamp.

Effect on Lubricants.—Methyl chloride dissolves practically all kinds of oils, so it has been found by experience that glycerin and white mineral oils are the only lubricants for compressors using this refrigerant. Because glycerin is hygroscopic, precautions must be taken to avoid the presence of water. Since methyl chloride often contains as much as 10 per cent of water, great care should be taken to obtain it of sufficient purity. The moisture in glycerin has been known to freeze in the cooling or evaporating coils of the refrigerating system and prevent the circulation of the refrigerant.

Relative Displacement Compared with Ammonia.—The cylinder of a compressor using methyl chloride will have a smaller displacement than one using sulphur dioxide for the same amount of refrigeration but requires larger displacement than an ammonia compressor.

Charts.—A pressure-temperature curve of methyl chloride is shown in Fig. 42.

Ethyl Chloride.—The odor of ether is a typical property of ethyl chloride (chemical symbol C_2H_5Cl). In its liquid form it is colorless, very volatile, and has a sweetish taste. Its vapor is very stable at the usual atmospheric temperatures and, for this reason, is suitable for household refrigerating machines and has also found considerable application in the refrigerating machines used on shipboard. Small quantities of ethyl chloride when mixed with air have very little effect upon the lungs and eyes. When more than 10 per cent by volume is in the air, it acts as an anæsthetic, and larger concentrations of the vapor may produce death by suffocation. Because of the tendency of this refrigerant to produce unconsciousness, it is not so safe as sulphur dioxide which is more irritating.

Inflammability.—Under some conditions, ethyl chloride is inflammable. When it is mixed with certain definite proportions of air, it burns with a greenish flame. When a mixture of from 5 to 14 per cent of ethyl-chloride vapor and from 90 to 86 per cent of air by volume is exposed to a spark or to a wire at white heat, there will be explosive combustion. Below or above these percentages, there will be no explosive effects. The flashpoint is below $-18°$ F. It is stated that by the addition of a small amount of methyl bromide to ethyl chloride, the mixture becomes non-inflammable and also non-explosive in air. The boiling point of ethyl chloride at atmospheric pressure is 55° F.

Effect on Metals.—Ethyl chloride has no corrosive effect on copper, copper alloys, iron, or steel.

Testing for Leaks.—Leaks in a system of piping containing ethyl chloride are difficult to locate, since this refrigerant, when expanded following compression, is below atmospheric pressure, and the tendency, therefore, is for air to enter the piping through leaks rather than for ethyl chloride to escape into the air.

Effect on Lubricants.—Ethyl chloride dissolves the oils and greases which are available for lubricating purposes. Experience has shown that glycerin is the only practical lubricant to be used with ethyl chloride, and the same precautions must be taken to avoid moisture as when methyl chloride is used.

Relative Displacement Compared with Ammonia.—Because of the light weight of ethyl chloride per unit of volume, the cylinder of the compressor using it for the refrigerant will be very large in comparison with ammonia and sulphur-dioxide compressors. A compressor using ethyl chloride as a refrigerant requires more than twice the cylinder displacement of one using sulphur dioxide and about seven times the displacement of one using ammonia, for the same amount of refrigerating effect.

Charts.—A temperature-pressure curve of ethyl chloride is shown in Fig. 42. It is possible to operate the compressor of a refrigerating system using ethyl chloride at lower pressures than are commonly used with other refrigerants. Methyl chloride, for example, requires considerably higher operating pressures than ethyl chloride, as will be seen from a comparison of the curves in the figure.

Carbon Dioxide.—The gas which gives the "sparkle" to ginger ale and other carbonated liquids is carbon dioxide (chemical symbol CO_2). This gas is probably more generally known as the one resulting from the combustion of fuels such as coal, wood, oil, etc. It is a heavy, colorless, and odorless gas. It is found in small amounts in atmospheric air. It is harmless to breathe except in extremely large concentrations; it is harmful then because of the lack of oxygen in the air. This gas is very stable and will withstand the temperature conditions in ordinary household service. When carbon dioxide is subjected to a pressure of little more than 500 pounds per square inch and the temperature is about 32° F., it solidifies into a snowlike substance.

Because carbon dioxide is not irritating to the membranes of the body and is not dangerous as a poison, it is often preferred for use in refrigerating systems in hospitals and ships. If a person breathes air containing 2 per cent by volume or carbon dioxide for any length of time, however, his efficiency will be reduced, and headache and drowsiness will result. If very large quantities are taken into the lungs, death may be produced by suffocation.

Inflammability.—Carbon dioxide is not inflammable and has actually a tendency to smother any kind of combustion.

Effect on Metals.—Carbon dioxide has no corrosive effect on copper, copper alloys, iron, or steel.

Testing for Leaks.—Leaks of carbon-dioxide gas are difficult to locate, for the reason that the gas is colorless and odorless under practically all ordinary conditions.

Effect on Lubricants.—Carbon dioxide has no effect upon oils and greases. When, however, it is used as the refrigerant, there will be very low operating temperatures, and, for this reason, the oil used must be suitable for low-temperature service. Glycerin is usually preferred as a lubricant for carbon-dioxide refrigerating machines, as it does not freeze at the low temperatures that are required and is not affected by acid.[1]

Relative Displacement Compared with Ammonia.—Because of the large weight per unit of volume of carbon dioxide, its refrigerating effect for a given volume is also large. A refrigerating machine using carbon dioxide requires only about one-fifth as much cylinder displacement as a machine using ammonia for the same amount of refrigerating effect.

Charts.—The pressure-temperature curve for carbon dioxide is shown in Fig. 43. The compressor-discharge pressures range

[1] Carbon-dioxide gas absorbs water to form a carbonic acid (chemical symbol H_2CO_3). It does not have so much affinity for water as ammonia.

from 800 to 1,000 pounds per square inch with a corresponding range of suction pressures from 200 to 300 pounds per square inch. Because of the high discharge pressures which are necessary, the compressor, the condenser, and the piping connecting them must be designed for very great strength.

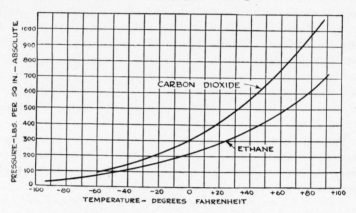

FIG. 43.—Pressure-temperature curves of carbon dioxide and ethane.

Ethane (C_2H_6) and Propane (C_3H_8).—Very little is known regarding the physiological properties of ethane; and the similar properties of propane are known only by inference from its effects on rats, as studied and reported by Dr. E. E. Smith as follows:

When the quantity of propane gas is about 5 per cent and is inhaled for an hour, slight drowsiness is produced, but when the quantity is moderately large (37.5 to 51.7 per cent) and is inhaled for two hours, muscular weakness is observed which is followed by mild anæsthesia. When the quantity of gas is as much as 70 per cent and is inhaled for several hours, there will be muscular spasms followed by anæsthesia.

The temperature-pressure curve of ethane is shown in Fig. 43. It will be observed that the curve for ethane approaches the pressure range of carbon dioxide but is not quite so high. The curve for propane is similar to the pressure-temperature curve of ammonia.

Butane and Isobutane (C_4H_{10}).—The physiological properties of butane are probably similar to those produced by propane, with a possibility that butane is more toxic. The physiological properties of isobutane are probably about the same as those of butane.

The pressure-temperature curve of butane is shown in Fig. 42. It will be noticed that this curve is somewhat similar to the pressure-temperature curve of ethyl chloride.

Ether.—Refrigerating machines of the piston type using ether as the refrigerant are bulky and cannot be used to produce intense cold, because the absolute pressure of ether vapor is only about 1.3 pounds per square inch at 4° F., and to make it evaporate at any temperature nearly as low as this would require an excessively large cylinder of the compressor. This large size would not only make the piston type of compressor clumsy and costly but would also involve much waste of power in mechanical friction. The tendency of air to leak into the system is another practical objection to the use of a pressure so low.

Data of Special Refrigerants.—Properties of several refrigerants which are suitable for use in centrifugal compressors where small differences between discharge and suction pressures are permissible are given in the accompanying table.

TABLE I

	Dieline[1] $C_2H_2Cl_2$		Trieline[1] C_2HCl_3		Carrene[1] CH_2Cl_2	
	"Standard-ton" temperatures					
	5° F.	86° F.	5° F.	86° F.	5° F.	86° F.
Absolute pressure, pounds per square inch...............	0.82	6.9	0.16	1.72	1.29	10.3
Volume of liquid, cubic feet per pound...............	0.0127	....	0.0109	....	0.012	
Volume of vapor, cubic feet per pound...............	63.00	8.5	240.00	25.20	48.3	6.8
Latent heat of evaporation, B.t.u. per pound...........	136.00	133.00	112.50	109.50	149.00	146.00
Entropy of liquid.............	0.0029	0.0425	0.00252	0.0368	0.0037	0.0535
Entropy of evaporation........	0.2930	0.2435	0.2420	0.2010	0.3200	0.2670
Entropy of vapor.............	0.2959	0.2860	0.2445	0.2378	0.3237	0.3205
Specific heat of liquid.........	0.270		0.233		0.340	
Specific heat of vapor (constant pressure)..................	0.1625		0.120		0.154	
Specific heat of vapor (constant volume)....................	0.1425		0.105		0.131	
Specific gravity of liquid (water = 1).....................	1.27		1.47		1.33	
Specific gravity of vapor (air = 1)	3.36		4.55		3.00	
Critical abstract pressure, pounds per square inch......	800[2]				1,490[2]	
Critical temperature, degrees Fahrenheit................	470[2]				380[2]	

[1] The refrigerant dieline is stable dichloro-ethylene, trieline, is trichloro-ethylene, and carrene is a water-white liquid at normal atmospheric conditions. It has a slightly sweetish odor similar to dieline but is non-combustible. Carrene is methylene chloride.

[2] Approximate

Heating and Cooling.—Refrigeration means the removal of heat from a substance in order to produce a low temperature. When heat is added to a substance, its temperature is raised; and when it is removed, its temperature is lowered. The removal of heat is sometimes called the *production of cold*, as though *cold* had a different meaning from *heat*. *Hot* and *cold* are terms which apply to effects produced upon our senses and indicate merely relative temperatures.

When coal burns in a stove, it gives heat to the stove, which, in turn, gives it up to the cooking pans and their contents. A spoon left in one of these pans becomes hot or absorbs heat until it and the contents of the pan have the same temperature. If a pan is taken from a hot stove and is placed in a basin of cold water, it loses some of its heat to the water and continues to do so until the water has the same temperature as the pan and its contents. A freshly killed fowl hung in a refrigerating compartment gives off heat and raises the temperature of the surrounding air. The air, in turn, has its heat removed by cold brine (indirect refrigeration p. 64) or by ammonia vapor (direct refrigeration), which circulates in the cooling or evaporating coils.

Measurement of Temperature.—If one's hand touches a piece of ice, the sensation of cold is noticed. If a live coal is touched, the sensation of heat is observed. Temperature, then, is the sensation which these bodies produce upon the senses or, more exactly, upon instruments used to measure the intensity of heat. The temperature of a substance may not show directly the quantity of heat in that substance. For example, if a pail contains 10 pounds of water at 60° F., and another contains 2 pounds of water at 150° F., the first pail, although at a lower temperature, has the greater quantity of heat. Temperature, therefore, reveals only the state or intensity of heat not the amount of heat in a body.

If two bodies have the same temperature, there is no transfer of heat from one to the other. But if one body is at a higher temperature than the other, heat will pass from the higher to the lower temperature.

If 122° F. is to be changed into centigrade degrees, it is first necessary to subtract from it 32 and then multiply this result $(122 - 32 = 90)$ by $^{100}/_{180}$ or $^5/_9$, and the result is 50° C. Using a short cut, the above methods of calculation may be stated as follows:

Centigrade degrees = $\frac{5}{9} \times$ (Fahrenheit degrees − 32°)

Fahrenheit degrees = $\frac{9}{5} \times$ (Centigrade degrees) + 32°

Measurement of Heat. Heat Units.—The most common way of measuring heat is to observe its effect in raising the temperature of a quantity of water. The quantity of heat is then determined from the rise in temperature of the water and its weight. The unit of heat is the *British thermal unit*, generally abbreviated B.t.u. The B.t.u. is the amount of heat required to raise the temperature of 1 pound of water 1° F. A more recent way of defining this heat unit is to state its value as $\frac{1}{180}$ of the heat required to raise the temperature of 1 pound of water from 32 to 212° F. at normal atmospheric pressure. This is generally called the *mean B.t.u.* The unit may easily be remembered by the phrase "1 pound of water, 1° F."

Latent Heat of Fusion.—The addition of heat to a substance may produce other changes besides one in temperature. The form or condition of the substance may be altered, as when iron melts or water boils. While this change of condition is taking place, there is no change in temperature, yet large quantities of heat are absorbed. If heat is applied to ice, its temperature rises to 32° F. When this point is reached, a further addition of heat does not change the temperature until all of the ice is melted. The amount of heat added to produce this change in condition at atmospheric pressure has been found by experiment to be 144 B.t.u. (see p. 91) for each pound of ice which is melted. The heat which is thus expended is called the *latent heat of fusion* of ice. Because of its capacity to absorb large quantities of heat in melting and because of its relative cheapness, ice is used extensively in reducing the temperature of warm substances, when, of course, the temperature need not be lower than 32° F. When ice is melted in a refrigerator and is changed to the liquid state as water, a great deal of heat is absorbed from the contents of the refrigerator, and this absorbed heat is carried away through the drain to the outside. Unless ice in the refrigerator melts,[1] it will not cool the contents of the refrigerator and the enclosed air.

---

[1] Except in emergencies, it is not a good plan to put newspapers over the ice in a refrigerator, nor is it good policy to put so-called "blankets" over ice in order to prevent its melting.

Heat of Liquid.—If water is heated in an open vessel over a fire, its temperature will rise until it reaches 212° F. Since the water absorbs heat and there is *no change in its condition*, the heat which is absorbed is said to be the *heat of the liquid.* To each pound of water, then, a certain number of B.t.u. is added, depending, of course, on the amount of heat already in the water. Since water freezes at 32° F., at this temperature it is said to have *no heat of the liquid.* If the temperature of 1 pound of water is raised from 32 to 212° F., the water absorbs 212 − 32 or 180 B.t.u., which is the heat of the liquid at 212° F.

Latent Heat of Evaporation.—Evaporation is changing a liquid to a vapor or a gas by the application of heat. The heat which is added to a liquid to bring it from 32° F. to the temperature of boiling is, of course, the heat of the liquid. When, however, the boiling point is reached, the temperature remains constant, and a relatively enormous amount of heat must be added to change the liquid to a vapor or a gas. This amount of heat added during the change from the liquid to the vapor or gas state is called the *latent heat of evaporation*, and although, *in principle*, this latent heat is exactly similar to the latent heat of fusion which is absorbed by a solid, as, for example, ice in melting, it is a very much larger quantity of heat in all practical cases which have to do with refrigeration.[1]

Evaporation takes place from the surface of liquids at all ordinary temperatures, but when heat is applied, it will take place more rapidly and at a higher and higher rate as the temperature is increased, until, finally, it takes place not only on the surface but also all through the body of the liquid at minute surfaces which are formed by little bubbles. When a liquid is boiling, there is a very much greater surface for evaporation, largely because of the formation of bubbles, than when there is only slow evaporation at the surface, and, consequently, the liquid will change to a vapor at a higher rate in proportion to this greater area of the effective surface for evaporation. These

[1] According to the molecular theory, during evaporation some molecules of a refrigerant, or, in fact, any liquid, find their way outside the surface of the liquid, and these "outside" molecules tend to fill the surrounding space; if this space is enclosed, there will be impact on the walls with a resulting pressure which is called the *vapor pressure* of the liquid. This amount of pressure has a definite relation to the temperature. When the temperature of a liquid is obtainable, it is possible to determine the vapor pressure of the liquid by reference to tables of its properties.

bubbles of vapor will form and collect into larger bubbles as they rise to the surface.[1]

When a liquid evaporates, work must be done upon it (1) to separate the molecules against their attractive forces, (2) to make space for the newly formed vapor by pressure against the surrounding medium, doing work against its pressure. The work of the first kind is called *internal latent heat;* the second, *external latent heat.* The sum of these two is the *total latent heat* given in the tables of the properties of refrigerants.

The *latent heat of evaporation* of a refrigerant may readily be given up by changing its vapor back to the liquid condition. To evaporate 1 pound of *liquid* ammonia at a temperature of 5° F. and a pressure of 34.3 pounds per square inch absolute, requires the addition of 565 B.t.u.; and to change 1 pound of ammonia *vapor* which is at a temperature of 5° F. into liquid ammonia, there must be removed from it 565 B.t.u.

The evaporation of any liquid causes a cooling effect. The more rapid the evaporation the greater the effect of cooling. Volatile liquids like gasoline, ether, and alcohol, which have large latent heats of evaporation, can be used for cooling. In refrigerating plants, cooling is produced by the evaporation of liquid ammonia, liquid carbon dioxide, or some other refrigerant.

Specific Heat.—In practical refrigeration work, it is necessary to consider not only the amount of heat absorbed in cooling different substances but also the amount of heat absorbed by the walls within which the substances are stored.

In a preceding paragraph, the B.t.u. was defined as the amount of heat necessary to raise the temperature of 1 pound of water 1° F. It has also been shown that all substances do not require the same amount of heat to raise their temperature 1° F. For example, if a pound of water and a pound of lead are heated over the same fire, the lead will have the higher temperature. This means that the quantity of heat which will raise 1 pound of water to a certain temperature will raise 1 pound of lead to a much higher temperature. Then, too, if these two substances have the same temperature and they are cooled to the same lower temperature, in doing so the water will give up more heat than

---

[1] Before the bubbles that are formed within the liquid can collect and rise toward the surface of the liquid, the vapor pressure within the bubbles must be sufficient to overcome the pressure on them due to the weight o the liquid over them.

the lead. In order to know how much heat is given off by a certain substance in cooling, it is necessary to know the specific heat of the substance. The specific heat of a substance is the amount of heat required to raise or lower the temperature of 1 pound of the substance 1° F. The specific heat of water is taken as the "point of departure" or the standard, and the specific heat of every other substance is determined by the relation of the amount of heat required to raise or lower the temperature of 1 pound 1° F. to 1, which is the adopted specific heat of water. Thus, the specific heat of alcohol is 0.60; of iron, 0.12, of ice, 0.50. To illustrate concretely, since the specific heat of ice is 0.5, the amount of heat which is necessary to raise the temperature of a given weight of ice 1° F. will raise the temperature of the same weight of water 0.5° F.

Example.—How many British heat units are required to lower the temperature of 500 pounds of aluminum from 100 to 40° F., the specific heat of aluminum being 0.22?

As it requires the removal of 0.22 B.t.u. to lower the temperature of 1 pound of aluminum 1° F. it will require the removal of 0.22 × 500 × (100 − 40) or 6,600 B.t.u. to lower its temperature from 100 to 40° F.

Example.—A storage room 50 by 25 by 10 feet is to have the air cooled from 70 to 32° F. At the lower (final) temperature, a cubic foot of air weighs 0.0807 pound and the specific heat at constant pressure is 0.237. How much heat must be removed from the air?

The room contains 50 × 25 × 10 or 12,500 cubic feet of air. Since 1 cubic foot of air at 32° F. weighs 0.0807 pound, the weight of air in the storage room when cooled is 12,500 × 0.0807 or 1,008.75 pounds. To cool each pound of air, at constant pressure, it is necessary to remove 0.237 B.t.u. for each degree Fahrenheit change in temperature. To cool 1,008.75 pounds of air from 70 to 32° F. requires 1,008.75 × 0.237 × (70 − 32) B.t.u. or 9,084.8 B.t.u. to be absorbed.

If this amount of heat is to be removed by means of melting ice, it will require 9,084.8 ÷ 144 or 63.1 pounds, since each pound in melting absorbs 144 B.t.u.

Heat Involved in Refrigeration Process.—When foods and other goods are placed in cold storage, there is first a reduction in temperature. To calculate the amount of heat to be removed, it is necessary to know the weight of the foods and other goods, their specific heats, and the required change in temperature. The sum of the products of these quantities for each kind of goods in cold storage gives the amount of heat which must be removed.

It so happens that some foods are usually kept frozen in cold storage. In this case, it is necessary to know the latent heat of fusion of the foods which are to be frozen, because this latent heat must be removed before actual freezing takes place. As the largest portion of all foods is water, they will freeze at *about* 32° F., and in freezing they require the removal of a large quantity of heat. Foods are sometimes cooled below 32° F. In such cases, in order to find the amount of heat to be removed, it is necessary to know the *specific heat* of the foods *before* they freeze and also *after* they are frozen. When the specific heat, the latent heat, the weight, and the final temperature are known, it will be possible to find the amount of heat (in B.t.u.) that must be removed.

Table II.—Heat Properties of Various Food Substances

Substance	Specific heat above freezing, B.t.u. per pound	Latent heat B.t.u. per pound	Specific heat below freezing, B.t.u. per pound	Temperature at which usually kept, degrees Fahrenheit
Beef..................	0.68	86	0.38	33–35
Veal..................	0.70	90	0.39	36
Pork.................	0.51	55	0.30	40
Mutton...............	0.67	84	0.37	32
Fresh fish.............	0.82	111	0.43	20
Oysters...............	0.84	114	0.44	30–35
Poultry...............	0.80	105	0.42	20–28
Eggs.................	0.76	100	0.40	31–33
Cheese...............	0.64	84	0.37	28–34
Butter...............	0.64	84	0.37	18–25
Milk.................	0.90	124	0.47	34
Cream...............	0.68	84	0.38	34
Vegetables...........	0.89	120	0.45	34–36
Beer.................	0.90	124	0.47	33–35
Fresh fruit...........	0.92	128	0.48	32–36
Game (to freeze)......	0.80	105	0.42	25–28

Example.—How much heat must be removed from 5 tons of poultry in cooling it from a temperature of 65 to 20° F.?

The amount of heat which is to be removed will be considered in three parts: (1) heat to be extracted in lowering the temperature from 65 to 32° F.; (2) latent heat at 32° F.; (3) heat removed in lowering the temperature from 32 to 20° F. In general, it is customary to find these three quantities for 1 pound of the substance which is to be cooled.

B.t.u.

1. Heat removed per pound from 65 to 32° F. = 0.80(65 − 32)..... = 26.4
2. Latent heat per pound at 32° F............................ = 105.0
3. Heat removed per pound from 32 to 20° F. = 0.42(32 − 20)...... = 5.04

Total heat removed per pound........................... 136.44

Total heat removed for 5 tons = 5 × 2,000 × 136.44 = 1,364,400 B.t.u.

Theoretical Displacement of Compressor.—The theoretical displacement of the cylinder of a compressor in a refrigerating system is calculated by multiplying together the weight of refrigerant in pounds per minute, which is circulated through the cooling coils of the evaporator, and the volume in cubic feet per pound of the refrigerant at the temperature of the suction side of the compressor.

If, for example, the weight of ammonia circulated per minute in pounds per ton of refrigeration is 0.4 and the volume of 1 pound of ammonia vapor at the suction temperature of the compressor (5° F.) is 8.15 cubic feet, the theoretical displacement of the ammonia compressor, in this case, is, then, 8.15 × 0.4 or 3.26 cubic feet per minute. This is the theoretical volume (cubic feet) of saturated ammonia vapor which will enter the suction pipe of the compressor from the cooling coil of the evaporator per minute, in order to produce a ton of refrigeration for the required temperature conditions. The actual displacement of a cylinder of a compressor must always be considerably larger than the theoretical value as calculated by this method, because the weight of ammonia vapor in the cylinder is always considerably less than the amount that is theoretically displaced by the piston. In other words, the actual displacement volume per ton of refrigeration must always be larger than the theoretical amount.

Superheating of Vapor Due to Compression.—The pressure on the suction side of a refrigerating system is the pressure in the cooling coils of the evaporator. The compressor takes the vapor from the evaporator and compresses it to a higher pressure. In doing this, a certain amount of work is done upon the vapor and its temperature is raised above the boiling point at the higher pressure. Vapor under these conditions is said to be *superheated*. If this additional heat is left in the vapor, the condenser will have to do more cooling than if there were no superheat.

Wet and Dry Compression of Ammonia.—There are two systems by which ammonia compressors are operated: (1) dry compression and (2) wet compression. If the ammonia vapor which is drawn into the cylinder of a compressor does not contain particles of liquid ammonia in suspension, the compression is said to be *dry;* and, conversely, if the vapor taken in by the compressor does contain particles of liquid ammonia in suspension, the compression is said to be *wet*.

With dry compression, the vapor of the refrigerant is superheated during compression, because work is being done on the vapor. The water jacket of the compressor reduces only slightly the amount of superheat and does not prevent entirely the superheating of the vapor of the refrigerant.

In a *wet-compression* ammonia refrigerating system, the heat produced by the compression of the ammonia vapor raises its temperature and causes the evaporation of the liquid ammonia which was injected. In evaporating, the latent heat of evaporation of the liquid ammonia is absorbed by the superheated compressed vapor, and its temperature is lowered. The evaporation of even a little liquid ammonia prevents superheating.

In the ammonia refrigerating system in Fig. 11, the liquid ammonia used for this cooling purpose is taken from the liquid receiver as shown by the piping.

Another means often used to prevent superheating is to inject cold oil into the cylinder at the beginning of the compression stroke. This oil absorbs the superheat. After leaving the compressor, the oil is removed from the compressed vapor by the *oil separator*. Oil injected in this way serves to seal the piston and valves, thus preventing leakage. It also partly fills the clearance space at the end of the stroke and causes the expulsion of nearly all of the vapor; this leaves the cylinder to take in nearly a full charge on the return stroke.

There is a difference of opinion as to which of these systems is the better. The presence of liquid refrigerant in the cylinder may result in disaster to the machine if the clearance space is small. The valves should be designed to permit the escape of any of the excess of the liquid on the compression stroke.

Comparative Value of Refrigerants.—In order to compare refrigerants, a practical range of temperature has been chosen, the standard temperature of the gas or vapor *after compression* being 86° F., and the lower temperature, that is, the temperature in the cooling coil of the evaporator, being 5° F. Table III shows the important properties of ammonia and carbon dioxide for these two temperatures.

Item 3 in Table IV, p. 89, shows that the *evaporation* of 1 pound of *ammonia* will produce a cooling effect of 474.4 B.t.u. per pound, while 1 pound of *carbon dioxide* in evaporating will produce a cooling effect of only 54.2 B.t.u. per pound. In order, therefore, to produce the same amount of refrigeration as is derived from 1 pound of ammonia, there must be 474.4 ÷ 54.2 or 8.75 pounds of carbon dioxide in circulation. In this respect, ammonia has a great advantage over carbon dioxide.

TABLE III

	Temperature, degrees Fahrenheit	Absolute pressure, pounds per square inch	Latent heat of evaporation, B.t.u. per pound	Specific volume, cubic feet per pound
Ammonia...........	86	169.2	492.6	1.77
	5	34.3	565.0	8.15
Carbon dioxide.......	86	1,039.0	27.0	0.47
	5	334.2	114.7	0.27

In order to produce a temperature of 86° F. at the end of compression, the absolute pressure of carbon dioxide will be 1,039 pounds per square inch; and for ammonia, 169.2 pounds per square inch. The pressure required when using carbon dioxide is 1,039.0 ÷ 169.2 or 6.04 times as great as that for ammonia. Such a high pressure requires a compressor and piping of heavy construction. When carbon dioxide is used as the refrigerant, pressures as high as 1,100 pounds per square inch absolute are frequent in tropical countries, as it is difficult to obtain a supply of cooling water with a sufficiently low temperature to permit having a discharge pressure much under this value. Pressures in ammonia refrigerating systems are neither very high nor very low but are above atmospheric pressure; hence, no special construction of the compressor or piping is necessary.

In producing a given cooling effect with carbon dioxide, it is necessary to circulate (as calculated in the preceding paragraph) 8.75 times as much carbon dioxide as would be required to obtain the same cooling effect with ammonia. Now, since the volume of 1 pound of carbon dioxide at 5° F. is 0.27 cubic feet, 8.75 times as much, or 2.36 cubic feet of carbon-dioxide gas, must be removed by the compressor as compared to 8.15 cubic feet of ammonia vapor (see table) for the same cooling effect.

The principal characteristic properties of five of the refrigerants most commonly used are given in Table[1] IV, p. 89. The comparison is made on the basis of the number of pounds of refriger-

[1] See MOTZ, "Principles of Refrigeration," p. 63.

TABLE IV.—CHARACTERISTICS OF REFRIGERANTS
(For standard temperatures of 86° F. in condenser and 5° F. in evaporator)

	Ammonia	Carbon dioxide	Sulphur dioxide	Ethyl chloride	Methyl chloride
1. Total heat content of vapor leaving evaporator, B.t.u. per pound...	613.3	101	162.3	165	154
2. Heat of liquid, leaving condenser, B.t.u. per pound..............	138.9	46.8	18.2	23	25.1
3. Refrigerating effect, B.t.u. per pound.......	474.4	54.2	144.1	142	138.9
4. Pounds of refrigerant per minute per ton refrigeration.............	0.42	3.70	1.40	1.41	1.45
5. Specific volume of vapor in evaporator, cubic feet per pound........	8.15	0.27	6.66	17.1	4.72
6. Theoretical displacement per minute per ton of refrigeration, cubic feet.............	3.44	0.99	9.26	23.95	6.83
7. Horsepower per ton of refrigeration..........	0.99	1.87	0.99	0.92	1.06

ant that must be circulated in the system per minute to produce one ton of refrigeration.[1]

A comparison is also made of the theoretical displacement of the compressor per ton of refrigeration and the theoretical horsepower required per ton of refrigeration. The values given in the table are based on a temperature of 5° F. in the cooling coil of the evaporator and a temperature of 86° F. in that portion of the condenser where the gas or vapor is in the saturated condition.

The number of pounds of refrigerant which it is necessary to evaporate per minute per ton of refrigeration is given in item 4 in the table, and the theoretical displacement of the compressor per minute per ton of refrigeration is stated in item 6. To obtain the *actual displacement* of a compressor from the values given in item 6, it would be necessary to increase the values given from 15 to 25 per cent. The *theoretical horsepower required per ton of refrigeration* (see p. 246) is shown in item 7, where a comparison of values shows that the horsepower per ton of refrigeration does

[1] For definition of 1 ton of refrigeration, see p. 91.

not vary a great deal for four of the refrigerants, these being ammonia, sulphur dioxide, methyl chloride, and ethyl chloride. On the other hand, the horsepower per ton of refrigeration required when carbon dioxide is used as the refrigerant is double the power needed for any one of the other four refrigerants in the table. The advantages of ammonia for use as the refrigerant in large refrigerating plants so much outweigh the disadvantages that it is used much more than any other refrigerant.

For the usual temperatures in a refrigerating system, ammonia is compressed to only relatively moderate pressures, and the necessary displacement of the compressor is also relatively small, as shown by item 6. The advantages of ammonia for use as the refrigerant in large refrigerating plants so much outweigh the disadvantages that it is used much more than any other refrigerant.

Evaporation and Condensation of Refrigerants.—Water and ammonia and other liquids act very much alike with reference to their boiling points and evaporation. At normal atmospheric pressure, water boils and becomes steam or vapor at a temperature of 212° F. Liquid ammonia boils and becomes a vapor at about 28° F. below zero (−28° F.). At more than atmospheric pressure, water must be raised to a greater temperature than 212° F. in order to boil. For instance, if the gage pressure is increased to 50 pounds per square inch, water will not boil or vaporize until its temperature is 298° F. If ammonia is at a pressure which is greater than that of the atmosphere, it will not become a vapor at −28° F. but at some higher temperature, according to the pressure to which it is subjected. For each pressure there is a definite temperature at which liquid ammonia or water will boil and vaporize. If liquid ammonia is heated at its boiling point, some of the liquid will evaporate and become a vapor and in doing so will take up its latent heat of evaporation. Then, if this ammonia vapor has its temperature lowered below the boiling point, it will give up its latent heat and condense to the liquid condition. Ammonia and other refrigerants take the condition of a vapor or a liquid according to whether the actual temperature is above or below the boiling temperature corresponding to the pressure. For example, if ammonia at a gage pressure of 28.4 pounds per square inch has its temperature raised above 15° F., it will be a vapor; if its temperature is below 15° F., it will be a liquid. Likewise, if ammonia is at a gage pressure of 181.1 pounds per square inch and has its temperature raised above 95° F., it is a vapor, and below 95° F. it is a liquid.

It follows then that increasing the pressure of a refrigerant raises the boiling and the condensing temperatures, and, conversely, decreasing the pressure lowers the boiling and the condensing temperatures. Any vapor, moreover, condenses at constant pressure when its temperature is lowered below the boiling point.

Refrigeration Units.—Refrigeration capacity is usually measured in terms of the standard commercial *ton of refrigeration per day*, meaning the quantity of heat in B.t.u. required to melt 1 ton of pure ice at 32° F. into water at 32° F. in 24 hours. The latent heat of fusion of ice is 144 B.t.u.[1] per pound at this temperature. A standard commercial ton of refrigeration per day is, therefore, a quantity of heat equal to 2,000 × 144 or 288,000 B.t.u. per 24 hours, which is sometimes called *refrigeration power*. Refrigeration capacity is simply calculated by dividing the total heat transfer in a day by 288,000. If, for example, a refrigerating plant transfers 3,000,000 B.t.u. in 24 hours, the refrigeration capacity of the plant is 3,000,000 divided by 288,000 or 10.41 tons of refrigeration per day.

The capacity of a refrigerating machine is usually expressed in tons of refrigeration or ice-making effect in 24 hours.

The joint committee of the American Society of Mechanical Engineers and the American Society of Refrigerating Engineers on Standard Tonnage Basis of Refrigeration recommends the following units:

a. A standard ton of refrigeration is 288,000 B.t.u.
This value is obtained by multiplying together 2,000 pounds (1 ton) and 144, which is the latent heat of fusion of ice at 32° F. in B.t.u. per pound.

b. The *standard commercial ton of refrigeration capacity* is the rate of cooling at 200 B.t.u. per minute.

c. The standard rating of a refrigerating system using liquefiable gas or vapor is the number of *standard* tons of refrigeration it performs under adopted pressures of refrigerants, namely: (1) the inlet (suction) pressure being that which corresponds to a saturation temperature of 5° F.[2] (−15°

[1] The U. S. Bureau of Standards has made a more exact determination in which it was found that the latent heat or fusion of ice was almost exactly 143.5. This figure may, however, be considered as so near to the usually accepted value, which is 144, that the latter number continues to be used as the standard value for all practical calculations.

[2] It should be pointed out that the temperature of the gas or vapor of the refrigerant coming to the compressor need not be 5° F. It can be higher but not lower. The temperature of the discharged vapor is often higher than 86° F. This temperature of the discharged vapor is then to be taken as the temperature corresponding to the saturation pressure.

C.); and (2) the outlet (discharge) pressure being that which corresponds to a saturation temperature of 86° F. (30° C.). There shall be 9° F. (5° C.) *subcooling*[1] of the liquid entering the expansion or throttling valve, and 9° F. superheating of the vapor entering the compressor. These pressures and temperatures are to be measured outside and within 10 feet of the refrigerating machine.

The following equivalents of a standard *ton of refrigeration per 24 hours* are convenient for reference:

B.t.u.
288,000 per day
12,000 per hour
200 per minute

Ice-making Capacity.—Although the standard for the usual commercial purposes is the *ton of refrigeration per 24 hours*, there is also another term which is sometimes used in the rating of refrigerating machines, especially in plants where the machines are used for making ice. This other unit is called *ice-making capacity* and means the number of tons of ice which a refrigerating machine can produce in 24 hours. This quantity is usually equal to about 50 to 75 per cent of the refrigerating capacity as expressed in tons of refrigeration per day. The heat transfer necessary to produce ice includes the following four items: (1) heat removal to cool the water to the freezing point; (2) heat removal to freeze the water at the constant temperature of 32° F. (3) heat removal to cool the ice to the temperature of the "brine bath"; (4) heat removal to make up losses.

In order to make these items clearer, the following example is given: Water at a temperature of 90° F. is to be used to make ice by the use of brine which has been cooled to 15° F. The first item of cooling as outlined in the preceding tabulation, therefore, is to cool the water from 90 to 32° F. This is a temperature change of 58°. It will be sufficiently accurate to assume that the specific heat of water is 1.0. Now, the difference in temperature times the specific heat of water is the quantity of heat change per pound of water which is cooled, and this quantity of heat is 58 B.t.u. It requires the absorption of 144 B.t.u. to melt 1 pound of ice, and the specific heat of ice is approximately 0.5, so that the amount of heat required to cool the ice to the temperature of the brine is equal to the temperature range multiplied by

[1] *Subcooling* means cooling the liquid refrigerant below the temperature at which condensation takes place.

0.5. The difference between 32 and 15° F. is 17° F., and the heat change necessary for this cooling is 17 × 0.5 or 8.5 B.t.u. per pound of ice. The total heat required, therefore, to *cool the water* to the freezing point to *make ice* and then to *cool the ice* to the temperature of the brine is 58 + 144 + 8.5 or 210.5 B.t.u. per pound. At least 10 per cent additional heat units must be added to make up the loss of heat through the insulation of the brine tank or coils and other incidental losses, so that the total quantity of heat which is required for ice making is 210.5 + (210.5 × 0.10) or nearly 232 B.t.u. per pound of ice. This last figure is equivalent, of course, to 2,000 × 232 or 464,000 B.t.u. per *ton of ice* which is made.

The relative wastefulness of making ice for purposes of refrigeration on a large scale compared with the direct use of some refrigerant is shown by the fact that, as calculated above, the heat requirement for producing a ton of ice is 464,000 B.t.u. per ton, while the refrigerating effect of a ton of ice due to its melting is only 144 × 2,000 or 288,000 B.t.u. per ton. The percentage of the refrigerating capacity that becomes available in ice-making capacity is, therefore, 288,000 ÷ 464,000, which is equivalent to 62.1 per cent.

Capacity of a Refrigeration System.—The common rating of refrigerating systems is in *tons of refrigeration*. By this is meant that the amount of refrigeration produced mechanically is equivalent to the quantity of heat absorbed by the melting of 1 ton of ice every 24 hours. This is the *unit of refrigeration*. If 1 ton of ice melts every 24 hours, the amount of heat required is then found by multiplying the latent heat of fusion of ice by the weight of the ice. This means that 144 × 2,000 or 288,000 heat units are required to melt 1 ton of ice. A refrigerating system which removes 28,800,000 heat units every 24 hours is said to have a capacity of 100 tons of refrigeration. This does not mean, however, that an ice-making plant having a capacity of 1 ton of refrigeration will produce 1 ton of ice every 24 hours.

Mechanical Equivalent of Heat.—It has already been shown that heat may be made to do work by the use of some form of heat engine. Since work and heat are interchangeable forms of energy there must be some relation between the B.t.u. and the foot-pound. By actual experiments, it has been found that 778 foot-pounds of work are equivalent to 1 B.t.u. This quantity 778 is called the *mechanical equivalent of heat.*

CHAPTER IV

COMPRESSORS FOR REFRIGERATING PLANTS

Compressors for Ammonia Refrigerating Systems.—The compressor in an ammonia refrigerating system is usually of the reciprocating rather than the rotating type. The reciprocating kind has a piston which moves up and down or back and forth when the compressor is operated. Every compressor has a suction or intake stroke and a discharge or "exhaust" stroke. During the suction stroke, the vapor of the refrigerant is drawn into the cylinder filling it as the piston moves in the direction which increases the cylinder volume to be filled. During this suction stroke, the suction valves of the compressor are open, and the discharge valves are closed. When the piston gets to the end of its suction stroke and the normal amount of vapor which the cylinder will hold has been drawn in, the suction valves close, the discharge valves remain closed, and the piston begins a stroke in a backward direction compared with the suction stroke. This "backward" stroke is called the *compression*, because, during this stroke, the vapor inside the cylinder is compressed into a smaller and smaller space until, near the end of the stroke, it occupies only a small part of the space it occupied before compression. The vapor is then at a high pressure and very hot. During the compression stroke, the pressure increases until it is slightly higher than that which is maintained in the *condenser;* and when this pressure is reached, at about three-quarters of the compression stroke, the discharge valves open, and the hot[1] compressed vapor is forced into the condenser.

Reciprocating Ammonia Compressors.—Reciprocating compressors are classified as (1) single-acting and (2) double-acting. A single-acting compressor takes in the vapor of the refrigerant to be compressed on only one side of the piston, so that only one

---

[1] The vapor of the refrigerant becomes very hot because of the expenditure of mechanical energy or work in compressing it from the low pressure in the cooling coils of the evaporator to the high pressure required so that it will force itself into the condenser against the pressure prevailing there.

94

charge is compressed in a revolution. This type of compressor does not require a stuffing box so intricate and expensive as the one in a double-acting compressor. A double-acting compressor takes in the vapor of the refrigerant on both sides of the piston so that two charges of vapor are compressed in a revolution. A double-acting compressor, therefore has approximately twice the capacity of a single-acting compressor having the same diameter of cylinder and length of stroke.

A compressor consists in its most essential parts of a cylinder in which a piston moves to and fro and the suction and discharge valves in this cylinder. In most cases, these valves are operated

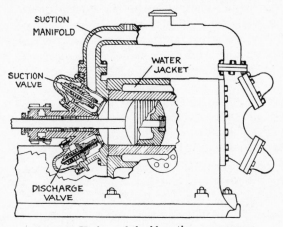

Fig. 44.—Horizontal double-acting compressor.

by springs so that they open when the pressure is in the direction to lift them and close when this pressure is released.

The available data regarding recent installations of refrigerating systems seem to show that there are in use considerably more vertical, single-acting compressors than horizontal double-acting compressors. Each type has its advantages. The strongest point in favor of the selection of the horizontal type of machine is the accessibility of the working parts all of which are near the floor, compared with the location of the same parts in a large vertical compressor. The construction of a horizontal compressor makes a compact arrangement that is easily accessible for operating, overhauling, and repairing. This type of compressor can be operated efficiently when working under *either wet or dry compression* (see p. 86). It is a dependable machine for either kind of operation, while the vertical type, unless very carefully designed, may give trouble when it must be operated with wet vapor. The horizontal type of compressor, furthermore, requires only a little more floor space than the vertical type, while the headroom it requires is only about one-half that of a vertical machine.

Piston of Compressor.—The piston of a horizontal double-acting compressor is generally a light and hollow semi-steel

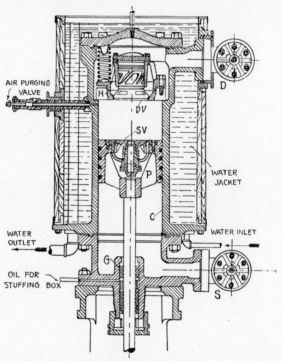

FIG. 45.—Cylinder of vertical single-acting compressor (uni-flow).

casting. The cylinders of many horizontal compressors have spherical heads, as in Fig. 44, and when this is the case, the faces of the piston must be of a shape similar to the ends of the cylinder. Such a piston consists of two parts, one part fitting against a tapered shoulder on the piston rod. A nut and locknut are then screwed onto the piston rod to fasten this half of the piston tightly against the shoulder. The other half of the piston is held in place by a locknut which completely fills a recess made for it in

mits the use in construction of some metals, as, for example, copper and its alloys, which cannot be used in contact with ammonia when water vapor may possibly be present.

In Fig. 65, the cylinder of a vertical, double-acting carbon-dioxide compressor is shown. This cylinder is made of a steel forging and is bored out of a solid block of metal. The small diameter of the cylinder makes it possi-ble to produce very high pressures with-out causing excessive forces in the piston rod, connecting rod, and crank.

The carbon-dioxide gas enters the cylinder C through the passage A and the suction valves B, B. The gas is compressed in the cylinder by the piston P and is expelled after compression at a very high pressure through the discharge valves D, D into the discharge passage E.

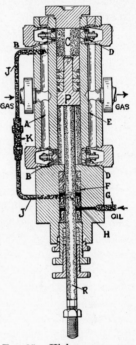

FIG. 65.—High-pressure car-bon-dioxide compressor.

The piston is fitted with metallic pis-ton rings, while cup leathers are used as packing in the stuffing box F.

Lubrication of this type of compressor is a special problem. A mechanical force-feed lubricator delivers oil through the pipe connection G to the lantern[1] of the stuffing box. From the point H, in the inner section of the stuffing box, a pipe J leads to the suction passage A through a check valve K. This pipe permits any carbon-dioxide gas leaking into the stuffing box along the piston rod R to return to the suction valves of the compressor. With this gas is carried any oil which has found its way from the oil lantern H. The distribution of this oil on the cylinder walls pro-vides the necessary lubrication and sealing-oil film over the piston rings. In a vertical-cylinder compressor, the pipe J extends upward from the stuffing box and enters the suction chamber or port above the center in order that the oil may pass into the cylinder through the top valve from which it is dis-tributed downward by the piston. In horizontal-cylinder com-

[1] The *lantern* is a space in the central portion of a stuffing box, not filled with packing into which the gas leaking through the packing can accumulate.

pressors, this connection enters the suction passage or port centrally.

Volumetric Efficiency and Clearance of Compressors.—The ratio of the volume of the vapor of the refrigerant which is actually handled to the volume of the piston displacement[1] is called the *volumetric efficiency.* It is customary when calculating volumetric efficiency, to express the volume of the vapor of the refrigerant which is actually handled in terms of the conditions of temperature and pressure in the cooling coils of the evaporator. For example, if the actual volume of the ammonia vapor taken into the cylinder of a compressor in 1 minute is (0.422 pound per ton of refrigeration) 3.44 cubic feet per ton and the piston displacement is 0.1 cubic foot per stroke for a 5-ton double-acting compressor, making 200 strokes per minute (100 revolutions per minute), the piston displacement per minute is 200 × 0.1 or 20 cubic feet per minute, and the volumetric efficiency is 3.44 × 5 ÷ 20, which is 0.86 or 86 per cent.

There are a number of reasons why the volumetric efficiency of a compressor is less than 100 per cent: (1) The amount of vapor of a refrigerant that will fill the volume of the piston displacement at the temperature and pressure in the cooling coils of the evaporator is always greater than the amount actually taken in. (2) The vapor of a refrigerant is heated by throttling when it enters the cylinder of the compressor, and this heating by throttling produces a higher temperature than that corresponding to the pressure; in other words, if the vapor is dry and saturated in the suction pipe, it will be superheated in the cylinder of the compressor. This superheated vapor of the refrigerant, being warmer than the vapor in the cooling coils of the evaporator, is obviously less dense and weighs less per cubic foot. (3) Another condition tending to reduce the actual volume of the vapor of the refrigerant that enters the cylinder is the lowering of density of the vapor of the refrigerant in the cylinder because its pressure is less than the pressure in the cooling coils of the evaporator. This lower pressure in the compressor cylinder is necessary in order to establish a flow of vapor from the cooling

---

[1] *Piston displacement* is the volume of the space in a cylinder swept through by the piston. It is calculated by multiplying the area of the piston (3.1416 × D^2 ÷ 4, where D is the diameter of the piston) by the distance the piston moves in a stroke of the compressor. When the dimensions for calculating displacement are in inches, the cylinder displacement is in cubic inches.

coils of the evaporator into the cylinder. This flow of vapor must occur necessarily at high velocity because of the rapidity with which the cylinder must be filled at each stroke of the compressor. (4) Still another reason for the reduced volume of the refrigerant entering the compressor cylinder is that there is a larger space inside the cylinder than is actually swept through by the piston. This "excess" volume is called the *clearance*. During the discharge stroke of a compressor, all of the compressed vapor of the refrigerant is forced out of the cylinder through the discharge valve as the piston in its cylinder advances on this stroke, with the exception of the vapor which is trapped in the *clearance space*. This trapped vapor remains and, on the next suction stroke of the compressor, expands down to the pressure in the cooling coils of the evaporator and fills a portion of the cylinder displacement, thus *limiting the amount of cylinder volume* that is available for the new charge of refrigerant. The higher the discharge pressure the more objectionable the clearance becomes.

Clearance of Compressor.—An important detail in the construction of a compressor is its clearance. The clearance of a compressor is the space between the piston and the cylinder head when the piston is at the end of its stroke. A small amount of clearance[1] is necessary, as the piston must be prevented from coming up against the cylinder head and doing damage. On the other hand, if the cylinder has a clearance too large, there will be an excessive amount of compressed vapor left in the cylinder at the end of the compression and discharge stroke, and then, on the next suction stroke, the vapor which is left in the cylinder at high pressure expands until its pressure falls to the suction pressure. At this point, the suction valve opens, and the cylinder begins to take in a new charge. The expansion of the vapor left in the cylinder reduces the available space for the new charge, a condition that greatly reduces the capacity of the compressor. The clearance space in a compressor should, therefore, be as small as it may be with safety, not exceeding 5 per cent of the cylinder volume.

[1] In some makes of ammonia compressors having vertical, single-acting cylinders, the amount of clearance is made as small as possible without the risk of the piston's coming into direct contact with the head of the cylinder. In some compressors of this kind, the distance between the piston in its highest position and the valves of the cylinder head is not more than $\frac{1}{64}$ inch.

Volume Delivered by Compressors or Pumps.—In order to determine the volume delivered by a compressor or pump, the piston displacement,[1] which is the volume swept through by the plunger or piston in each stroke, must be calculated.

Volume Delivered by Single-acting Compressor.—If a compressor makes 50 strokes per minute, then the plunger or piston displacement per minute is found by multiplying the plunger or piston displacement per stroke by 50. A standard United States gallon is 231 cubic inches, so that the *displacement per minute* expressed *in gallons* is the plunger or piston displacement per minute in cubic inches divided by 231. There are always some leakage and other losses in a compressor, so that the actual volume delivered will be somewhat less than the theoretical displacement as explained above. The losses are due to incomplete filling of the cylinder of the compressor at each stroke and leakage through the valves and around the plunger or piston.

Volume Delivered by Double-acting Compressor.—The displacement of a double-acting piston type of compressor is calculated in very much the same way as the displacement of a single-acting compressor or pump. The method of calculating the displacement of a double-acting piston type may be explained by taking the case of a compressor with a cylinder 15 inches in diameter, a piston stroke of 30 inches, a piston rod 3 inches in diameter, the compressor making 120 strokes per minute. The area of the piston on the side where there is no piston-rod area to consider is 176.7 square inches. The area of the piston rod is 7.1 square inches. Deducting 7.1 from 176.7 square inches, the effective area of the side of the piston to which the piston rod is attached is 169.6 square inches. Since there are 120 strokes of the piston per minute, half this number, or 60, are effective for the discharge of compressed gas or vapor at one end of the cylinder, and the other 60 strokes for the discharge at the other end. The displacement of the compressor *per minute* at the end with the larger piston area is $(176.7 \times 30) \times 60$ or 318,060 cubic inches, and the displacement of the compressor *per minute* at the other end is $(169.6 \times 30) \times 60$ or 305,280 cubic inches.

---

[1] Piston displacement is explained more in detail on p. 110. In some pumps, the total area of the plunger or piston is not effective, because of the attachment of a piston rod. When a piston rod is used, reducing the effective area of a plunger or piston, the area of the rod must be deducted from the total area of the face of the plunger or piston.

The total displacement per minute is 623,340 cubic inches per minute.

Adiabatic Compression.—When the vapor of a refrigerant is compressed or expanded without a loss or gain of heat (from another source), the compression or expansion is called *adiabatic*. In the analysis of what takes place in the cylinder of a compressor in a refrigerating system, it is assumed that the compression is adiabatic, meaning, there is no transfer of heat between the vapor of the refrigerant and the cylinder walls, just as if the compression took place in a cylinder made of a material which is a non-conductor of heat. In many of the problems which are to be calculated in this subject, it will be assumed that the vapor of the refrigerant enters the cylinder of the compressor during the suction stroke as a dry and saturated vapor, that is, in the form of a vapor containing no particles of any of the *liquid* refrigerant which may be in the cooling coils of the evaporator; in other words, the vapor of the refrigerant is not superheated at the *beginning* of the compression stroke. In most cases, however, at the *end* of the compression stroke, the vapor of the refrigerant is superheated to a considerable degree, meaning that the temperature is a number of degrees above the saturation temperature corresponding to the pressure.

Pressure after Compression.—In a mechanical refrigerating system, the pressure to which the vapor must be compressed depends on the temperature of the cooling water supplied to the condenser. In a system using ammonia as the refrigerant, the temperature of the cooling water should be between 50 and 80° F. In the ammonia table on page 386, it will be seen that, under these temperature conditions, the ammonia vapor must be compressed to some value of absolute pressures between 89.2 and 153.0 pounds per square inch or, in gage pressures, between 75 and 138 pounds per square inch.

Pressure before Compression.—When liquid ammonia evaporates at atmospheric pressure, the temperature of the ammonia is 28° *below* the Fahrenheit zero (-28° F.), a temperature much below that required for commercial refrigeration. The suction pressure of the compressor in every commercial ammonia refrigerating plant is, therefore, greater than atmospheric. The *suction pressures* generally used in practice are from 20 to 50 pounds per square inch absolute. With this pressure in the low-pressure piping, air leakage is prevented, and the size of the compressor can be reduced for given requirements.

CHAPTER V

HOUSEHOLD MECHANICAL REFRIGERATION

Modern Household Refrigeration Systems.—Automatic mechanical household refrigeration was introduced about 1910. Before this time, the ordinary ice-cooled refrigerator was the common device for preserving and storing foods in the home. The development and use of the electrical refrigerator has been rapid. According to statistics of the U. S. Census, there are between 20,000,000 and 30,000,000 families in the United States, of whom about one-third live under more or less urban conditions, which are distinctly favorable to extensive use of mechanical refrigerators. Since 1920, the equipment of homes with these devices has progressed steadily. Fortunately for the industry, household machines have been brought to such a stage of perfection that the amount of servicing has constantly diminished.

A study of various foods shows that at temperatures ranging from about 40 to 50° F. the bacteria multiply about one-four-hundredth as rapidly as in the range between 50 and 60° F. From this it can be seen that a household refrigerator should cool the stored goods to temperatures below 50° F. This temperature is rather difficult to obtain in an ice-cooled refrigerator.

Fungi may be classified as follows: (1) molds, (2) yeasts, and (3) bacteria. The growth of bacteria can be shown by the fact that one bacterium will produce, after 1 hour, 4 bacteria; after 2 hours, 16 bacteria; after 5 hours, 65,543 bacteria; and, after 15 hours, 1,000,000,000 bacteria.

Household refrigerating systems may be divided into the following two classes: (1) the *compression system*, which is electrically driven, such as the Frigidaire, Kelvinator, Servel, and similar makes; and (2) the *absorption system*, in which the necessary energy is supplied from either an electric heater or a gas burner, as in the household absorption system. Further explanation of this system is made on pages 157–166.

The advantages of the compression system are that the pressures involved need not be very high and either air or water may be used for condensing the refrigerating medium. The disadvantage is that a somewhat noisy belt or gear drive is generally used, while the electric or gas-heated absorption system is practically noiseless, as it has no moving parts. The principal disadvantage of the absorption system is that high pressures are necessary as in all systems using ammonia refrigerant, and a supply of water is generally required for cooling purposes, a fact which considerably increases the operating expense of small machines.

The following table shows the comparative operating cost for these systems:

Compression System (Electric)	Absorption System (Gas Heated)
Average electric-power consumption 50 kilowatt-hours per month	Gas consumption.... 1,500 cubic feet per month
Cost of electrical power: First 20 kilowatt-hours............ 8.5 cents	Cost of gas.......... $1.15 per 1,000 cubic feet
All over 20 kilowatt-hours............. 3.0 cents	Water consumption 5 to 8 gallons per hour or
Total cost of operation. $2.60 per month	500 to 900 cubic feet per month
	Cost of water........ $0.75 to $2 per 1,000 cubic feet
	Cost of gas.......... $1.75 per month
	Cost of water........ $0.35 to $1.80 per month
	Total cost of operation. $1.10 to $3.55 per month

From the above table it can be seen that the average operating cost is approximately the same in both systems. These figures apply to cabinet refrigerators having a capacity 6½ cubic feet and a "cooling" temperature of 40 to 45° F. inside the box. The ice-melting capacity is, in each case, about 75 pounds of ice in 24 hours, so that the *equivalent* cost of ice would be about 12 cents per 100 pounds without considering depreciation and interest.

Refrigerants for Household Systems.—The refrigerants suitable for use in household refrigerating systems are sulphur dioxide, ethyl chloride, methyl chloride, ammonia, carbon dioxide (not commonly used in America but used extensively in Europe), butane, isobutane, methane, ethane, and propane. These refrigerants can be classified into two groups: (1) non-inflammable and (2) inflammable. The non-inflammable refrigerants are carbon dioxide and sulphur dioxide. The remainder of the group may burn when mixed in some proportions with air and must, therefore, be classified as inflammable. Not all of the above refrigerants are widely used in household machines. Those most commonly found are sulphur dioxide, methyl chloride, and ammonia. Isobutane and butane have been used to some extent.

General Electric Company Refrigerating Unit.—The General Electric household refrigerator has been designed to occupy as little space as possible and to eliminate all exposed moving parts. It has been arranged to simplify the interchange of refrigerating units and to reduce to a minimum the possibility of gas leaks. An automatic control maintains constant refrigerating temperature. The refrigerant used in this machine is *sulphur dioxide*.

The General Electric unit resembles in many ways the Audiffren oscillating-cylinder refrigerating machine (see p. 51), which has been successfully used for 25 years. There are four principal parts in the refrigerating unit; namely, (1) compressor, (2) float chamber, (3) evaporator, and (4) automatic temperature control.

Compressor.—The compressor of the General Electric unit is shown in Fig. 66. It has a single *oscillating* cylinder C, and its piston is driven by an eccentric on the shaft of the electric motor M. The compressor is single acting. The compressor and motor are in a steel case which is provided with a steel base plate. The joint between the case and the base plate is made thoroughly leakproof by means of a tongue-and-groove type of lead seal. Lubrication is by the forced-feed method that operates by means of a plunger type of oil pump which operates on the permanently sealed oil supply, somewhat as the piston of the compressor operates on the refrigerant. The oil pump is not shown in the figure.

In order to reduce the starting torque of the compressor, an "unloader" valve H is used. This valve is held up against its seat by oil pressure during the normal operation of the compressor but opens at the low oil pressure when starting, thereby allowing the pressure on the outside and inside of the compressor cylinder to become equalized through a bypass. At the time of starting, a check valve *G* closes and thus prevents the vapor of the refrigerant from leaking back into the evaporator through the suction line. The entire mechanism is mounted within a steel case by means of a three-point suspension, so as to absorb motor noises and vibrations. This makes the machine practically noiseless. The suction pipe is a tube which is wound around the compressor

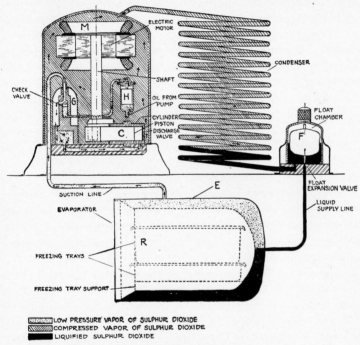

LOW PRESSURE VAPOR OF SULPHUR DIOXIDE
COMPRESSED VAPOR OF SULPHUR DIOXIDE
LIQUIFIED SULPHUR DIOXIDE

FIG. 66.—Diagram of General Electric icing unit.

between the base plate and intake opening of the cylinder to permit the free movement of the suction pipe without danger of breaking.

Float Chamber.—The float chamber *F* is located on the top of the refrigerator cabinet at the right of the compressor case. Its purpose is to accumulate the liquid refrigerant, and when there is a sufficient quantity of liquid in the chamber, the float valve[1]

[1] The pressure and temperature to be maintained in the evaporator determine the adjustment for opening this float valve.

lifts and allows the liquid refrigerant to flow into the coil of the evaporator.

Evaporator.—The evaporating device is located on the inside of the cover of the cabinet and is an integral part of the unit. The evaporator E is made of three tested steel shells which are nested together and welded at the open ends. The inner and intermediate shells have circular cross-sections. Between the nearly square outer shell and the intermediate shell is the space for the evaporator coil. There are two other, separate compartments; the larger one, which is between the intermediate and inner shells and not shown in the figure, contains a freezing mixture. Because of its high latent heat of fusion, the freezing mixture can store up a large amount of refrigeration; that is, it has a capacity of heat absorption which depends on the quantity of freezing mixture. The practical effect of this freezing mixture is to reduce the number of operating periods and, therefore, also the number of times the motor must be started. Every time the unit is started, there is a much greater burden on the machine than when it is in continuous operation. The float valve F permits the liquefied refrigerant to pass through the expansion valve and enter the evaporator, where the refrigerant evaporates and absorbs heat from the freezing mixture and thus causes it to solidify. When this solidified freezing mixture melts, it absorbs heat from the interior of the refrigerator cabinet and thereby cools the food.

In a central recess R in the evaporator E there are two ice trays, one of which is used to make a small quantity of ice cubes, while the other is used for making frozen desserts or a large supply of ice.

Control of Temperatures.—The temperature-regulating device is located in a control box placed on the top of the refrigerator cabinet to the left of the compressor, as shown in Fig. 67. This control performs three functions: (1) It starts and stops the electric motor as the temperature changes in the evaporator; (2) it cuts off the current whenever there is an overload, thus preventing damage to the motor; and (3) it reduces the torque to be overcome by the motor when starting.

Temperature control is secured by means of a "sylphon-bellows" type of *pressure-regulating* valve (Fig. 68) to which a copper tube is attached at one end while the other is fastened to the back of the evaporator. This copper tube contains sulphur dioxide from the refrigerating system. At high temperatures in the evapo-

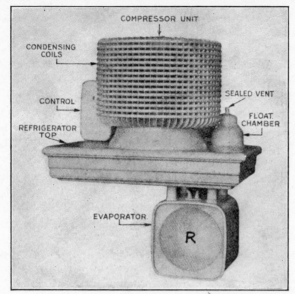

FIG. 67.—General Electric icing unit showing parts in place.

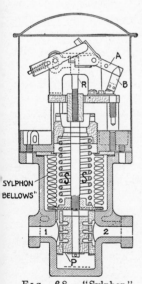

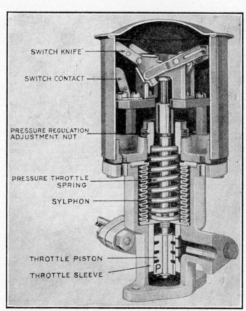

FIG. 68.—"Sylphon" bellows for electric switch operation.

FIG. 69.—Sectional pictorial view of "Sylphon" bellows for electric switch operation.

rator, the sulphur dioxide evaporates and increases the pressure in the tube and in the sylphon-bellows valve, so that the latter expands and closes a switch at the top of the device, *which* starts the motor.   On the other hand, a decrease in temperature in the evaporator causes a reduction in pressure in the sylphon-bellows valve, opens the switch, and cuts off the electric current of the motor, thereby stopping the compressor.   This device is used in a number of makes of household refrigerating systems.   It is shown pictorially in Fig. 69.

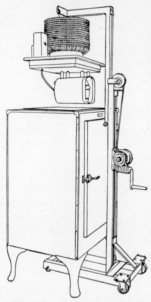

A thumbscrew adjustment is provided so as to decrease or increase the tension of the spring in the folds of the sylphon-bellows valve.   This adjustment permits the temperature-control unit to be set for the proper temperature in the refrigerator.   In order to prevent damage from overload, an overload tripping switch is provided in the electric circuit to prevent an excessive current.

The installation of this refrigerating unit consists only of placing it in position at the top of the cabinet; and since there are no pipe connections to be made, it is easily installed in an apartment or a house.   Figure 70 shows a crane for conveniently removing and replacing this unit in a refrigerator.   A portable refrigerating unit is shown in Fig. 71.

Fig. 70.—Portable crane for removing General Electric icing unit.

At the factory, the standard method of testing this machine is to submerge the evaporator in a brine bath held at a temperature of 20° F. while the condenser for the refrigerant is at room temperature.   With these conditions, one of the small units has a refrigerating capacity of 320 B.t.u. per hour, when the electric-power input is 150 watts and the room temperature is 100° F. The condenser gage pressure is 110 pounds per square inch while the suction pressure corresponds to a vacuum of 4 inches of mercury.

When this refrigerating unit is installed in a room having a temperature of 100° F., it will run about 70 per cent of the time when the doors of the refrigerator are kept closed. Under this condition, the average suction pressure is slightly lower than during the brine test method above, and the refrigerating capacity of the machine will be slightly reduced.

FIG. 71.—Portable General Electric icing unit, and refrigerator.

The Frigidaire Compression Refrigerating System.—The Frigidaire system made by the Delco-Light Company (General Motors Corporation) is of the compression type and operates according to the following cycle: The heat is absorbed from the refrigerator cabinet by the evaporating refrigerant, which is *sulphur dioxide*, and is carried away by the cooling water or air, whichever cooling medium is used for the condenser. The compressor, driven by an electric motor, serves to keep the refrigerant circulating through the system and increases the pressure of the refrigerant so that it may be readily liquefied in the condenser. The liquid sulphur dioxide which has been condensed drops into a pocket or sump of the compressor from which it is forced by difference of pressure through a tube into the cooling coil of the evaporator. The flow of the liquid sulphur dioxide into the cooling coil is controlled by an expansion valve of the float type, as shown in Fig. 72. This valve serves two purposes: (1) to maintain a pressure on the liquid line so as to keep the sulphur dioxide in the liquid state at "room" temperatures, (2) to allow the liquid sulphur dioxide to flow into the cooling coil of the evaporator rapidly enough in order to replenish the refrigerant which has been evaporated in the coil. The method of operation of this float valve can be seen more clearly in Fig. 97. The evaporation of the liquid sulphur dioxide in the coil of the evaporator takes place continuously but is more rapid when the compressor is running. This is due to the fact that the operation of the compressor reduces slightly the pressure in the coil of the evaporator. The float expansion valve (Fig. 72) is

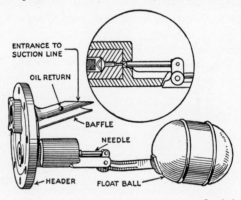

ENTRANCE TO SUCTION LINE

OIL RETURN

BAFFLE

NEEDLE

HEADER   FLOAT BALL

Fig. 72.—Float valve for operating evaporator on flooded system.

located in the header of the cooling unit and at all times maintains the proper level of the liquid sulphur dioxide in the coil of the evaporator, regardless of the surrounding temperature. When the liquid sulphur dioxide in the coil evaporates, the float drops, permitting the needle of the expansion valve to open slightly and thus allowing additional liquid refrigerant to enter the cooling coil. After the refrigerant enters, the level rises, and the float shuts off the supply. It is easily seen that the control is entirely dependent on the quantity of liquid in the cooling coil and, in turn, is dependent upon the rapidity with which the liquid sulphur dioxide evaporates.

Cooling Unit.—The cooling unit consists of a header containing the float type of expansion valve (Fig. 72) and a system of coils of the evaporator designed to bring about the transfer of heat from the air in the refrigerator to the refrigerant contained in these coils. The cooling unit does not consist merely of a coil of tubing but has a definite shape for the particular function that it has to serve.

Control of Lubrication.—Since the compressor piston must be lubricated to reduce friction, and the lubricating oil must make a perfect seal between the piston and its cylinder to prevent leaking of the vapor, it is fortunate that sulphur dioxide and oil have an affinity for each other. The liquid sulphur dioxide, when it comes into contact with the oil which has passed through the cylinder of the compressor, absorbs part of this oil, so that the resulting liquid which passes to the coils of the evaporator is not pure sulphur dioxide but a solution of oil and sulphur dioxide. It is necessary, therefore, to provide some means by which the

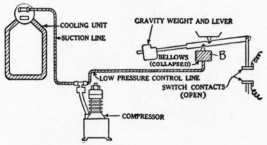

Fig. 73.—Low-pressure regulator with "Sylphon" bellows (compressor not running).

oil can be returned to the compressor from the cooling coil. When the mixture of sulphur dioxide and oil in the cooling coils evaporates, the sulphur dioxide passes off into the suction line of the compressor in the form of a vapor, leaving the oil behind. The oil, being lighter than liquid sulphur dioxide, floats in the coils of the evaporator and is drained off through small holes in a curved suction pipe which discharges it into the crankcase of the compressor.

Motor Control.—The unit is equipped with a *low-pressure control*, as shown in Figs. 73 and 74, instead of a thermostatic control, like the device shown on page 157. A mechanical refrigerating unit controlled only by the temperature of the food compartment is dependent for its ice-making and dessert-freezing capacity on the heat leakage through the walls of the refrigerator cabinet.

The pivot at the top of the sylphon bellows *B* will move sufficiently to cause the electric supply switch of the motor to open or close. When the switch contacts are closed, the motor operates the compressor, causing a lowering of the pressure and temperature in the cooling coils of the evaporator and the suction (low pressure) line of the compressor until the temperature in the coils of the evaporator is somewhere between 8 and 28° F., depending on the temperature required. When the temperature in the evaporator and the pressure in the low-pressure line are sufficiently low, the electric switch opens and stops the motor.

The temperature of the food compartment may be further controlled by means of an adjusting damper. This damper when closed retards the circulation of air and causes the temperature

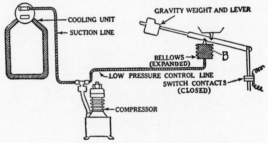

Fig. 74.—Low-pressure regulator with "Sylphon" bellows (in operation).

in the food compartment to rise, while opening the damper causes a lower temperature. The damper also serves as a drip shield for the cooling unit. This prevents moisture collecting on the bottom of the cooling unit from falling into the food compartment when the cooling unit is being defrosted (p. 129).

There are two general types of Frigidaire household refrigerating machines. The machine and equipment most generally used in private houses and apartments has a condenser which is cooled by air circulation, while the larger machine, suitable for hotels, restaurants, and stores has provision for cooling the condenser and the cylinder of the compressor by water circulation.

Frigidaire Refrigerating System with Water-cooled Compressor.—In the Frigidaire refrigerating systems, in which the compressor cylinder and the condenser are cooled by water, some means of controlling the quantity of water is necessary. The water supplied to the condenser is controlled by a sylphon bellows *B*, shown in Fig. 75, which begins to expand when the gage pressure in the condenser is about 55 pounds per square inch. At this pressure, a lever *L* and a gravity weight *W* are raised and cause the water valve to open so that more water

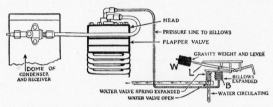

Fig. 75.—Regulation of cooling water valve by low-pressure control.

circulates in the condenser. When the cooling water in the condenser is at a comparatively high temperature, the pressure in the condenser will also be high. This is necessarily so, because, as the temperature of the cooling water increases, the vapor of

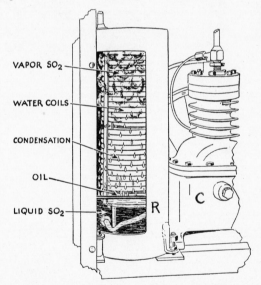

Fig. 76.—Water-cooled condenser and oil receiver of compressor.

the refrigerant has to be subjected to higher pressure. Expansion of the sylphon bellows produced by an increase in pressure will cause the water valve to open wider and allow more water to pass through the condenser coils. It is then easily seen that the supply of water is controlled entirely by the pressure in the condenser. When the motor and also the compressor are stopped by opening the control switch, the pressure in the condenser will gradually become lower. The cooling water, however, will continue to flow through the condenser coils until the pressure in the condenser has been reduced enough to cause the sylphon bellows to collapse and close the water valve. As the cold cooling water passes through the condenser coils, it absorbs heat, thus lowering the pressure and thereby reducing the starting load of the compressor when it is again started. Figure 76 shows the method of operation of a water-cooled Frigidaire condenser and the connection of the receiver *R* to the crankcase *C* of the compressor for the purpose of draining the oil from the liquid receiver into the crankcase.

Compressor.—The compressor is of the single-acting type having two cylinders, which are driven by an electric motor. The motor is geared to the shaft of the compressor. The motor pinion is made of a noiseless composition, meshing with a cast-iron gear on the compressor shaft and running in a bath of oil. Oil is supplied to the bearings of the motor by a device on the compressor which causes the oil to be thrown into a small reservoir from which a tube runs to both the front and rear bearings of the motor. This method of oiling the motor bearings is automatic and supplies adequate lubrication. The compressor runs at a relatively slow speed and is well lubricated by the oil which returns normally from the cooling unit. The compressor, being of the closed type, has a stuffing box which is placed around the crankshaft and sealed with oil to prevent loss of the refrigerant. The stuffing box (Fig. 77) contains a special packing material held in position by a heavy spring. As shown in the figure, a bronze thrust collar is fitted on the fan end of the compressor shaft. This thrust collar is held firmly in place by means of a spring *S* and retaining plate *P*. A sylphon bellows is fastened to the thrust collar at one end and at the other end is clamped to the compressor by means of a retaining plate. A gasket is placed between the sylphon bellows and the compressor casing to make a vapor-tight joint. A satisfactory shaft

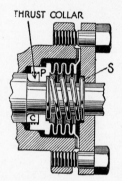

Fig. 77.—Stuffing-box of Frigidaire compressor.

stuffing box to prevent entirely and permanently the leakage of the refrigerant is an essential requirement in any compressor for household refrigeration.

Spring Rod Suspension.—Spring suspension rods, as shown at *R*, in Fig. 78, are used to support the compressor unit and prevent the transmission of noise and vibration to the base of the machine and then to the building. This suspension is adjustable so as to

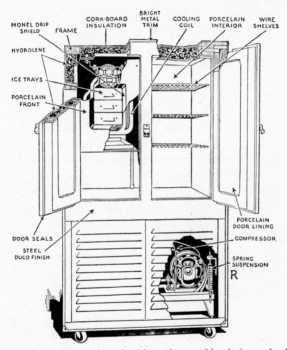

Fig. 78.—Spring suspension of refrigerating machine in base of cabinet.

provide for the leveling of the motor and compressor. Being of the three-point type, the suspension is easily adjusted.

Condenser.—The Frigidaire water-cooled condenser consists of a long copper tube for cooling water, coiled into a tank *T*, in Fig. 79, which serves also as the *liquid receiver*, in which the liquid refrigerant accumulates. The condenser is shown more in detail in Fig. 76. The compressed vapor, on coming into contact with the surface of the coils containing the cooling water, liquefies and drops to the bottom of the receiver.

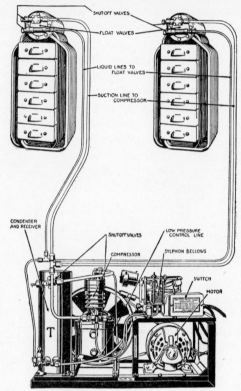

FIG. 79.—Frigidaire single-cylinder compressor, control device, condenser and cooling units.

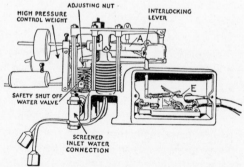

FIG. 80.—Details of Frigidaire low-pressure control switch.

coils with provision for hanging them on copper supports. The inside surface of the cooling coils, therefore, cools the ice trays, and the outside surface of the coils chills the air which circulates through the food-storage space of the refrigerator cabinet.

Figure 78 shows a typical metal cabinet for a Frigidaire equipment. The exterior is made of sheet steel finished with white Duco enamel. Two-inch cork board is used for heat insulation in the walls and doors of the refrigerator. Either an air-cooled or a water-cooled compressor unit may be used in this cabinet,

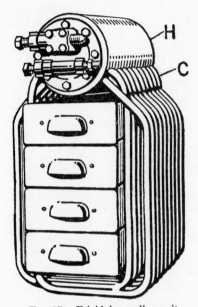

Fig. 87.—Frigidaire cooling unit.

and the compressor units may be placed in the compartment in the bottom of the cabinet or in the basement, cellar, or other out-of-the-way place.

If the refrigerator is to be used in an apartment, the most satisfactory arrangement is to put the compressor unit in the lower compartment of the refrigerator. If, on the other hand, the refrigerator is to be used in a private house, where there is room in the cellar or basement, it is preferable to place the compressor unit there—in the first place, because looking after the equipment will be easier if it is located where the parts, especially the motor, are easily inspected, and, in the second, because the efficiency of the equipment will usually be better so situated than where the compressor has about the same temperature as the hot air in the kitchen of a house or apartment. Some of the cooling units made for Frigidaire equipment are provided with two small drawers for ice trays and one large drawer, twice the size of the smaller ones, for refrigerating puddings or making large blocks of ice.

Automatic Control.—The automatic-control switch is operated by a copper sylphon bellows, which expands and contracts with the changes of pressure of the refrigerant in the coils of the evaporator, this pressure being, of course, that of the low-pressure line of the refrigerating system. The control switch is mounted on the same base with the compressor and motor and operates a quick make-and-break switch.

New Designs for Apartments.—Recently, the Frigidaire Corporation has introduced small noiseless air-cooled units, for

Fig. 87a.—Frigidaire air-cooled unit with radiator type of condenser.

use especially in apartments where noise is to be avoided. The new features of this design are a lightweight "noiseless" electric switch for starting and stopping the motor, and a radiator type of condenser as shown in Fig. 87a. The condenser is cooled by a positive circulation of a stream of air which enters at the back of the refrigerator cabinet and is discharged over the condenser and compressor upon a tightly closed front in the base of the cabinet.[1]

The flow of air through the apparatus is intended to be U-shaped. The air is drawn in by the suction of the fan-shaped

[1] There are no louvres or other similar openings in the front of this type of cabinet.

spokes of the fly-wheel on the shaft of the compressor, discharges over a radiator type of condenser and the cylinder of the compressor. Since there is no opportunity for this air to pass out through openings in the front of the refrigerator cabinet, the direction of flow of the air is reversed in direction and is discharged through an exhaust fan on the shaft of the electric motor, the air thus making a U-shaped circuit.

Another innovation in the design of this unit is the mounting of the whole apparatus on cylindrical-shaped pieces of rubber, one at each corner. This mounting on rubber is to eliminate vibration and consequent noise.

Fig. 88.   Fig. 89.

Figs. 88–89.—Water coolers equipped with Frigidaire cooling units.

Interesting recent applications of Frigidaire refrigerating units are in water coolers using bottled water (Fig. 88) and those having water-pipe connections with the city water supply (Fig. 89).

Kelvinator Refrigerating Unit.—A popular type of household refrigerating equipment is made by the Kelvinator Corporation. The Kelvinator refrigerating equipment is made only in the small sizes suitable for household use, all being arranged for cooling the condenser by air circulation. None of the designs is intended for water cooling. The compressors for this system of refrigeration are intended to be operated by electric motors. Refrigerating equipment of this kind may be used for cooling any standard make of refrigerator of which the cooling-space volume is not more than 70 cubic feet. The *refrigerant is sulphur dioxide.*

Large outfits are provided with a two-cylinder compressor, but the size most often used has a single-cylinder machine. The compressors are of the reciprocating single-acting type. The piston of the compressor slides in steel sleeves. The suction valves are in the piston, and the discharge valves are flat disks located in the side of the compressor cylinder. The Kelvinator apparatus was one of the earliest successful household refrigerating machines on the market. The improvement in the con-

Fig. 90.—Single-cylinder Kelvinator compressor with air-cooled condenser.

struction of small compressors that really made the household refrigerating machine safe for general use was the application of a sufficiently tight, durable, and self-lubricating stuffing box

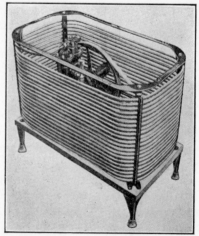

Fig. 91.—Two-cylinder Kelvinator compressor with air-cooled condenser.

around the shaft of the compressor. Instead of having an ordinary stuffing box, which requires adjustment and lubrication, a sylphon-bellows type of vapor seal of self-aligning, self-lubricating antifriction material is used. The electric motor drives the compressor by means of a "V" belt, one end of which is on a pulley on the shaft of the motor, and the other end of which is on the rim of a flywheel which has fan blades between the hub and the rim instead of spokes. A single-cylinder Kelvinator refrigerating machine is shown in Fig. 90, where the combined flywheel and fan are clearly shown. This size of compressor is operated by a ¼-horsepower electric motor. The refrigerating equipment shown in Fig. 91 is essentially the same as in Fig. 90, except that it has a two-cylinder compressor with a larger con-

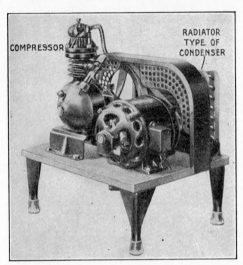

FIG. 92.—Kelvinator compressor with radiator-type of condenser.

denser coil. It has a larger compressor and condenser coil to provide for a larger capacity.

Condenser.—The condensing equipment in most of the Kelvinator units consists of a continuous coil of ½-inch seamless copper tubing wound spirally around the compressor and the electric motor. The condenser coil, compressor, and motor are mounted on the same base, making a very compact unit which may be conveniently installed either in a space provided for it in the base of a refrigerator cabinet or in the basement of a house. Figure 92 shows a single-cylinder Kelvinator compressor with a condenser of the compact "radiator" type. Figure 93 shows a single-cylinder Kelvinator unit as it would be installed in the basement of a house. The two-cylinder compressor is recommended for use in refrigerator cabinets having a volume of more than 20 cubic feet.

Refrigerating Element.—In the Kelvinator equipment, the cooling unit (Fig. 94) consists of the brine tank, the cooling coils of the evaporator inside the casing of the brine tank, the expansion valve, the thermocoil, and the thermostat. When this equipment is to be installed in the ice box of an ordinary refriger-

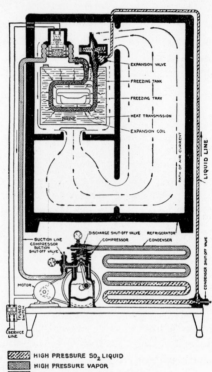

HIGH PRESSURE SO₂ LIQUID
HIGH PRESSURE VAPOR
LOW PRESSURE SEMI LIQUID AND VAPOR
LOW PRESSURE VAPOR

FIG. 93.—Diagram of flow of refrigerant in Kelvinator refrigerating machine (dry system).

ator cabinet, the cooling element is placed in the ice box, and the compressor, electric motor, and condenser coil are usually placed in a basement, cellar, or some other out-of-the-way place. Even when there is a space in the base of a refrigerator cabinet which is suitably arranged or specially designed to be occupied by the combined compressor, motor, and condenser unit, it is generally preferable not to use the space for this purpose, if the compressor unit can be conveniently located somewhere where it is easily accessible. Under these circumstances, manufacturers usually recommend the location of the compressor unit in the cellar or basement. Machinery of this kind, when located in a basement cellar or similar place, should, however, be protected by some wood or wire casing to prevent animals from being caught between the belt and the flywheel, as might easily happen if these parts were exposed.

Brine Tank.—The Kelvinator brine tank has a casing of sheet copper which is tinned on its outside surface. The cooling unit shown in Fig. 94 has three freezing compartments. The various sizes of Kelvinator outfits have from two to four of these freezing

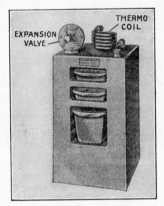

Fig. 94.—Kelvinator cooling unit.

compartments, according to the capacity of the equipment. There is a tray for freezing 21 cubes of ice, making 2½ pounds. The largest-size Kelvinator equipment is provided with a double-size freezing tray which will make 8½ pounds of ice. The brine tank is filled with calcium-chloride brine. The cooling coils of the evaporator are placed in the brine tank in such a way that they surround each of the freezing compartments of the cooling unit.

Expansion Valve.—The sulphur dioxide leaves the condenser in the liquid form and passes at through the copper tubing to the expansion valve (Fig. 95) at the top of the cooling unit. The refrigerant is discharged through the expansion valve at a reduced pressure into the cooling coils of the evaporator. The automatic expansion valve lowers the pressure of the refrigerant from 2 inches of vacuum (about 14 pounds per square inch absolute) to 3 pounds per square inch gage (about 18 pounds per square inch absolute), depending on the size of the brine tank and the number of feet of tubing in the coil of the evaporator. The expansion valve is of the balanced-pressure type, being designed so that when the pressure is increased on the low-pressure side L of the valve by the boiling of the refrigerant, the valve acts against the pressure on the liquid or high-pressure side H and automatically shuts off the supply of liquid refrigerant to the valve when a sufficient quantity has been admitted. Then, again, when the suction pressure of the compressor is sufficiently reduced on the low-pressure side, the valve automatically opens

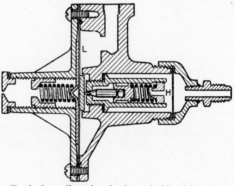

Fig. 95.—Typical needle valve for household refrigerating system.

again to admit more liquid refrigerant into the cooling coil of the evaporator.

Automatic Control.—The Kelvinator refrigerating system has an automatic thermostatic control operated by means of a thermostat which is inside the thermocoil shown in Fig. 94 at the top of the cooling unit. The thermostat is arranged so that it opens the electric circuit of the motor when the temperature in the refrigerator becomes too low and closes the circuit when the temperature becomes too high. A sylphon-bellows type of thermostat is used. This device is very simple, as it consists merely of a corrugated metal bellows filled with sulphur dioxide. The contraction and expansion of the bellows due to changing temperatures in the refrigerator operates a quick make-and-break electric switch. Under ordinary conditions, the Kelvinator units are designed and installed to operate from 6 to 7 hours a day when the temperature of the air outside the refrigerator is about 65 to 70° F.   The actual running time of the equipment will, of course, vary with the room temperature, the quality of the insulation in the walls, and the volume of the refrigerator cabinet.

Operating Temperature.—When a Kelvinator equipment is properly installed in a refrigerator cabinet, it may be expected that the temperature in the food spaces will be at least 10° F. colder than when ice was used under the same conditions.   The reason for this is that the surface of the brine tank is usually kept fairly constant at about 20° F., while the *surface* of a cake of ice is, of course, always 32° F.

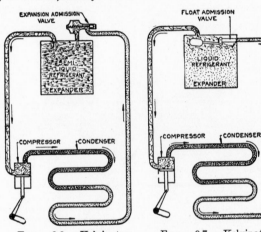

FIG. 96.—Kelvinator "dry system" of operation of evaporator.   FIG. 97.—Kelvinator "flooded" system of operation of evaporator.

Dry and Flooded Systems of Expansion.—When the Kelvinator refrigerating system is installed so that a compressor provides refrigeration for only one cooling unit, as is the case in most private houses and in single apartments, the "dry" rather than the "flooded" system of expansion is used.   The reason for this choice is that the dry system permits placing the cooling unit either above or below the condenser, as may be most convenient, and that it requires a smaller amount of refrigerant than the flooded system, thus reducing the cost of refrigerant.

The flooded system is used, however, in cases where two or more cooling units are to be refrigerated by the same compressor, as by this system the liquid refrigerant can be supplied to the coil of the evaporator in any one of a number of cooling units as it may be needed. The float valve like Fig. 72 in the coil of the evaporator operates in the flooded system to permit the liquid refrigerant to enter the coil of each evaporator until the supply is adequate, regardless of any inequality in the demand for refrigeration in the several units. Figures 96 and 97 shows the application of the dry and the flooded systems in Kelvinator refrigerating units.

Servel Compression Household Refrigerator.—The Servel compression refrigerating unit consists of compressor, motor, condenser, float valve, cooling coil of the evaporator, and pressure-control switch. The cycle of refrigeration is as follows: The refrigerant, which is *methyl chloride,* is admitted by means of a float-type expansion valve (Fig. 98) into the cooling coils of the evaporator which are in the refrigerator cabinet. In the

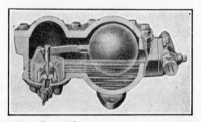

FIG. 98.—Servel float type of expansion valve.

coil of the evaporator, the liquid methyl chloride evaporates and takes up heat. From the evaporator the methyl-chloride vapor is drawn into the suction side of the compressor where it is compressed and discharged at high pressure into the condenser. In the condenser, the methyl-chloride vapor becomes liquid again and flows back at high pressure into the float-type expansion valve to be re-expanded.

Compressor.—The compressor, shown in Fig. 99, is the vertical reciprocating type and is lubricated by means of the splash system. The crankshaft and the connecting rods are made of forged steel, and the bearings are of cast babbitt metal. The suction or inlet valves which are located in the piston are automatically operated by the difference in pressure on the two sides of the valves. The discharge valves are flat-spring plates and are also automatic. A crankshaft stuffing box, marked 13 in Fig. 99, consists of a steel spool with three bronze collars, all tightly clamped to and revolving with the crankshaft. On each side of these bronze collars is a stationary steel disk.   The outer rims of the disks are held apart by steel spacers.   Between each disk and the bronze collars, heavy graphite grease is packed for lubricating purposes.   The outer rims of these disks are clamped into the compressor casing so as to make a metal packing in the stuffing box which requires very little attention.

Motor.—The electric motor used for driving the compressor is mounted on a hinged base which permits the belt which drives the compressor to be automatically taken up as it stretches.

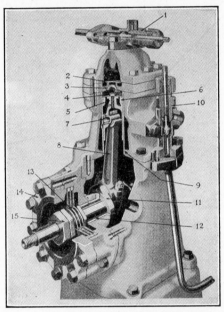

Fig. 99.—Servel compressor showing construction of stuffing box and piston.

The belt tension is maintained at constant tension by use of an eyebolt and spring fastened to the hinged base.

Condenser.—Copper tubing ⅜ inch in diameter and 105 feet in length is used to make the coils of the condenser.   For the air-cooled unit, the air is kept moving through the condenser coils by means of a fan driven by the same belt which drives the compressor.   At each end of the condenser coil, there are valves which are closed when it is necessary to keep the methyl chloride in the condenser, so that repairs can be made on other parts of the refrigerating unit.

Float Valve.—The hollow ball of the float-type expansion valve (Fig. 98) is connected to a lever arm to which a needle valve is attached. The weight of the ball float holds the needle valve against its seat, thus preventing the liquid refrigerant from leaving the valve chamber. As liquid refrigerant accumulates within the chamber, the float rises, opens the needle valve, and permits the liquid refrigerant to pass into the cooling coils

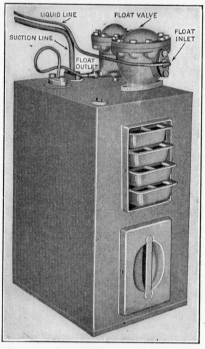

Fig. 100.—Servel cooling unit showing location of float valve.

of the evaporator. This flow of refrigerant takes place because of the difference of pressure within the condenser and evaporator.

Evaporator.—The cooling coils of the evaporator are made of copper tubing contained inside a copper shell which is filled with a 40 per cent solution of alcohol and water.

Control Switch.—The electric control switch is usually mounted on the base provided for the compressor and the motor. This switch is wired in series with the circuit of the electric motor. The opening and closing of the switch is controlled by a plunger attached to a sylphon bellows for temperature control. This sylphon is connected into the suction line of the compressor between the evaporator and the compressor. The pressure in the sylphon bellows must, therefore, be approximately the same as in the evaporator. The sylphon is set to open and close the electric control switch between two definite pressure limits. By this means, it is possible to obtain nearly constant pressure in the evaporator with correspondingly constant refrigerating temperature. The solution of alcohol and water acts as a means of storing refrigeration. Heat flows from this alcohol-and-water solution to the coils of the evaporator, where it is absorbed by the methyl chloride when it changes its condition from liquid to vapor. Since this vapor cannot escape from the coils, the pressure of the vapor in the coils increases. This increase of pressure causes the sylphon to lift the plunger, which closes the control switch and starts the motor and compressor. The electric control switch, electric motor, compressor, condenser, and cooling unit (Fig. 100) of the Servel compression system are shown in Fig. 101. Detailed views of a somewhat similar electric control switch are in Figs. 68 and 69.

Welsbach Household Refrigerating System.—A household refrigerating machine using the double-acting type of horizontal compressor is made by the Welsbach Company of Gloucester, N. J. The refrigerant used in this apparatus is *ethyl chloride*. In normal operation in a room where the temperature is between 75 and 80° F., the discharge gage pressure at the compressor is from 20 to 25 pounds per square inch, and the suction pressure is a little less than atmospheric, so that the suction side of the system operates in a vacuum. An electric motor furnishes the motive power, which is transmitted to the flywheel of the compressor by means of a belt, as shown in Fig. 102.

The compressor is cooled by air circulated by means of a ventilating fan consisting of fan blades which take the place of spokes in the flywheel. The air-cooled condenser is made of ⅜-inch copper tubing. The cooling unit, shown in Fig. 103, contains the expansion coil and a tank filled with a non-freezing solution of glycerin and water, together with sets of ice trays. There is a downward slope of the coil of the evaporator away from the expansion valve, to permit the drainage of circulated lubricant back to the compressor. Automatic temperature control in the cooling unit is accomplished by means of a mercury switch mounted on a two-metal coil (shown at *S* in the upper

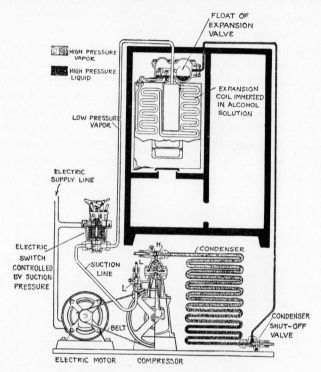

Fig. 101.—Piping arrangements of Servel compression refrigerating system for household service.

Fig. 102.—Welsbach refrigerating machine.

right-hand corner in Fig. 103 and more in detail in Fig. 113).
The cooling unit has four ice trays.

Herringbone Gear Compressor for Household Refrigeration.—
A household refrigerating machine made by the Belding-Hall
Company uses a compressor of the gear type. The gears are
operated at the same speed as the electric motor to which they
are directly connected in somewhat the same way as shown in
Fig. 104. They rotate in a sealed chamber and are supplied
with a small amount of oil to seal them, so that they effectively
compress the refrigerant which is trapped between the tops of the
gears and the sides of the gear casing. The refrigerant used in

Fig. 103.—Welsbach cooling unit.

this system is *sulphur dioxide*. The compressor, motor, and
condenser coil are mounted on a single base, which may be
placed on top of a refrigerator cabinet or in the basement, as
desired. The electric motor is directly connected to the shaft of
one of the gears of the compressor by means of a flexible coupling.

In the typical illustrative apparatus shown here, the expansion
valve and the cooling coil of the evaporator are at the lower part
of the figure. A small low-pressure receiver (marked "expanded
gas") in the suction line is provided to prevent frost from going
back to the compressor when the refrigerating unit is placed on
top of the refrigerator cabinet. The condenser in this apparatus
and also the compressor are cooled by the circulation of water, as
shown in the figure. Water cooling is sometimes necessary to
keep sufficiently cool the oil in which the gears of the compressor
operate.

Rotary-pump Type of Compressor for Household Refrigeration.

—A household refrigerating machine which has a rotary-pump type of compressor is shown in Fig. 105. This is the "Icemaid" household refrigerating unit, made by the Lamson Company of Syracuse, N. Y. The refrigerant is ethyl chloride. The electric motor which is used as a source of power is directly

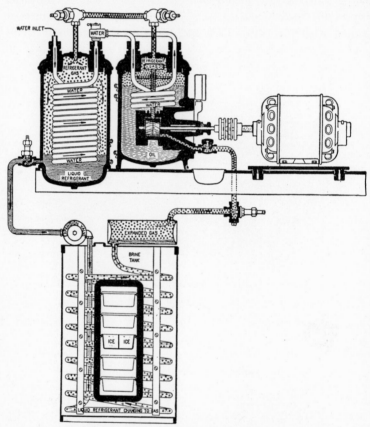

Fig. 104.—Refrigerating unit operated by gear-type compressor.

connected by means of a flexible coupling to the shaft of the rotary compressor. The condenser is a tubular-honeycomb type somewhat like the radiators on some automobiles. It is located between the electric motor and the rotary compressor and is cooled by a fan on the shaft of the motor, as shown in the figure. The circulated air, after passing through the honeycomb condenser, is discharged over the rotary compressor to keep it cool. The flow of refrigerant into the coils of the evaporator is controlled by a pressure-regulating device on the low-pressure or suction side of the compressor. By this means, more than one evaporating coil can be operated with a single compressor. The starting and stopping of the motor is regulated by a thermostatic switch which is controlled by a thermal device located within the brine tank in the cooling unit. The electric current is made or broken within a tilted glass vacuum tube containing a small

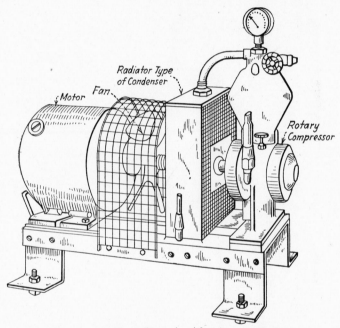

Fig. 105.—Refrigerating unit with rotary compressor.

quantity of mercury, so that the spark made by breaking the current occurs between a hard alloy point and a mercury surface.

An interesting compressor of the rotary type is part of the equipment of the Williams household refrigerating system made by the Simplex Refrigerating Corporation of Brooklyn, N. Y. A sectional drawing of this rotary compressor is shown in Fig. 106. *Ethyl chloride* is used as the refrigerant. The shaft of the compressor is directly connected to that of the electric motor by means of a flexible coupling. It is stated that this compressor has a volumetric efficiency of about 82 per cent and that its

mechanical efficiency compares favorably with that of the reciprocating types. The compressor and condenser are cooled by
air circulation from a fan type of blower mounted between an
electric motor and the compressor.

The cooling coils of the evaporator are operated on the flooded
system. By this method, the cooling coils of the evaporator are
filled with liquid refrigerant and are connected into a vertical
header from the top of which the vapor of the refrigerant is taken

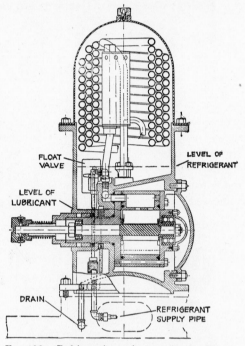

FIG. 106.—Refrigerating unit operating in oil bath.

into the suction pipe of the compressor. The hot refrigerant,
after being liquefied in the condenser, is discharged into a small
chamber at the left-hand side of the compressor, which is fitted
with a float valve, as shown in the figure. This float valve
regulates the flow of liquid refrigerant so that it discharges into
the coils of the evaporator at the same rate at which it is being
condensed. The utilization of the flooded system makes the
heat transmission through the walls of the cooling coils of the
evaporator much more rapid than if the coils were almost entirely
filled with the vapor of the refrigerant.

An interesting type of vertical, single-acting compressor is shown in Fig. 107. The condenser consists of a spiral coil placed around the cylinder of the compressor. An exterior casing around the condenser coil provides a space for the circulating

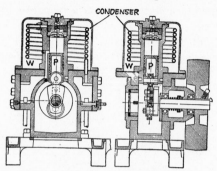

FIG. 107.—Compressor with eccentric drive.

water which is used to cool both the condenser and the cylinder of the compressor.

The *"Icemaster" household refrigerating unit* is shown in Fig. 108. The reciprocating compressor and the electric motor are not direct connected, and the motor drives the compressor *C* by

FIG. 108.—Compressor for household service operated with gear box to reduce speed of electric motor.

means of reduction gears in the gear box *G*. A fan on the shaft of the motor provides air circulation for the condenser coil *R* of the radiator type. The refrigerant is *methyl chloride*.

Removing Air from Small Compression Refrigerating System. When a household unit is installed, it is necessary to remove all air from the various parts of the system. In order to remove it, a bypass pipe must be provided between the condenser shut-off valve and the suction shut-off valve. The charging drum is connected into the system at some point in this bypass line. A suitable pipe fitting (usually a tee) must be provided for connecting the charging drum into the bypass line. In order to remove the air in the system by "pumping down" with the compressor, it is necessary to have only a small opening through the main discharge shut-off valve.[1] The shut-off valve at the condenser as well as also the suction shut-off valve may then be opened slightly. The valves are now set so that the air in the condenser, the float-valve chamber, and the suction piping can be drawn through the bypass line into the compressor and discharged from the system through the small opening in the discharge shut-off valve. The air in the piping which connects the charging drum to the bypass line will be removed during this process. The air in the cooling coils of the evaporator will also be drawn through the suction valve and will be discharged from the system. If the system includes a cooling unit which is filled with brine, or other solution, not readily frozen, as a part of the evaporator, the filler cap must be removed, so that if there are any leaks in its expansion coil, the cooling unit will not collapse. The compressor may be started and its operation continued until the suction pressure is pumped down to a vacuum of approximately 27 to 28 inches of mercury, when the compressor may be stopped, for a few minutes. If the system holds this vacuum, it is tight.

It is very important that the system should be charged with the proper quantity of refrigerant. This quantity will vary with the size of the system and the distance of the compressor from the cabinet of the refrigerator. After having obtained the required vacuum in the entire system, it is important not to permit any air to enter during the actual charging of the system. To be sure of this, the refrigerant must be put into the system before any valve or connection in the system is disturbed. The charging drum containing the refrigerant having been connected to the suction valve through the tee in the bypass connection, the valve on the charging drum can be slightly opened to permit the refrigerant to enter the system until the *gage* pressure increases

---

[1] Some small compressors have a main discharge shut-off valve with a plug in it which may be removed to obtain a small opening through the valve when it is closed.

to about 10 to 15 pounds per square inch. When this pressure is reached, the valve on the charging drum may be closed. The discharge shut-off valve may then be opened as well as the condenser shut-off valve. When the valve on the charging drum is again opened, the pressure of the refrigerant in the charging drum will force the refrigerant through the compressor and into any such device for pressure control as a sylphon bellows. Now, if the main electric switch on the motor is closed, and if the pressure within the system is great enough, the control switch will start the motor and the compressor. When this charging operation starts, the valve on the charging drum should be opened only slightly. As the refrigerant is drawn from the charging drum, it will become chilled, and frost will accumulate, unless the charging drum is placed in a pail of warm water. Care should be taken that the *gage* pressure of the vapor of the refrigerant in the condenser does not exceed 30 pounds per square inch. If it should get above this limit, it may be reduced somewhat by removing the charging drum from the hot water and allowing it to cool. When the system is completely charged, the valve on the charging drum should be closed, and the operation of the compressor continued, to test the automatic starting and stopping. In all this charging operation, it is necessary to watch the gage in order to determine just how the pressure-control switch is working. If the pressure control is satisfactory, the suction shut-off valve may be opened, and the bypass connection may be removed if there is a sufficient amount of refrigerant in the system. The quantity of refrigerant in the system can be ascertained by weighing the drum before and after charging. The whole installation should be thoroughly tested for leaks.

"Icyball" Refrigerating Device.—An interesting household refrigerating device called "Icyball" is made by the Crosley Radio Corporation. This contrivance is shown in Fig. 109 in the upright position, as it would be placed in an ice box or a small refrigerator, the "cold ball" inside, and the "hot ball" outside. The two balls with the connecting piece of tubing T are tightly and permanently sealed, so that the liquid refrigerant contained inside cannot evaporate. When this device is being used to cool an icebox, for example, it operates by the method of the expansion of the compressed vapor of the refrigerant through the equivalent of a very small orifice in the connecting tubing T, the flow of the vapor of the refrigerant being from the cold ball

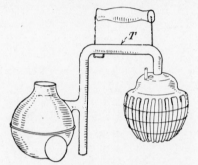

FIG. 109.—"Icyball" refrigerating device.

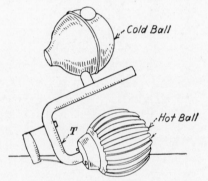

FIG. 110.—"Icyball" device in position to charge hot ball.

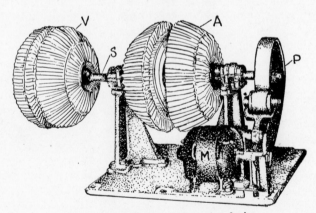

FIG. 111.—Audiffren refrigerating device.

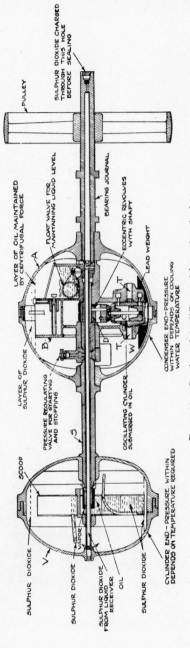

Fig. 112.—Section of Audiffren refrigerating device.

into the hot ball. When the pressures have become equalized, there will be no further cooling of the ice box. When this is the case, the device is removed from the ice box and turned on its side, as shown in Fig. 110, so that the liquid refrigerant (the "cold ball") flows by gravity into the hot ball. The refrigerant is *sulphur dioxide.* The next step is to heat the hot ball over a fire, preferably a portable heater of some kind, with the cold ball immersed in cold water. As the heat passes up around the fins on the hot ball, it evaporates some of the liquid refrigerant in the hot ball, causing its vapor to pass through the connecting tube T into the cold ball, when it condenses. When the hot ball has been sufficiently heated, it is taken off the fire and immersed for a few minutes in water for cooling. The liquid refrigerant in the cold ball now begins to evaporate and passes very slowly back into the hot ball. The evaporation of the liquid refrigerant in the cold ball produces a low temperature in the cold ball, which, in turn, cools the ice box in which it is placed.

Audiffren Refrigerating Machines.—The household refrigerating apparatus manufactured by the Audiffren Machine Company of New York City is shown by an exterior view in Fig. 111 and a section view in Fig. 112. A similar equipment, much too large, however, for household use, has been in commercial use for over 15 years (a detailed description of this larger apparatus is given on p. 51). *Sulphur dioxide* is the refrigerant used.

Compressor.—All the operating parts of the compressor are completely closed and sealed in the revolving "dumb-bell" shown in the figure. This consists of two bronze oval-shaped balls supported on a hollow shaft. The device is operated by a belt transmitting the power from an electric motor to the pulley shown at the right-hand side of the figure. The hollow shaft revolves in two babbitted bearings, and as the shaft revolves, one of the balls is heated by the substances which it cools, while the other is cooled in the larger sizes by water in a tank; but the smaller sizes of this device are air cooled, so that it is not necessary to provide water-pipe connections.

Thermal Electric Switches.—Some electric switches are operated from a bimetallic thermostat; but are not successful, because it is difficult to make it operate on a temperature *range* as low as 4 or 5° F. An improved bimetallic switch, called *mercoid control,* is shown in Fig. 113. This type of electric switch has recently found considerable application in household refrigerating devices. It consists of a two-metal member mounted on a glass tube, as shown in the figure. The tube contains a small amount of mercury which flows from one end to the other. When the mercury is at the left-hand end of the tube, the electric circuit is completed through the contact points A and B, and when it is tilted so that the mercury is at the right-hand end, as shown in the figure, there is no connection between A and B, and the circuit is broken. In this way, a quick make-and-break contact is secured. In order to avoid the corrosion produced by the arcing of the spark when the circuit is broken,

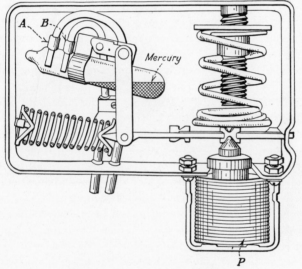

Fig. 113.—Mercoid electric switch.

the glass tube containing the mercury is filled with an inert gas in which an electric spark produces no combustion or oxidation.

Electrolux Servel Gas Refrigerator.—The gas-heated refrigerator made by the Electrolux Servel Corporation is an example of the absorption-system type of refrigeration as applied to household purposes. For many years, the gas engineer has been looking for a household refrigerating system that would utilize gas instead of electricity for its energy supply. This kind of refrigerating unit is highly desirable for the gas manufacturer, as the demand for gas for such refrigerators balances seasonally, to some extent, the requirements for house heating in the winter months.   The refrigerant is ammonia, which is not considered so safe for household use as some other refrigerants.

The refrigerating unit, as shown in Fig. 114, consists of a generator *G*, rectifier *R*, condenser *C*, absorber *A*, liquor-heat exchanger *B*, gas-heat exchanger *D*, and evaporator *E*.   Heat is supplied to the generator *G* by the gas flame of a Bunsen burner, which heats the strong ammonia liquor at the bottom of the generator.   This heat causes an increase in pressure in the lower

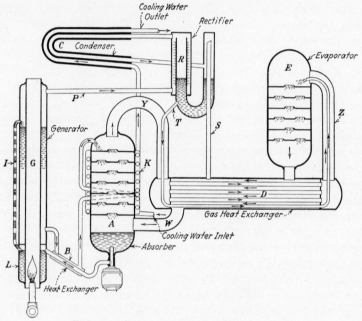

Fɪɢ. 114.—Servel gas-heated refrigerating unit.

section *L* of the generator, which forces slugs of strong ammonia liquor to rise through the interconnecting line *I*, thus feeding strong ammonia liquor into the top of the generator.   When still more heat is added to the strong liquor in the generator, a mixture of ammonia and water vapors passes from the generator through the pipe *P* into the rectifier *R*.

When the strong liquor in the generator has been reduced in concentration, a weak liquor is thus formed, which, because it has lower density than the strong liquor, settles to the bottom of the generator.   The weak liquor, because of the difference in level and also of pressure, is forced through the liquor-heat exchanger *B* into the bottom of the absorber *A*.

The ammonia and water vapors formed in the generator enter the rectifier *R* in which heat is removed from the mechanical mixture of the vapors by the evaporation of liquid ammonia, thus causing the water vapor to condense. The water thus formed by condensation then absorbs ammonia vapor, so that an ammonia solution of strong concentration is returned to the generator *G*, through the pipe *P*.

The rectifier *R* is used, therefore, to separate the water vapor from the ammonia vapor, permitting the ammonia vapor to pass through to the condenser *C* where the cooling water removes a sufficient amount of heat to cause the ammonia vapor to liquefy. In the liquid state, the ammonia flows from the rectifier *R* through a pipe *T*, which passes through the lower part of the gas-heat exchanger *D* and discharges the liquid ammonia into the top of the evaporator *E*. In the evaporator, the liquid ammonia flows over trays which have openings permitting it to fall over one row of trays after the other until it is evaporated. Hydrogen gas enters the top of the evaporator *E* through *Z* and mixes with ammonia vapor, causing the partial pressure of the latter within the evaporator to be low enough to obtain a low temperature. The law (Dalton's) of *partial pressures* is thus utilized, as the total pressure in the evaporator is the sum of the pressures of the hydrogen gas and the ammonia vapor. By admitting the hydrogen gas along with the ammonia to the evaporator, the partial pressure of the latter will be lower than if the ammonia vapor was used alone, thus giving a low evaporating temperature. After the liquid ammonia has evaporated, the ammonia vapor and the hydrogen gas, acting as a mechanical mixture, pass downward through the gas-heat exchanger *D*, where they cool the liquid ammonia flowing from the rectifier to the evaporator through the pipe *T* as well as the hydrogen gas which is passing into the evaporator.

The evaporation of the ammonia is due to its fall in pressure from 180 pounds per square inch in the generator to a partial pressure of 30 pounds per square inch in the evaporator. This is accomplished by an ingenious application of a law discovered by John Dalton, over a century ago, that the total pressure of a mixture of gases is equal to the sum of the pressures that each gas in the same space would exert if the other gas were absent. Now, the evaporator is filled with an atmosphere of hydrogen gas which gives a partial pressure of 150 pounds. When the ammonia which has been liquefied under a pressure of 180 pounds comes into the chamber where the pressure due to hydrogen is only 150 pounds, it evaporates at a rate sufficient to make up the difference between the two (30 pounds), and this causes the cooling. The hydrogen is kept from getting into the other part of the apparatus by a curved tube filled with water, through which ammonia can pass but not hydrogen.

The mechanical mixture of hydrogen gas and ammonia vapor, after passing through the gas-heat exchanger D, enters the bottom of the absorber A through the passage W. The ammonia then rises and mixes with the cool weak liquor entering the absorber at the top. This weak ammonia liquor flows over trays in the absorber which have numerous small holes, so that the weak liquor falls like rain and mingles with the rising mechanical mixture of ammonia vapor and hydrogen gas. The concentration of the weak liquor is such that it readily absorbs ammonia vapor, thereby causing the strength of the solution to increase so that it becomes a strong liquor. The strong liquor accumulates at the bottom of the absorber, and because of a difference in pressure, its vapor flows through the passage Y into the left-hand end of the gas-heat exchanger D. In this exchanger, heat is absorbed from the weak liquor, which is on its way to the absorber, thus increasing the temperature of the strong liquor about to enter the generator G.

Cooling coils K in which water is circulated are provided to remove the partial heat of absorption generated by the absorption of ammonia vapor by the weak liquor. These cooling coils are made of copper and are placed around the exterior of the casing of the absorber A. The hydrogen now left free of ammonia is allowed to pass through the tubes of the gas heat exchanger D and the passage Z into the evaporator E.

The condenser C consists of adjacent copper and steel coils, one containing water, and the other ammonia. These coils are in direct contact, and heat flows by conduction from the ammonia to the water. In order to obtain large contact surfaces, a copper wire is soldered to the adjacent coils in order to increase the rate of heat transfer. The cooling water is supplied at the bottom of the cooling coils K of the absorber A and is discharged directly into the cooling coils of the condenser. The temperature of the cooling water at the outlet of the condenser is maintained at about 90° F. by permitting a limited quantity of water to pass through the cooling coils. This temperature is controlled entirely by a sylphon-bellows temperature regulator. The quantity of water required is about 5 to 8 gallons per hour.

The generator, evaporator, absorber, rectifier, and gas-heat exchanger are made of heavy steel tubing interconnected by steel pipes. All the joints are made by oxyacetylene welding. These parts will withstand a pressure as high as 3,000 pounds per

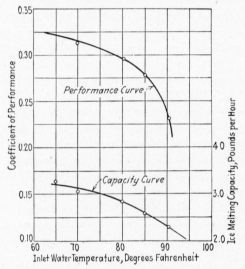

Fig. 115.—Effect of varying cooling-water temperature. Gas rate 2.5 cubic feet per hour. Room temperature 70° F. Quantity of water 7 gallons per hour.

square inch, although the maximum charging pressure is only about 200 pounds per square inch.[1] An apparatus of this kind requires an automatic mechanism which is regulated by temperature for shutting off the gas supply at the end of the boiling period and, also, for adjusting at the right time the cooling water going to the condenser and to the absorber.

This system has a very satisfactory safety feature, in that the radiating surface (the outside surfaces of the evaporator, heat exchangers, absorber, condenser, and rectifier) is large in pro-

[1] In order to prevent any destructive effect of the ammonia on the metal parts, a little ammonium bichromate is added to the ammonia which circulates in the system.

portion to the heating surface. These will dissipate heat by radiation almost at the same rate that it is supplied to the generator.

A fusible plug is fitted into the gas-heat exchanger at the end toward the absorber, in order to provide an emergency outlet for the ammonia in case of exterior heating by the outbreak of fire in the room or building. This fusible plug is made of a metal which melts at 200° F.

Figure 115 shows the effect of the coefficient of performance and ice-melting capacity for varying inlet-cooling-water tem-

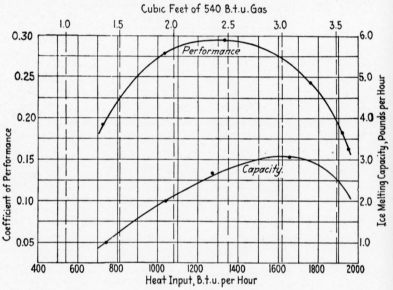

Fig. 116.—Effect of varying amount of heat supplied. Water temperature 70° F. Room temperature 70° F. Quantity of water 5 gallon per hour.

peratures when the rate of gas consumption is 2½ cubic feet per hour, the room temperature is 70° F., and 7 gallons of water are used per hour. It is interesting to note that the curve of coefficient of performance falls off rapidly at temperatures of inlet cooling water above 80° F.

Curves showing how the coefficient of performance and the ice-melting capacity are affected by the amount of heat supplied are given in Fig. 116. These curves are based on a heating value of the gas of 540 B.t.u. per cubic foot. The coefficient of performance has its maximum value when the total heat supplied is about

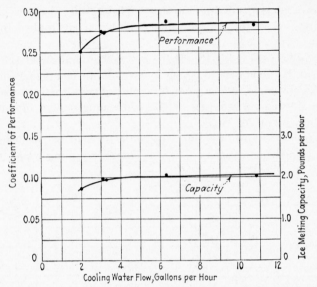

FIG. 117.—Effect of varying quantity of cooling water. Cooling water tempera-ture 70° F. Room temperature 70° F. Heat input 1,025 B.t.u. per hour.

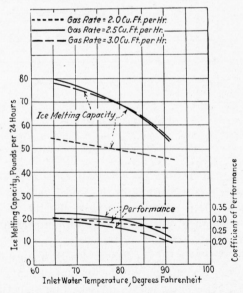

FIG. 118.—Effect of varying cooling-water temperature for three rates of gas con-sumption. Room temperature 70° F. Quantity of water 7 gallons per hour.

1,300 B.t.u. per hour, while the ice-melting capacity has its highest value when the total heat supplied is about 1,620 B.t.u. per hour. The rate of gas consumption for average operation is shown by the curves to be between 2 and 3 cubic feet per hour.

A curve showing how the coefficient of performance and the ice-melting capacity are affected by the quantity of cooling water in gallons is given in Fig. 117. For rates of flow of cooling water of about 4 gallons per hour and above, the coefficient of performance and ice-melting capacity do not change appreciably.

In Fig. 118, there are curves showing the effect of cooling-water temperature upon efficiency and ice-melting capacity of the refrigerating system, for three rates of gas consumption. It is interesting to note the wide divergence in the values of ice-melting capacity for gas rates of 2 and 3 cubic feet per hour.

Some of the important factors in the operation of this refrigerating system are: (1) The maximum performance is obtained when the heat input is about 1,300 to 1,350 B.t.u. per hour, which is approximately equivalent to 2.4 cubic feet of gas per hour; (2) the lower the average temperature of the cooling water the better is the performance; (3) refrigeration for domestic purposes may be obtained when the temperature of the cooling water is 90° F. and the room temperature is 100° F.; (4) maximum capacity of the machine is obtained when the heat input is about 1,620 B.t.u. per hour, which is equivalent to approximately 2.9 cubic feet of gas per hour;[1] (5) room temperature affects the efficiency of the machine slightly but not enough to interfere with its operation for the ordinary range of temperature; (6) in case the cooling water fails and the gas continues to burn, refrigeration will stop, and the maximum pressure will not increase more than about 25 per cent above the normal working pressure.

Gas-control Device.—Figure 119 shows the gas-control valve used in the Electrolux-Servel refrigerating system. In essential parts, it consists of the thermal bulb E which is filled with a vapor which when expanded by heat increases the pressure in the tube T and on the top of the diaphragm F. The depression of the diaphragm F and the valve disk K on the valve stem S due to pressure in the tube T is resisted by the spring G. The

---

[1] The capacity for this heat input is approximately 3.3 pounds of ice-melting capacity, which is equal to about 79 pounds of ice-melting capacity per 24 hours. This represents a daily gas consumption of about 70 cubic feet.

gas for the Bunsen burner which supplies heat to the generator of
the refrigerator is taken into the gas-control valve at C, passes
through the opening between the valve disk K and its seat J,
and discharges through the outlet connection H.

These gas-control valves are set at the factory to adjust the
flow of gas to a pressure of 5 inches of water at the Bunsen burner,

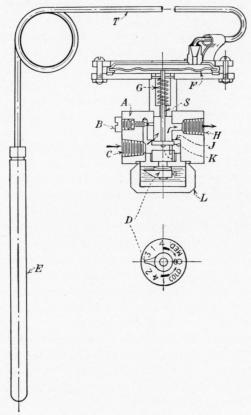

Fig. 119.—Gas-regulating valve.

which supplies heat to the generator of the refrigerator. In
order to change the adjustment for gas pressure, the pointer on
the disk D is turned clockwise to reduce the height of the gas
flame and counterclockwise to raise the flame. The setscrew A
is used to adjust the height of the pilot light. At the tip of the
screw A, there is always a small opening for the passage of gas
when the valve disk K is completely closed against its seat J.

Figure 120 shows a Servel refrigerator cabinet and gas range combined for the requirements of small apartments.

Household Absorption Refrigerating System Using Water as Refrigerant.—A French household absorption machine invented by R. Follain is interesting because water is the only medium of refrigeration employed. This is doubly advantageous, since water everywhere is cheap and absorbs a larger quantity of heat on evaporation than any other substance known. In this apparatus, the evaporation is hastened, and, therefore, the cool-

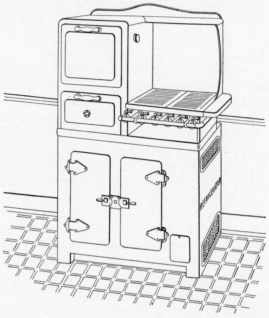

Fig. 120.—Refrigerator and gas range for small apartments.

ing effect is intensified through the creation of a vacuum above the surface of the water in an airtight tank by the injection of a steam jet in a constricted tube. The water vapor and steam are condensed in an adjoining chamber by a spray of cold water. Several such systems can be arranged in series in order to secure the desired reduction of temperature. Such a machine will cool 1,100 pounds of water from 77 to 37° F. with the use of about 7.9 pounds of water utilized as steam for the injector and 450 pounds of water for cooling at average yearly temperatures.

CHAPTER VI

OPERATION OF REFRIGERATION SYSTEMS

Operating Practice for Compression System. Starting a Compressor.—The reciprocating engine-driven compressor of a refrigerating system should always be started slowly and carefully, for the reason that the machine is handling powerful chemicals at high pressures. When starting a water-cooled compressor, it is necessary to provide, first, a flow of cooling water through the condenser and also through the water jacket of the compressor. It is during the starting operation that the cylinder of the compressor is most likely to become too hot.

Before steam is admitted to an engine driving a compressor, the main discharge valve at the compressor must be open, while the main suction valve and the valve on the main liquid line *A*, in Fig. 121, must be closed. The packing in the stuffing box of the compressor should be examined to make sure that it is not too tight and that the oil cups supply sufficient oil to the bearings. In the operation of starting, the engine cylinder should be "warmed." If a slide-valve engine is being used, this can be done by opening the drain cocks and letting into the cylinder just enough steam to warm it. The drain cocks should not be closed until the engine has run for a little while. In the case of a Corliss engine, which does not have drain cocks, warming is accomplished by opening the throttle valve of the engine a little and unhooking the wristplate and rocking it back and forth so that a small amount of steam enters each end of the cylinder, being careful that the valves are hooked to the wristplate. Then the wristplate should be attached to the rocker arm and to both dashpot rods. The throttle valve may then be opened only wide enough to bring the engine past dead center; and after operating for a few strokes, the suction valve of the compressor may be opened slightly. If the compressor cylinder "knocks," the suction valve should be closed a little, a knocking sound indicating that liquid refrigerant is entering the cylinder. Since the liquid is not compressible, its presence may cause a cylinder

137

head of the rigid type to be broken off. If there is no knocking, the suction valve should be opened more and more at intervals until it is wide open. Usually, an increase in the opening of the suction valve causes the engine to run more slowly, and it will then be necessary to provide more steam to keep it turning over.

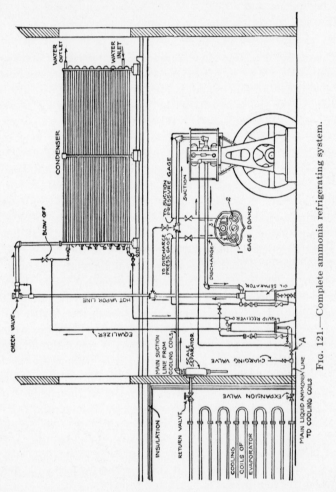

Fig. 121.—Complete ammonia refrigerating system.

Most compressors, and especially those driven by electric motors, are equipped with a by-pass connection so that only a small amount of power will be needed for starting. When starting a motor-driven compressor, the valves on the main discharge and suction lines should be closed, and the valve on the by-pass connection opened. When the motor is running at low speed, the valves on the main discharge and suction lines should be opened and the valve on the by-pass closed. The speed of the compressor should then be adjusted so as to bring the suction pressure to the desired value, after which the expansion valve can be opened and adjusted to the proper conditions.

In order to shut down a motor-driven compressor, reverse the order of operations as above. When the compressor is motor driven it should be remembered that the power required to operate with high suction pressure is much greater than with a low suction pressure. It often happens that the suction pressure is high at the start and because of this about 40 per cent more power is required than under operating conditions.

When a refrigerating plant has been shut down for several hours, the evaporation of liquid refrigerant in the cooling coils of the evaporator will probably generate a high pressure that will be indicated on the suction gage. This pressure will be reduced when the compressor is started and the suction valve is opened. In a plant using ammonia as the refrigerant, for example, until the suction gage registers a pressure of at least 5 or 10 pounds per square inch, the compressor must not be run above three-quarter speed; half-speed is even better. In the meanwhile, the temperature of the discharge pipe of the compressor should be observed. If it gets too hot to be touched comfortably by the hand (110 to 120° F.), the speed of the compressor should be reduced by slowing the engine.

With the expansion valve still closed, the valve on the main liquid line A, in Fig. 121, may now be opened, and then the expansion valve should also be opened a little at a time to admit a fine stream of liquid ammonia into the cooling coils of the evaporator.

When the suction pressure increases and the suction pipe becomes cold, the engine may be operated at full speed. It is a good plan to put one's hand on the suction pipe from time to time to observe whether or not it is getting colder, as it should be when the compressor is operating properly.

As the expansion valve is gradually opened wider, more frost will appear on the cooling coils of the evaporator as far back on the suction pipe as the suction valves. This is an indication that the expansion of ammonia into the coils is going on properly. In an ammonia refrigerating system, the expansion valve is adjusted properly when the suction gage reaches the desired operating pressure.

Temperatures, Pressures in Compression System of Refrigeration.—The vapor of a refrigerant will not be condensed unless its temperature is higher than that of the condenser cooling water. The discharge pressure of the compressor, therefore, must always be high enough to keep the vapor of the refrigerant at a sufficiently high temperature. It is important, however, that there should not be too much difference in temperature, for efficiency of operation requires the smallest possible temperature range. The best effects are obtained when the condenser cooling water is as cold as possible, in order that the discharge pressure of the compressor may be so low that the ammonia will not be at an excessively high temperature.

In the cooling coils of the evaporator, the temperature of the vapor of the refrigerant depends on the suction pressure. By adjustment of the suction pressure, then, the temperature of the refrigerant in the cooling coils of the evaporator can be controlled. The suction pressure can be *increased* by two methods: (1) by opening the expansion valve a little or (2) reducing the speed of the compressor. This pressure is *decreased* similarly by closing the expansion valve slightly or increasing the compressor speed. The speed of the compressor and the amount of opening of the expansion-valve control, also, the discharge pressure; but the effects of compressor speed and expansion-valve opening on the discharge pressure are opposite to their effects on the suction pressure. A high discharge pressure is maintained by high compressor speed; and low discharge pressure is maintained by low speed.

If a temperature of 32° F. is to be maintained by a brine cooling system, it will be found necessary to keep the suction-gage pressure in a plant using ammonia as the refrigerant at 25 to 28 pounds per square inch, in order that the ammonia may be enough colder than the brine to insure a rapid transfer of heat from the brine to the ammonia. This difference in temperature should be 10 to 15° F. Similar conditions in a direct-expansion system require a suction-gage pressure of the ammonia vapor of 33 to 35 pounds per square inch.

If it is desired to secure a rapid freezing temperature (0° F. or lower), the suction-gage pressure of ammonia vapor will have to be kept as low as 5 pounds per square inch; while 20- to 25-

pounds-per-square-inch gage will give the proper temperature
(10 to 20° F.) for making ice.

Shutting Down an Ammonia Compressor.—Methods of
shutting down the compressor in an ammonia refrigerating
system vary according to the length of time it is desired to keep
the compressor out of operation.

To shut down for 2 or 3 hours, the suction-gage pressure should
be reduced to not more than 5 pounds per square inch, by operating, if possible, the compressor with the valve on the main
ammonia liquid line *closed*. It may happen that the compressor
will tend to overheat while thus reducing the suction pressure.
In this case, the speed of the compressor should be reduced until
the compressor is no longer getting hotter. When the suction
gage indicates the proper reduction in pressure, the compressor
should be stopped. Then, and not until the compressor has
come to a *dead stop*, the main suction and the discharge valves
should be closed. It is important that the main discharge valve
should never be closed while the compressor is still operating.

After the engine driving the compressor has been stopped, the
ammonia vapor will be likely to escape at the compressor stuffing
box, unless precautions are taken. To avoid this, it is a good
practice to tighten the packing of the stuffing box when shutting
down. Finally, the cooling water should be shut off.

For a longer period of shutdown (a day or more), it will also
be necessary to close the expansion valve after "pumping down"
the suction pressure.

If the shutdown is to last not more than about $\frac{1}{4}$ hour, only
the valve on the main liquid line A, in Fig. 121, need be closed;
and when this valve is closed, the engine driving the compressor
may be stopped.

Opening the Cylinder of a Compressor.—As in the case of
any similar machine, the cylinder of a compressor needs such
occasional care as cleaning or regrinding of valves. To remove
the valves for this purpose, the main suction valve (marked S, in
Fig. 122) is closed, and the compressor is operated for about a
dozen revolutions. After stopping the compressor, the main
discharge valve should be closed, and the blank flange should
be removed from the valve Z. A pipe connection, as shown at Y,
should be made from the valve Z into a bucket of water. When
this valve Z is opened a little, the vapor of the refrigerant in the

compressor will pass into the bucket of water, making it possible to open the cylinder.

Oil for Compressors.—The compressor cylinders of a refrigerating plant are subject to unusual conditions of service and need special grades of oil. The oil which is used should be free from animal or vegetable matter and should not freeze, thicken, or gum at low temperatures. High-grade paraffin petroleum oils

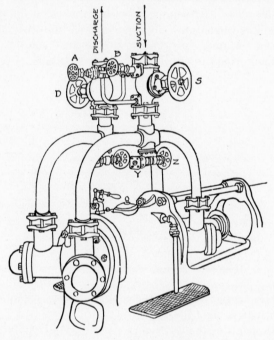

Fig. 122.—Bypass connections on ammonia compressor.

will meet these requirements satisfactorily in plants using ammonia as the refrigerant.

When oil is used too freely in the compressor, it is likely to find its way into the condenser and cause trouble there. It should be used sparingly but in sufficient amount to produce the necessary lubricating effect. Once a week or oftener, the oil which has passed through the oil separator into the condenser or other parts of the system should be cleaned out by the method of circulating hot ammonia vapor through the pipes to make the oil more fluid than it would otherwise be. Then the mixed oil and ammonia should be "pumped" through the compressor into the oil separator.

Oil Separator.—The discharge-pipe line of the compressor shown in Fig. 121 is provided with an *oil separator*. This separator is necessary to remove from the refrigerant the oil supplied to the cylinder of the compressor to lubricate the piston and to remove, also, the small amount of oil provided for the stuffing box and which may leak into the cylinder. Unless removed, some of this oil will remain mixed with the vapor of the refrigerant and will be carried into the condenser where it will collect on the walls of the pipes, preventing the efficient transfer of heat and reducing the effectiveness of the condenser. Briefly, an

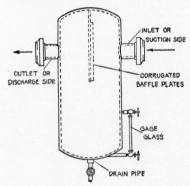

FIG. 123.—Oil separator with baffle plates.

oil separator is used to remove the oil before the vapor of the refrigerant enters the condenser.

The oil separator, shown in some detail in Fig. 123, is simply a vertical cylinder connected to the discharge pipe of the compressor so that the flow of vapor of the refrigerant is intercepted by baffle plates, as shown. Some of the vapor passes through holes in the corrugated baffle plates, and some vapor passes around the plates. The pipe connections leading, respectively, to the compressor and to the condenser are at the top of the cylinder. The vapor of the refrigerant enters the oil separator at a high velocity, and the sudden change in direction of flow of the vapor, caused by the baffle plates, tends to leave the oil on the baffle plates and the inside wall of the separator, to which it clings. It then trickles down to the bottom, where it collects and is drained off. Some oil separators are made with the discharge pipe of the compressor passing halfway down on the inside, and others have a special passage with fins placed along the path of the vapor for the purpose of separating the oil. An oil separator generally has a gage glass connected to it at one side, as shown in Fig. 123. At the top and bottom of the gage glass are cocks, which, when open, show the depth of oil in the separator. Except when testing the depth of oil in the separator, these cocks should be kept closed to prevent the possible escape of the refrigerant.[1] From the top of the oil separator, a small pipe usually extends to the gage board, where a gage indicates the pressure in the discharge line of the compressor. Figure 124

Fig. 124.—Ammonia condenser, oil separator, and purifier.

shows the location of the oil separator in a recently equipped plant.

In Fig. 121, there is a check valve in the pipe line connecting the oil separator to the condenser. The purpose of this check valve is to prevent the liquid refrigerant from passing back from the condenser into the compressor, as might happen if it were not removed from the condenser rapidly enough to prevent flooding. If liquid ammonia should flow back into the cylinder of the compressor, there would be danger of damaging the cylinder head.

[1] The objection to oil separators with baffle plates is that they cause considerable loss of pressure by the sudden change of direction of the flow of the vapor. Such a loss of pressure is the result of the change of kinetic energy into useless heat and, therefore, is an "irreversible" heat process.

Charging an Ammonia Compression Refrigerating System.—
In charging an ammonia refrigerating system, the compressor
must first be operated with the discharge pipe disconnected so
that the discharge is into the atmosphere till a vacuum of at
least 26 inches of mercury is indicated by the suction gage.
Then the discharge pipe is to be attached to the connection for
it on the compressor cylinder. After weighing and recording the
weight of the ammonia shipping drum, which usually contains
about 100 pounds, the ammonia drum should be connected to
the charging valve, and the valve marked *A*, in Fig. 121, which
is between the liquid receiver and the charging valve on the main
liquid ammonia line should be closed. In this way, the ammonia

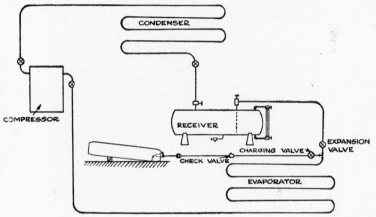

FIG. 125.—Pipe connections for charging ammonia compression refrigerating
system.

in the liquid receiver is kept from passing into the cooling coils of
the evaporator, and the ammonia in the shipping drum is allowed
to expand into the evaporator from which ammonia vapor is
drawn into the compressor. The main discharge and suction
valves on the discharge and suction pipes at the compressor
should then be opened as well as also the expansion valve and
the valve at the high-pressure gage. The system is ready to be
put into operation when the cooling water begins to circulate in
the coils of the condenser. The ammonia vapor can then be
drawn from the cooling coils of the evaporator, passed into the
compressor, where it is compressed, discharged into the condenser, where it is condensed, and, finally, drained into the
liquid receiver.

The piping connections for charging an ammonia refrigerating system are shown in Fig. 125.

Some precautions are necessary in connecting the ammonia shipping drum to the system. A connection of ⅜-inch pipe should be made and bent suitably for connecting the drum to the charging valve of the system. The ammonia drum should be placed and blocked so that the back end is higher than the valve end, and the outlet valve should point upward. After a tight connection has been made between the ammonia drum and the charging valve, the compressor should be started and operated very slowly. At the same time, the flow of water should be started through its water jacket, if the compressor has one, because a compressor heats very quickly.

The next operation is to open, first, the charging valve and then the valve on the ammonia drum. The valve on the drum must be opened very cautiously, a little at a time. If the odor of ammonia is strong, this valve should be shut off, and the connections to the drum should be tested for leaks. When the connections are tight, the valve on the drum may be opened wider.

Soon after the valve on the drum is opened, a coating of frost begins to accumulate on the cooling coils of the evaporator, and gradually this coating of frost extends backward to the charging valve and to its connection to the drum. This frost accumulates because the pressure in the coils of the evaporator is low while the pressure in the drum is high, so that when the charging valve is opened, the liquid ammonia vaporizes at the low pressure in the charging pipe. The evaporation of the ammonia reduces the temperature so much that the moisture of the air settles on the pipe and freezes.

While this part of the charging operation is going on, the compressor is running and discharging the ammonia vapor into the condenser as soon as it forms. If it were not for this rapid removal of the ammonia vapor from the coils of the evaporator, a high pressure would be produced in them.

When the frost begins to approach the back end of the drum, it indicates that nearly all the ammonia has been removed from the drum. After a while, the frost on the charging pipe begins to disappear. If a blowtorch is applied near the outlet of the drum at this time, the rate of evaporation will be increased, and the drum will be emptied more rapidly.

After all the frost has disappeared from the drum and its connections, the compressor should be stopped, and the suction-gage pressure should be carefully observed. If, after a few moments, there is no appreciable rise in pressure, the drum is empty and may be disconnected. If, however, at this time, the suction-gage pressure rises to atmospheric, the drum is not empty.

In the operation of disconnecting the empty drum, the charging valve should first be closed, and then the valve on the drum. When breaking the connection, one should work slowly and keep one's hands, if not protected, as far as possible from joints, because it is likely that the connections still contain some liquid ammonia which causes burns if touched with bare hands.

If a newly installed system is being charged for the first time, not all the ammonia which will be needed should be put into the system at one time. It is best to charge the system with one-half the necessary amount of ammonia and operate the plant long enough to circulate it throughout the system. Air will collect at the top of the condenser; and this air should be drawn off through the blowoff or "purge" valves, before charging with more ammonia. The ammonia which is still needed may then be added preferably at two different times, circulating the ammonia and drawing off the air through the blowoff or "purge" valves of the condenser between times of filling with ammonia.

When an ammonia drum appears to be empty, it should be weighed, and the weight of ammonia which has been taken out should be checked with that of a full drum. This checking insures fair weight by the dealer and makes certain that the drum is entirely empty. In case more than one ammonia drum is needed, another drum may be attached with the same precautions as before. Before opening the valve of an ammonia charging drum, one should observe that the suction gage of the compressor indicates a vacuum.

After the system has been charged with ammonia, leaks may occur. These are easily detected either by the smell of ammonia or by means of sulphur sticks.

When the system is operating, the liquid ammonia should be about 1 foot deep in a vertical liquid receiver. Quantities required vary with the length of the piping in the system; but, in general, those given in the following table will be about the proper amounts:

For ice making..................... 45 pounds of ammonia per ton of
ice-making capacity.
For direct-expansion refrigeration...... 25 pounds of ammonia per ton of
refrigeration.
For brine-circulation refrigeration...... 13 pounds of ammonia per ton of
refrigeration.

Removing Refrigerant from the System.—The refrigerant
should not be withdrawn from a refrigerating system and placed
in shipping drums without weighing the amount of refrigerant
placed in each drum. There is great danger of overfilling a
drum. The proper connections for removing the refrigerant
from the system are shown in Fig. 126.

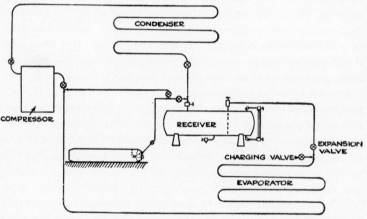

Fig. 126.—Pipe connections for removing ammonia from compression refrigerating system.

Weight of Refrigerant to Be Evaporated.—The weight of
refrigerant which is to be evaporated per minute can be calculated by multiplying together the following quantities: (1)
actual capacity of the refrigerating system in tons of refrigeration, (2) number of pounds of refrigerant which is evaporated
per minute per ton of refrigeration. In a practical example of
finding the *second* of these quantities, the temperature of the
liquid ammonia may be assumed to be at the standard values of
86° F. when it leaves the condensor and 5° F. after it passes
through the expansion valve and vaporizes in the cooling coils
of the evaporator. The refrigerating effect for these temperature
conditions is 474.4 B.t.u. per pound. By definition, 1 ton of
refrigeration is equivalent to the removal of heat at the rate of

200 B t.u. *per minute.* The weight of refrigerant, therefore, which must be circulated and evaporated in a minute for each ton of refrigeration to obtain the required temperature after the refrigerant has passed through the expansion valve is 200 divided by 474.4 or 0.422 pound of refrigerant *per minute* per ton of refrigeration.

Weight of Liquid Ammonia Evaporated in Passing through Expansion Valve.—The total amount of heat which a pound of liquid ammonia will take up in the expansion coil of the evaporator will depend only on the temperature of the liquid ammonia before it enters the evaporator, provided, of course, that all the ammonia is in the liquid form. Now, it happens, always, that some of the liquid ammonia is evaporated when the ammonia in the liquid form passes through the expansion valve, and whatever proportion of a pound of ammonia is in the *vapor form* when it reaches the expansion coil of the evaporator cannot be used for cooling by the method of expansion in the evaporator.

In most cases, in the practical operation of refrigerating plants, the temperature of the liquid ammonia as it enters the expansion coil of the evaporator is nearly the same as its temperature when it leaves the condenser; and this temperature is usually a number of degrees above the temperature of the evaporating ammonia in the expansion coil. Because of this higher temperature of the liquid ammonia, it is necessary to evaporate part of the liquid ammonia in order to cool the remainder from the temperature at which it leaves the condenser to the temperature existing in the expansion coil of the evaporator. This means that just before the liquid ammonia comes to the expansion valve, it is entirely in the liquid state but that immediately after it passes through the expansion valve and is on its way to the expansion coil of the evaporator, it is a mixture of liquid and vapor.

As an example illustrating this point, it will be assumed that the temperatures in the system are of the usual standard values. That is, the temperature of the ammonia vapor entering the condenser is 86° F., and the temperature in the expansion coil of the evaporator is 5° F. The ammonia must, therefore, be cooled in its passage through the condenser and through the expansion valve from 86° F. to the lower temperature or through a range of 81° F. The temperature of the ammonia vapor, when becoming liquid in the condenser, is reduced from 86° F.

to nearly the temperature of the water used for cooling the condenser; and the rest of the temperature reduction must come about by the evaporation of part of the liquid ammonia. The heat required to cool the liquid ammonia from 86 to 5° F. may be found by subtracting from the total heat in the liquid ammonia at 86° F. the total heat in the liquid ammonia at 5° F. These values of total heat of the liquid ammonia may be taken from Table of Properties of Ammonia in the Appendix; in this table, it is found that the total heat of the liquid at 86° F. is 138.9 B.t.u. per pound and that the total heat of the liquid ammonia at 5° F. is 48.3 B.t.u. per pound. The difference of the total heats of the liquid is, therefore, 90.6 B.t.u. per pound. For purposes of illustration, it may now be assumed that the ammonia is cooled by means of very cold circulating water to a temperature of 66° F. A certain amount of every pound of liquid ammonia must, therefore, be cooled from 66 to 5° F. (temperature in the evaporator). The total heat in the liquid ammonia at 66° F. is 116.0 B.t.u. per pound, and the total heat of the liquid ammonia at 5° F. is 48.3 B.t.u. per pound. The difference or 67.7 B.t.u. per pound must, therefore, be absorbed from the liquid ammonia in order to cool it from the temperature at which it leaves the condenser (66° F.) to the temperature in the evaporator.

The above calculations show that when cold water is available for use in the ammonia condenser, the cooling effect theoretically available in the expansion coil of the evaporator is 565.0 B.t.u. per pound (latent heat of evaporation at 5° F.) less 67.7 B.t.u. per pound, or 497.3 B.t.u. per pound. On the other hand, if the cooling water which is available is at a relatively high temperature, so that the liquid ammonia leaves the condenser, at 86° F., the cooling effect in the expansion coil of the evaporator due to each pound of ammonia is 565.0 − 90.6 or only 474.4 B.t.u. per pound.

Percentage of Ammonia Evaporated by Cooling between Condenser and Evaporator.—The amount of ammonia which must be evaporated in order to reduce the temperature between the condenser and the evaporator is easily expressed as a *percentage*. In other words, this is a percentage loss of refrigerating effect due to this reduction in temperature. When the liquid ammonia leaves the condenser at 66° F., the percentage by weight of ammonia which must evaporate so that its temperature as it enters the expansion coil of the evaporator may be 5° F. is 67.7 ÷ 565.0 = 0.12, or 12 per cent.

Now, if the liquid ammonia leaves the condenser at 86° F., with other conditions the same, the percentage of each pound of ammonia evaporated in the cooling between the condenser and the evaporator is 90.6 ÷ 565.0 = 0.16 or 16 per cent. In each case, the latent heat of evaporation is, of course, 565.0 B.t.u. per pound.

This percentage of ammonia which must be evaporated to provide for the cooling between the condenser and the evaporator is really the percentage of "wetness" of the ammonia vapor after it has passed the expansion valve and enters the expansion coil. The *quality* of a vapor is usually expressed as a decimal and is the difference between unity and the decimal fraction corresponding to the percentage of wetness. In the first case above, when the liquid ammonia leaves the condenser at 66° F., the *quality* of the ammonia vapor entering the expansion coil of the evaporator is 1.00 − 0.12 or 0.88.

Effects of Cooling-water Temperature on Refrigerating Effect.—A comparison of the cooling effects when ammonia leaves the condenser at 66 and at 86° F. shows the desirability of cooling the liquid ammonia to a temperature as low as possible in the condenser. In other words, it shows strikingly the improved refrigerating effect from using cold water for cooling the condenser.

Testing Ammonia Compression Refrigerating Systems for Leaks.—When a new refrigerating compressor is installed, the operating engineer should obtain a set of instructions from the manufacturer, for each machine has its special features and requires special directions for operating, testing, and charging. Some general information, however, may be given which applies to any of the standard types.

Every new plant, when it is installed, should be thoroughly tested before going into use. It is possible that machinery leaving the factory in perfect condition may not be received in such condition. The handling in shipping may cause breakage or inaccurate adjustment.

The most important test is for leaks. This test should be made before admitting any ammonia into the system. The first step is to open the suction pipe at the compressor and to seal it either by screwing a cap over it, or by closing the main

suction valve on the end of the pipe. Then permit a free circulation of air through the whole system by opening the main
discharge valve, the expansion valve, and any other valves
which would interfere with the flow, being careful, however, to
shut off the suction-pressure gage, for the operation of testing is
likely to damage it. Now start the compressor gradually and
let it run slowly. In this way, air passes into the compressor
cylinder through the suction valve, is compressed, and is forced
through the system. When the high-pressure gage indicates a
pressure of 200 to 250 pounds per square inch, stop the compressor and close the main discharge valve tightly. For a few
moments, while the air cools, there will be a falling off of the
pressure. When the air has cooled, the needle of the gage should
remain stationary, *indicating that there are no leaks* and that the
system is tight.

If the gage shows a continued falling off in pressure, there are
leaks. To locate them, a thick lather of soap and water should
be applied to all the piping with a broad flat brush. At the point
or points of leakage, the lather will be expanded into soap bubbles
by the escaping air. Submerged parts of the system, if there
are any, such as the condenser or brine tank, may also have
leaky coils. Escaping air in these submerged parts is detected
by a column of bubbles, which forms on the coils and rises to the
top of the water or brine.

Two methods are effective for repairing small leaks. One is
to solder the defective portion of the pipe. The other is to
apply a paste of glycerin and litharge, protecting the paste, until
it hardens, by binding over it a sheet of rubber. Large leaks
cannot be repaired by these means, and the leaky section of
pipe must be removed and replaced by a perfect one.

After testing with compressed air, a new plant is sometimes
given a vacuum test. To do this, the suction pipe is connected
as for normal operation, and the discharge pipe is disconnected.
The valve or cock on the suction gage is now opened, and the
one on the discharge or pressure gage is closed. The compressor
is operated slowly, as before. The air which was in the system
will be sucked into the compressor cylinder and will pass out
through the discharge valve. Thus, as the air is pumped out of
the system, the suction gage will drop and indicate a vacuum.
The main suction valve should then be closed to seal the system.
If the suction gage holds its reading, the system is free from leaks.

Testing for Leakage of Ammonia Vapor.—In the regular operation of an ammonia refrigerating plant operated with compressors, those in charge of the machinery must be constantly on the lookout for the leakage of ammonia vapor through the piston-rod packing and valve stems. In all kinds of plants using ammonia, there is the danger of leakage at the joints in the piping. It is very difficult to keep the packing around the piston rod perfectly tight at all times, and tightness becomes especially difficult to maintain when the piston rod is not centrally located at all times in the stroke. One reason for this difficulty is that the piston rod will eventually wear away more in the middle of the stroke than at the ends, and this unequal wear may become so great that it will be necessary to turn down a rod in a lathe. If the wear in the crosshead shoe is not adjusted carefully from time to time, there will be present another cause for excessive wear on the piston-rod packing.[1]

The test most commonly used to determine whether or not there is leakage of ammonia vapor through the piston-rod packing, valve stems, and pipe joints is to burn a stick of sulphur near the place where leakage is suspected. A leak of ammonia vapor will be indicated by white fumes, as already stated on page 71. Condensers of the atmospheric and shell-and-tube types may also be tested with sulphur sticks, when the tested surfaces are dry and the gage pressure in the condenser is about 200 pounds per square inch.

A double-pipe condenser may be tested for leaks by the use of sulphur sticks, but, obviously, the method of testing with sulphur will not work out so well with this type of condenser as with other types and under other conditions. For this reason, a double-pipe condenser is usually tested for leaks by adding what is called *Nessler's solution* to a sample of the cooling water which is discharged from the condenser while it is operating. In order to make the test, a sample of the cooling water should be collected in any kind of glass vessel, and, if any ammonia is present in the sample, the water will be colored when a few drops of Nessler's solution are added. It will turn yellow, if relatively small leaks are present, and dark brown, if the leaks are large.

[1] Records of leakage of ammonia in refrigerating plants in Philadelphia and Chicago show that the average loss of ammonia by leakage in well-operated plants adds an expense of about 2 cents per ton of ice.

Thus, large leaks of ammonia from the expansion tank can be tested by Nessler's solution added to the brine, and the brine in the freezing tank of an ice plant can also be tested in the same way. If the brine has been made by the addition of sodium chloride to water, Nessler's solution can be added to the brine in the same manner as it would be put into the cooling water of the condenser. On the other hand, if the usual kinds of calcium brine are to be tested for ammonia leakage, it is necessary to remove the calcium by adding to the sample of brine after dilution with water enough sodium carbonate to precipitate the calcium and then adding Nessler's solution to the filtrate. If the filtrate turns brown after Nessler's solution has been added, there is a leakage of ammonia into the sample being tested. The addition of sodium to the calcium brine before testing with Nessler's solution is necessary, because Nessler's solution always forms a precipitate in calcium brine whether or not ammonia is present. It will be observed, however, that if there is no leakage of ammonia into the brine, the sample being tested will be white when the Nessler's solution is added, and will have a yellow color when only a trace of ammonia is present.

Testing with Nessler's Solution and Litmus Paper.—The formula for Nessler's solution is as follows: Dissolve 17 grams of mercuric chloride in about 300 cubic centimeters of distilled water; dissolve 35 grams of potassium iodine in 100 cubic centimeters of water. Add the former solution to the latter, with constant stirring, until a slight permanent red precipitate is formed. Next, dissolve 120 grams of potassium hydrate in about 200 cubic centimeters of water; allow the solution to cool, and then add it to the previous solution and make up with water to 1 liter. Add mercuric-chloride solution until a permanent precipitate again forms. Allow to stand till settled, and decant the clear solution for use. Put it in glass-stoppered *blue* bottles and set aside in a dark place in order to prevent decomposition.

Litmus paper, of the kind which can be purchased in any drug store for testing alkaline reactions, can be used to test water or brine for the presence of ammonia. A portion of a strip of this kind of prepared paper is simply dipped into the sample of water or brine to be tested. If ammonia is present, the moist part of the paper will turn blue. Small amounts of ammonia leakage will change the color of the paper scarcely at all, while a large amount of leakage will turn it to a deep blue. Litmus paper will not, however, give reliable tests of calcium brine, as a strong calcium brine will turn it blue in the same way that ammonia does.

Stick Test to Check Operating Conditions.—The liquid receiver should always be provided with an adequate gage glass, so that the depth of liquid can always be readily determined. The gage glass should be protected with four wires, as shown in Fig. 127, and should also have automatic safety valves, like those in Fig. 128, which will shut off the connections if the glass is broken. The level of the liquid in the receiver is always changing, and if a plant is being operated with more than one

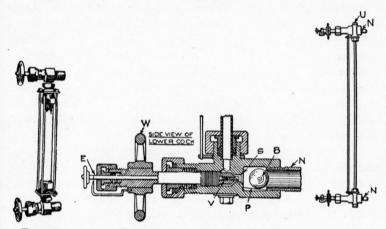

Fig. 127.—
Metal guards
for gage glass.

Fig. 128.—Safety water gage glass connections.

temperature in a group of expansion coils, there is likely to be continual trouble in maintaining the capacity of the plant unless the person in charge can tell at any moment how much liquid ammonia there is in the system back of the expansion valve. If it happens that the level in the liquid receiver is drawn down so much that there is no supply, then liquid ammonia and uncondensed gas will flow as a mixture into the coils of the evaporator, where the uncondensed gases will have the effect of choking the coils and thus reducing the refrigeration capacity.

In this connection, it is convenient to have some means of determining whether or not the operating conditions in the coil of the evaporator are satisfactory. The *stick test* is often used to determine whether or not the proper temperature is being carried in the coils of the evaporator. The method of testing is to scrape away the frost on a pipe of the coil to be investigated and then to apply a moistened finger to the surface of the pipe. If the temperature in the pipe is below 15° F., the finger will stick to the surface of the pipe, and a considerable pull will be required to remove it. On the other hand, if the finger does not stick to the pipe, it shows that the necessary low temperature is not maintained.

Draining Oil from the Oil Separator and Liquid Receiver.— Figure 121 shows the *liquid receiver* and the *oil separator* placed side by side. This is the usual arrangement, and, in most cases, they are connected by an *oil drum*, which is located beneath them. A small connection between the main suction pipe and this oil drum is also usual.

In order to drain the oil separator, the valve between the separator and the oil drum is opened, and, after allowing ½ hour for the oil to flow into the drum, this valve is closed, and the one between the oil drum and the main suction pipe is opened. The best results are obtained when this latter valve is opened only a little. When white frost gathers on the connection between the main suction pipe and the oil drum, there is an indication that the ammonia which was mixed with the oil is being drawn off into the suction pipe. After this frost has disappeared, the valve may be closed, and then, after waiting 20 minutes for the oil to settle in the oil drum, it may be drawn off into a bucket by opening the drain valve at the bottom of the oil drum.

Since oil collects only very slowly in the liquid-ammonia receiver, it will not be necessary to draw it off so frequently as from the oil separator. The method of drawing oil from the liquid-ammonia receiver is similar to that for draining the oil separator.

The Bypass.—Bypass pipes are provided in most compressors for the purpose of changing the suction pipe into a discharge pipe or the discharge pipe into a suction pipe. It consists of two connections each with a valve, one leading from the discharge pipe to the suction pipe, and the other from the suction pipe to the discharge pipe. Figure 122 shows a common arrangement of the *bypass valves*, as marked at A and B. The *main discharge valve* is lettered D, and the main suction valve S. If D and S are closed and A and B are opened, ammonia will discharge through the small bypass connection *from* the discharge side of the compressor *into* the main suction line. Through the other bypass connection, ammonia will be drawn from the main discharge line into the suction pipe of the compressor.

Pumping Out the Condenser of an Ammonia Refrigerating System.—Whenever repairs or cleaning make it necessary to open the condenser, the ammonia must be removed by pumping through the bypass pipes (see p. 172). In the process of removing the ammonia from the condenser, the valve at the condenser on the liquid-ammonia line between the condenser and the liquid-ammonia receiver should now be closed, in order to shut off that part of the system containing the main discharge line, oil separator, and condenser from the part containing the main suction line, cooling coils of the evaporator, main liquid line, and liquid receiver. It is a good plan to trace out these parts on Fig. 121. The main discharge and suction valves should then be closed, and both bypass valves should be opened. The system is now to be reversed, so that the compressor draws the ammonia from the condenser through the discharge line and forces it into the opposite side of the system (through the main suction line) into the cooling coils of the evaporator. For this transfer of ammonia, the compressor must be operated at very low speed, and the expansion valve should be wide open. The ammonia enters the cooling coils of the evaporator at high pressure and, consequently, also at high temperature and will be condensed. To operate the compressor at high speed would be likely to damage the system, since the compressor is now discharging high-pressure ammonia vapor through a small pipe.

When the discharge-pressure gage indicates that a vacuum has been established in the condenser, the two bypass valves should be closed tightly, and the work of repairing the condenser may begin. It will also be possible to open any other parts *on the same side* of the system. The opening of any part of the system in which a vacuum has been established admits air into the system and destroys the vacuum. Before more ammonia is admitted into this side of the system, the air must be removed. Provision is made for removing air from the system shown in Fig. 122 by the valve *Z*, which has a blank flange instead of the connection *Y*. To establish a vacuum by means of this valve, the main discharge and suction valves *D* and *S*, respectively, are closed, and the bypass valve at *A* is opened, the blank flange is removed, and a pipe is attached to the valve Z as shown at Y. Because the air which is drawn off may probably contain strong ammonia fumes, it is a good idea to run the free end of the pipe outside the room so that the discharge will not foul the inside air. Having opened the valve Z, the compressor should be started at a very low speed, and the air is removed from the condenser through the bypass of the compressor into the main discharge pipe and is expelled through the pipe leading from Z. When this side of the system is cleared of air, the discharge-pressure gage will indicate the presence of a vacuum. Now the valves Z and A may be closed, the blank flange at Y replaced, and the main discharge valve D opened.

To put the system once more in regular operation, the flow of condenser cooling water should be started, and the main suction valve S should be opened very slowly, all the usual precautions for starting the compressor being observed.

Removing Ammonia from Evaporator.—The method of removing ammonia from the cooling coils of the evaporator is somewhat different and does not require the use of the bypass pipes. First, in order to prevent any more ammonia from passing into the coils of the evaporator, the main liquid line valve (marked A, in Fig. 121) is closed. The compressor is then operated as in regular service, allowing the flow of condenser cooling water to continue. After a time, the suction-pressure gage will indicate a vacuum, and the frost will leave the suction pipe, showing that the ammonia has been pumped through the condenser into the liquid-ammonia receiver. When the compressor has been stopped and both the main discharge and suction valves have been closed, the suction side of the system may be opened for repairing.

In emptying the oil separator or the liquid-ammonia receiver for repairs, the compressor should be stopped, and the liquid ammonia in the receiver should be emptied into the cooling coils of the evaporator. When this has been done, the valve on the main liquid line (A, in Fig. 121) should be closed, and the ammonia should be removed in the same way as it is taken from the condenser, that is, the remaining ammonia should be discharged (by using the bypass) through the compressor into the cooling coils of the evaporator, taking care to operate the compressor very slowly. The ammonia is thus stored in the coils of the evaporator while the repairs are being made.

Operating Practice for Absorption System.—Under ordinary conditions, in plants having *low pressures* in the absorber and evaporator, it is probably best to pass all the cooling water through the absorber first and then through the condenser,[1] after which the water may be used in the rectifier or weak-liquor cooler. In *high-pressure* plants, it may be desirable to pass all of the water through the condenser and then all or part through the absorber, after which it may then be used in the rectifier and in the weak-liquor cooler.

Operating Data of Absorption System.—In the following example, relating to an absorption refrigerating system, the strengths of solutions, temperatures, and pressures are not actual values from tests but are given here merely to illustrate what takes place in the different parts of the system.

Referring now to Fig. 15, it will be assumed that the strong liquor entering the generator has 29 per cent of ammonia and that its absolute pressure is 175 pounds per square inch. The steam applied to the heating coils of the generator has an absolute pressure of 65 pounds[2] per square inch, the temperature corresponding to this pressure being 298° F. The liquor in the generator will then be heated by the steam to a temperature of about 270° F.

If, for example, ammonia vapor containing 10 per cent of water vapor leaves the generator at a temperature of 270° F. and rises through a rain of strong liquor, in the analyzer, there is an exchange of heat, and the strong liquid is heated by the hot vapors. Strong liquor from the exchanger, having a temperature of, say, 210° F. and a strength of about 29 per cent, enters the top of the analyzer, as indicated in the figure. This strong liquor then flows over the edges of the pans and falls from one to

[1] The statement is generally made that the temperature of the cooling water going to the condenser should be as low as possible. In the case of low pressures (and low temperatures) in the absorber and evaporator, there is not the necessity, in most plants, for having the lowest possible temperature of the cooling water going to the condenser.

[2] The boiler should generate steam at an absolute pressure somewhat greater than 65 pounds per square inch. In case the pump is driven by steam, this pressure at the steam cylinder of the pump should be high enough so that the exhaust from the pump can be used in the steam coils of the generator at an absolute pressure of 65 pounds per square inch. In case extra steam should be needed for the generator steam coil, it can be supplied from the boiler through a throttling valve, which will reduce the boiler pressure to the desired pressure for the steam coils in the generator.

the other until it passes down into the top of the generator.   If
the temperature of the strong liquor, when entering the analyzer,
is 210° F. and, as a result of the transfer of heat, the temperature
is raised to 225° F., some of the ammonia will be driven out of
the strong-liquor solution.   This ammonia vapor then passes on
with the hot vapors from the generator through the horizontal
pipe connecting the analyzer and the rectifier.   The strong
liquor entering the generator from the analyzer has now a temperature of about 225° F. and a strength of about 28 per cent of
ammonia.   On reaching the generator, it is again heated by the
steam coils to a temperature of 270° F., and its strength is reduced
to about 21 per cent of ammonia.   It then leaves the generator
as weak liquor at a temperature of 270° F. and a strength of 21
per cent of ammonia.

The vapors rising from the generator and passing up into the
analyzer are at a temperature of 270° F. and contain some water
vapor.   This water vapor is cooled in the analyzer by the strong
liquor, so that some of it is condensed, and the condensation
returns to the generator.   The remaining vapor, containing
about 7 per cent of water vapor, is cooled to about 235° F. and
passes out of the analyzer into the rectifier.

If the mixture of ammonia and water vapors enters the rectifier
at a temperature of 235° F. and the strong liquor from the
absorber enters the rectifier at a temperature of 110° F., in the
exchange of heat the ammonia vapor will be cooled to about
135° F.   At this temperature, it passes to the condenser at a
gage pressure of 165 pounds per square inch.   The strong liquor
is heated to a temperature of 150° F. in passing through the
rectifier.   From here the strong liquor then passes into the
exchanger.

The exchanger, shown in Fig. 15, is of the double-pipe type
(p. 27).   It transfers heat from the hot weak liquor to the cool
strong liquor.   The weak liquor entering the exchanger has a
temperature of 270° F., while the entering strong liquor has a
temperature of 150° F.   The temperature of the strong liquor is
then increased to about 210° F. and passes out of the exchanger
into the analyzer.

The weak liquor, after being cooled in the exchanger, enters
the weak-liquor cooler.   This cooler is also of the double-pipe
type.   In this cooler, the weak liquor gives up heat to the cooling
water supplied from the condenser.   It is then cooled from 175°

F. to the temperature of the absorber, which is about 110° F. The cooling water leaving the condenser has a temperature of about 85 to 89° F. As a large quantity is available, it will cool the weak liquor through a large range of temperature without raising its temperature very much.

After leaving the cooler, the weak liquor passes through a regulating valve. This valve reduces the gage pressure from 165 pounds per square inch to 15 pounds per square inch, this being the pressure of the anhydrous-ammonia vapor in the evaporating coils of the brine cooler. The regulating valve is generally of the automatic type, and it adjusts itself so as to maintain a constant pressure of the weak liquor entering the absorber.

After the water vapor has been removed from the ammonia vapor in the rectifier, the ammonia vapor passes over into the condenser at a gage pressure of 165 pounds per square inch and a temperature of 135° F. Owing to the fact that it is super-heated, it must first be cooled to about 89° F. before it will condense. After it is condensed, it may be cooled a few degrees more in the condenser, so that it will enter the liquid receiver at a temperature of about 85 to 87° F. From the liquid receiver, the liquid ammonia flows through the expansion valve into the coil of the evaporator in the brine cooler. In the coil of the evaporator, it evaporates at a gage pressure of about 15 pounds per square inch and a temperature of 0° F. The resulting ammonia vapor then passes into the absorber, where it mixes with the weak liquor from the weak-liquor cooler. The weak liquor, now having a strength of 21 per cent, a temperature of 125° F., and a gage pressure of 15 pounds per square inch, absorbs the ammonia vapor. This absorption of ammonia increases its strength to 29 per cent at 110° F. The resulting strong liquor is then pumped into the rectifier again.

Heat is generated when the absorption of ammonia vapor takes place. This excess heat must be carried away, so that the weak liquor may absorb a large quantity of ammonia vapor, thus producing a stronger liquor. This excess heat is often carried away by the cooling water, which has already been used in the condenser and now passes through the cooling coils in the absorber.

In some plants, the cooling water from the condenser is not used to cool the weak liquor as shown in Fig. 15, for the reason that since this condenser cooling water has already acquired a great deal of heat, it would not be very effective in cooling the absorber. In this case, an independent water supply for the absorber is used.

The strengths of the strong and weak liquors are controlled by four conditions: (1) absorber pressure, (2) generator pressure, (3) steam pressure in the generator coils, (4) speed of the liquor pump. In order to obtain the best results, this system must be operated with strengths of strong and weak liquor that will give 1 pound of liquid anhydrous ammonia for every 7 to 8 pounds of strong liquor. In order to do this, the strength of the strong liquor should be as strong as possible, to correspond with the pressure and temperature in the absorber. On the other hand, the weak liquor should be as weak as possible. The temperature and pressure in the generator are generally fixed by the temperature of the cooling water for the condenser. The only remaining variables to adjust are the steam pressure in the generator coils and the speed of the pump.

Before the system can be operated satisfactorily, it will be necessary to equip it with pressure gages as follows: (1) steam pressure gage for the generator coils; (2) ammonia pressure gages for the generator, condenser, evaporating coils, and absorber. Also, there should be provided gage glasses (water gages) on all apparatus where it is necessary to know the amount of the liquid contained. These may be provided with self-closing safety cocks.

A ball type of safety water gage is shown in Fig. 128. The complete gage is shown at the right-hand side of the figure, and a section of the lower gage cock is shown at the left. The gage cocks are connected to the receiver or drum, where they are to be used by means of extra-heavy nipples N, which should be inserted into the cock so that the ball B may move freely back and forth on the inclining plane P. The plug in the upper cock is large enough to permit inserting the gage glass from that end. In case the glass breaks, the pressure of the liquid or vapor forces the balls B in the cock, as shown in the figure toward the left against the seats S, so that they prevent any flow into the gage glass. The gage cocks at top and bottom should then be closed by turning the handwheels W in a clockwise direction. After a gage glass has been replaced, the "unseating" stem E should be screwed in far enough so that it will press the ball B off the seat S before the cocks are opened by the movement of the handwheels *W*. The cocks should be opened slowly, and the balls *B* will then slide back on the inclined planes *P* to the position shown in the figure. An approved method of protecting the gage glass by means of four rods is illustrated in Fig. 127.

A gage glass should not be longer than 2 feet, but, in some cases, where the depth of the liquid to be measured exceeds 2 feet, two gage glasses, one above the other, should be used instead of one.

In a refrigerating system, air is likely to leak in, and some means must be provided to rid the system of it. For this reason, *purge valves* should be connected at all points where air is likely to collect.

Some means must be arranged to *charge the system*. For this purpose, charging valves are provided. The usual place for charging the liquid ammonia in an absorption system is shown in Fig. 15 just below the pump. This valve may be used to drain off the liquor when repairing or for taking a sample. The valve *V* may be used to obtain a sample of the weak liquor.

Testing a New Absorption System.—The method of testing a new absorption system for tightness is similar to that used in testing a compression system. The system should be subjected to an air pressure of about 250 pounds per square inch (gage) and allowed to stand at this pressure. If the pressure remains constant after the air has cooled, the system is tight, and it should not be necessary to test it with a vacuum.

As a new system will contain air, the latter should be removed before charging the system with liquor. In doing this, the discharge side of the liquor pump should be disconnected. The free end of the system should now be sealed by closing the valve. All other valves of the system should be opened so as to permit the air to pass over to the pump, thus preventing an accumulation of air in a portion of the system after the pumping. The pump should be started for the purpose of removing the air from the system through the absorber, continuing until the vacuum gage shows the lowest possible pressure that can be obtained. The valve on the suction pipe should now be closed, and the discharge end of the pump reconnected. The system is now ready to receive its charge of liquor.

Another way of removing air from the system is by the use of the venturi tube, as shown in Fig. 130. This method is the better, as through it a high vacuum can be easily obtained. As shown in this figure, the venturi tube consists of a short length of pipe which narrows down to a small diameter at the middle and enlarges again to the original diameter of the pipe. A connection is made at the narrow section. When a stream of water is supplied to the tube at the proper pressure, the stream will pass the connection at the narrow section with a very high velocity. Some air is caught by the water and is carried along with it. Thus, there is a removal of air. When removing the air from an

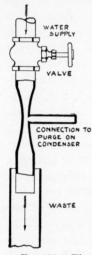

absorption system with one of these venturi tubes, the tube should be connected to the water supply of the condenser, and the *purge pipe* (p. 199) *at the top of the condenser* should be joined to the connection at the narrow section of the venturi tube. By running the water through the tube, the air is removed from the system, and a high vacuum is obtained.

Charging an Absorption Refrigerating System.

After a good vacuum has been obtained in the system, it may be charged with liquor. The first step is to connect a shipping drum filled with aqua-ammonia liquor to the charging valve. The charging valve and the valve on the connection of the shipping drum should then be opened. After this is done, the air valve on the shipping drum is also opened. This produces a difference of pressure on the liquor, forcing it into the system. The system should be only partly charged

Fig. 130.—Ejector for connection to condenser.

at first. It should then be operated for a time until the remaining air in the system collects in the condenser. This air should then be expelled, after which the remainder of the required charge may be admitted. When the drum is nearly empty, great care should be taken to prevent air from entering the system. If the system is fully charged at first and is then started, the liquor will expand and cause an overcharge. This will flood the condenser and may damage some parts of the system.

When enough liquor has been added so that there is a slight pressure instead of a vacuum in the system, the ammonia pump should be started, steam should be allowed to enter the generator coils, and the condenser cooling water should be started. The liquor should be heated until the gage pressure in the generator is about 100 pounds per square inch. The ammonia vapor will then begin to condense and collect in the liquid receiver.

When a sufficient quantity of liquid ammonia has collected, the expansion valve may be opened. The system is now in operation so that the water may be turned on the absorber, the liquor pump started, the air expelled, and the remaining charge of liquor put in. Enough liquor should now be put into the system so that, when operating under normal conditions, there will be about 1 foot of liquid ammonia in a vertical liquid receiver.

Recharging an Absorption System.—After a season of continuous running, an absorption system will lose some of its ammonia by leakage. Not only is anhydrous ammonia lost in this manner, but there is also a leakage of liquor. Such losses tend to reduce the liquor's strength and make it necessary from time to time to charge the system with new ammonia or liquor. This should be done during the months of the year when refrigeration is not essential. At such times, the plant can be shut down, and charging can be done more conveniently than when it is in operation. If the strength of the charge becomes too low, it can be easily strengthened by adding liquid anhydrous ammonia until the strength is again normal. On the other hand, if the charge has reduced in volume only, more liquor must be added. The amount of liquor in the system can be determined by the gage glasses on the absorber and generator. The strength of the liquor can be determined by taking a sample and testing it with a hydrometer.

Strengthening the Charge of Aqua-ammonia Liquor.—When ammonia is absorbed in water, its specific gravity changes and becomes less than that of water, which is, of course, unity. In order to obtain the specific gravities of liquids, a calibrated instrument called a *hydrometer* is used. It is made of a glass tube and is hollow so that it will float. At one end, there is a bulb partly filled with lead shot or mercury. The hydrometer will float upright when placed in a solution. If it is a direct-reading hydrometer, the number corresponding to the level of the liquid indicates the specific gravity. The stems of hydrometers, however, are often marked with an arbitrary scale of degrees, called the *Baumé scale*. The point on this scale which is marked 10 degrees is the specific gravity of water or 1 on the specific-gravity scale. The Baumé scale is generally used for measuring different strengths of aqua-ammonia liquors.

When the charge needs strengthening, a shipping drum containing liquid anhydrous ammonia should be connected to a charging valve on the coils of the evaporator. As it is possible to find the amount of liquor in the system and its strength, the amount of anhydrous ammonia to be added to give the liquor the proper strength can be calculated. Methods are given on page 242.

For charging with anhydrous ammonia, the shipping drum should be placed on platform scales and connected to the charging valve by means of a flexible connection. The weight of the drum should be noted. While charging, the scales should be kept balanced, in order to determine the amount of ammonia that has passed into the system. When the system has received all but 10 to 15 pounds of its new charge, the charging valve should be closed, and the system put in operation for 2 or 3 hours. This permits the new anhydrous ammonia to become thoroughly absorbed in the liquor. The remainder can then be put into the system. If the charge has become both weakened and reduced in amount, it is best to charge the system with liquor having a strength of about 26° Bé. This liquor should be added until the strength is normal.

In charging the system with liquor, the shipping drum should be connected to the charging valve, and the drum should be raised above the liquor pump, as otherwise the pump is likely to "race." This is because the suction pressure is reduced and the pump has less resistance then than when handling liquor. The vapor thus formed in the cylinder of the pump can then be condensed by pouring cold water upon the cylinder, which will sometimes stop this trouble. Racing can be entirely prevented by simply raising the charging drum well above the pump.

Leaks in an Absorption System.—The absorption system is more likely to have leaks than is the compression system, as considerable pitting or corrosion occurs. The generator and the exchanger coils are especially subjected to corrosion. Because of this, a constant watch must be kept, and all leaks given immediate attention. All of the generator coils should be kept well covered with liquor, as corrosion takes place more rapidly when the coils are uncovered than when covered. These coils should be carefully inspected when the plant is shut down, to make sure that they are in good condition.

In plants equipped with an analyzer, a mixture of ammonia and steam is formed in the generator and enters the analyzer. This water vapor causes corrosion and leaks in the analyzer pans.

Some water may even collect in the liquid receiver. A sample should be taken occasionally from the receiver and tested by evaporating it in a glass test tube. If the water remaining is as much as 20 per cent by volume of the original sample, the analyzer pans are probably leaking.

When leaks occur in the exchanger, there results a mixing of the strong and weak liquor. This changes the strengths of these liquors, the strong liquor becoming weaker and the weak liquor becoming stronger. When such a leak is large, it may be detected, in extremely bad cases, by the cooling of the weak-liquor pipe between the exchanger and the generator. The cooling of this pipe is due to the fact that the strong liquor is pumped through the leak into the weak-liquor connections, so that the former enters the generator at the top and bottom.[1] A leak in the exchanger may also be detected by closing the valve in the weak-liquor line from the generator to the exchanger. The valve in the weak-liquor feed line to the absorber should first be closed. The liquor pump should be started very slowly, and then the valve in the weak-liquor feed line should be opened wide. If the pump speeds up, there is a serious leak in the exchanger. The reason for this is that when the valves in the weak-liquor feed line to the absorber and in the weak-liquor line from the generator to exchanger are both closed, the pump will be doing work against the pressure of the generator. Now, if there is a leak in the exchanger, and the valve in the weak-liquor feed line to the absorber is opened, the pump will work against a lower pressure. This is because the strong liquor is passing through the short circuit made up of the exchanger, the leak, and the weak-liquor cooler. From the weak-liquor cooler, the liquor returns to the absorber.

Boil-overs.—By *boil-over* is meant the result of liquor's entering some part of the system in which it does not belong. This is generally caused by the accumulation of condensed steam in the steam coils of the generator. This accumulation of water reduces the active steam surface. In attempting to maintain the desired generator pressure, the engineer turns on more live steam, to make up for the reduced heating surface of the steam coils. Now, if the condensation in the steam coils should stop, the liquor will receive too much heat and boil over into the condenser.

[1] In such case, there will be an increase in pressure in the generator, with, probably, the stopping of refrigeration.

In order to prevent this, a steam trap should be connected to the steam coils. This trap will drain the steam coils without loss of steam.

A boil-over sometimes occurs as a result of the ammonia's being low in the system. The liquor is then likely to be syphoned over from the generator into the absorber. This is the result of too rapid absorption of ammonia. For this reason, the gage glass on the generator should be frequently observed. By so observing, it is easy to determine when the level of the liquor in the generator is getting too low.

Effects of Air on the Refrigerating System.—There is some air in the piping of a refrigerating system, even if a very low vacuum is pumped when filling the system with the refrigerant. If the piping is simple and not very extensive, the circulation of the refrigerant will collect this air and carry it along with the vapor of the refrigerant into the compressor. After the air and vapor are compressed, they are carried along to the condenser, where the air separates from the refrigerant, for the reason that, as the latter condenses, it settles to the bottom of the condenser while the liberated air accumulates at the top. Usually, there is enough liquid refrigerant below the layer of air at the top of the condenser to prevent its passing out and circulating through the system; but, nevertheless, this air must be considered a hindrance to the operation of the plant, because that portion of the condenser occupied by the air cannot be reached by the vapor of the refrigerant. In other words, the effective condensing surface is reduced; and that surface which is still *available* is overworked to produce the proper condensing capacity. Another effect of this air accumulation is that more cooling water is used than is actually required for the normal operation of the condenser.

In large refrigerating systems with many feet of pipe in the condenser, if there is not enough liquid refrigerant in the condenser to seal its outlet, nearly all the air circulates and is compressed with the vapor of the refrigerant. This causes the cylinder and the discharge pipe of the compressor to become excessively heated, because, when air is compressed, its rise in temperature is greater than the increase in temperature when the refrigerants most commonly used are compressed. By thus increasing the temperature in the cylinder of the compressor, the presence of air brings about a corresponding increase in the discharge pressure. It must be remembered, too, that energy is lost and the efficiency of the system reduced by the continuous compression and expansion of such air which does no work in refrigeration.

A good method of ridding an ammonia refrigerating system of air is to attach a small pipe to the blowoff valve on the top of the condenser, so that an extension of this pipe is downward. In case an "equalizer" or some other pipe is also connected to this blowoff valve, the equalizer may be shut off by closing its valve, so that the opening of the blowoff valve will not drain the refrigerant from other parts of the system. The end of the pipe which is attached to the blowoff valve should be immersed in a pail of cold water, with the open end a little below the surface. The blowoff valve should then be opened slightly, and large bubbles will form in the water and rise to the surface. These bubbles are due to the mixing of the air flowing from the condenser with a small amount of ammonia. The ammonia, however, does not rise but separates from the air and mixes with the water.[1] When all the air has been expelled, the flow through the pipe will be only ammonia vapor, which enters the water with a crackling sound and gives it a milky appearance. When the system has been cleared of air as nearly as possible, the blowoff valve should be tightly closed.

York Purge Drum.—Foreign gases in the condenser of a refrigerating system are indicated when the temperature of the liquid refrigerant leaving the condenser is below the temperature corresponding to the condenser pressure. The difference between the two temperatures is the amount of subcooling of the liquid refrigerant. With liquid *ammonia* leaving the condenser at 80° F. and the condenser gage pressure at 160 pounds per square inch (corresponding to 88° F.), the amount of subcooling is 8° F., indicating a definite weight of foreign gases in each cubic foot of the condenser space. As the amount of subcooling increases, the weight of foreign gases per cubic foot increases likewise, and the weight of ammonia vapor per cubic foot decreases.

By a method called *purging*, all the foreign gases can be eliminated from the main condensing system, but the amount of ammonia vapor lost will be greatly in excess of the amount of foreign gases that are purged.

---

[1] The ammonia and water in the pail may be set aside for cleaning purposes. It is a much stronger solution than ordinary household ammonia.

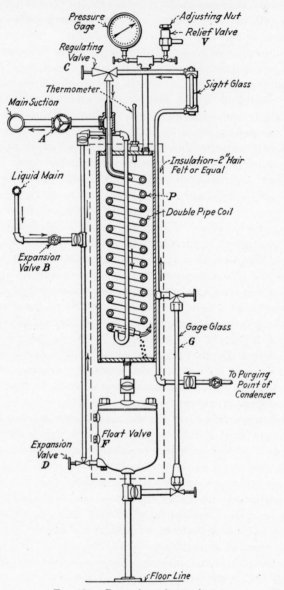

Pressure Gage

Adjusting Nut

Relief Valve V

Regulating Valve C

Thermometer

Main Suction

Sight Glass

A

Liquid Main

Insulation-2"Hair Felt or Equal

P

Double Pipe Coil

Expansion Valve B

Gage Glass G

To Purging Point of Condenser

Float Valve F

Expansion Valve D

Floor Line

FIG. 131.—Purge drum for condenser.

The York double-pipe purge drum is an intensely cold condenser, with an automatic means of discharging into the atmosphere only at the highest practical pressure. The subcooling of the liquid refrigerant in the purge drum thus becomes as large as possible, and the weight of foreign gases in each cubic foot of the drum space is far in excess of the weight of ammonia vapor, making the loss of ammonia a minimum.

The usual method of connecting the purge drum into the system is indicated in Fig. 131. The suction line leading from valve A should be connected into the lowest suction pressure available. The liquid expansion line leading to valve B may be taken from any desired point supplying liquid refrigerant. The foreign gas line leading to valve C may be taken from any point in the condensing system, preferably not too close to the hot-vapor inlet connection.

The best place for purging is at the top of the liquid-ammonia receiver, provided that there are no liquid seals between the receiver and the condenser. Another good point for purging is at the lower portion of a shell-and-tube condenser, about 12 inches above the liquid level.

In the operation of this purge drum, the adjusting nut on the relief valve (at the top of the figure) must be turned down tightly, and then the regulating valve C and the main suction valve A may be opened. When liquid accumulates in the float-valve chamber F, the expansion valve D should be opened a little. The temperature in the insulated drum P will then fall to within about 15° F. of the temperature corresponding to the suction pressure of the compressor. The regulating valve C should be throttled so that a continuous stream of bubbles rises through the liquid ammonia which gathers in the gage glass G. The relief valve V may then be adjusted to "blow" very slowly and continuously at 10 pounds per square inch below the condenser pressure. Full opening of this valve will permit the pressure to drop from 10 to 15 pounds per square inch and will cause a waste of ammonia.

The foreign gases mixed with ammonia vapor travel downward through the inner pipe coil in the drum P, while the liquid ammonia enters between the coils at the bottom and travels upward in the annular space, thus maintaining the low temperature in the drum through the outer coil and cooling the incoming mixture through the inner coil. The countercurrent flow and the intimate contact of the cooling surfaces increase the heat transfer, so that there results a low temperature and efficient performance.

The ammonia vapor condensed in the inner coil flows from the open end of the coil into the float-valve chamber F. From there it is automatically expanded into the annular space of the double coil, thus assisting in the cooling of the hot vapor which comes from the liquid ammonia receiver.

Defrosting Pipes.—Frost results from the moisture in the air's collecting and freezing on the cold pipes of a refrigerating system. If the coat of frost or ice is very thick on the pipes, the capacity of these pipes is reduced, the frost or ice acting as an insulator. If the frost is thin, as shown by a gray color of the pipes, their capacity is not much reduced. In case a heavy coat of frost occurs, it is necessary to lower the suction pressure in order to maintain the required temperature; and this puts more work on the compressor. Frost must be removed before it becomes too thick. In the direct system, this may be done by passing the vapor of the refrigerant *from the compressor* through the frosted coils for a short time. The frost or ice will then be loosened from the coils and may be scraped off. At times, it may be necessary to bypass the refrigerant from a section and let it stand idle until the frost is melted. When this method is to be used, additional coils should be operated while others are being freed from frost.

In laying out refrigerating coils, the pipes should not be placed close together, as the frost may extend from one pipe to the next, making the coil a mass of ice.

Sometimes, in the indirect system, the method is used of defrosting the cooling coils by allowing brine at ordinary temperatures to pass over their surfaces until the frost is melted. In order to do this, a spray pipe is placed over the coils; and from this spray pipe, the brine is sprayed on the top of each coil.

Amount of Piping Required.—When estimating the amount of piping to be used in refrigerating work, simple rules based on experience are generally used, for the reason that the data for the transmission of heat through the walls is too limited for accurate calculations. In general, a plant will operate more efficiently if the piping allowance is too large rather than barely enough. Because of this, manufacturers usually recommend the use of large sizes of piping. It should be remembered that large amounts of piping add to the first cost of the refrigerating plant.

Size of Pipe and Temperature Range.—If an insufficient amount of pipe is used in a refrigerating system, a greater cooling effect can be obtained by increasing the range of temperatures between the inside and the outside of the pipe. In the case of the direct system, this greater cooling effect can be obtained by lowering the suction pressure. On the other hand, a pipe having large surfaces can be used by decreasing the temperature range between the inside and outside of the pipe. In the direct system, this would be accomplished by increasing the suction pressure, thus reducing the work of the compressor. In general, then, it can be said that, in all cases of heat transfer, the smaller the range of temperature the more efficient the heat transfer will be.

Amount of Piping for Suction, Discharge and Liquid Lines.— The laying out of headers and connections at the compressor should be given considerable care in order to eliminate changes of direction in the flow of the vapor or liquid, as changes of direction cause losses. The flow of vapor through cylinder ports as well as discharge and suction bends causes a loss of pressure. The area of a discharge port is sometimes designed for a velocity of about 10,000 feet per minute. In this case the ports should be straight, and large-radius bends should be used if there is a sudden change in direction.

Size of Discharge Piping.—The size of piping in the discharge line of a compressor is determined by the quantity of refrigerant flowing in a given time. This can be calculated by finding the number of pounds of refrigerant circulated per minute and the specific volume of the refrigerant for the condition at the discharge port of the compressor. This quantity being in cubic feet per minute must be divided by the velocity in feet per minute in order to find the area of the pipe in square feet. The size of pipe required can then be found in Table XXV in the Appendix. The velocity of vapor through the discharge lines may be taken at about 6,000 to 7,000 feet per minute.

The size of discharge pipe is often computed by the use of the following equation based on the piston displacement

$$\text{Average velocity} = \frac{\text{Piston area} \times \text{stroke} \times 2 \times \text{revolutions}}{\text{Area of pipe}}$$

where the piston area is square inches, stroke is inches, revolutions are revolutions per minute, and area of the pipe is square inches. The above equation is for a double-acting or a twin-cylinder single-acting compressor.

Size of Suction Piping.—The design of the suction piping is more important than that of the discharge piping. In the discharge line the effect of pressure loss is to reduce the volumetric efficiency of the compressor and increase the work of compression; while wire-drawing in the suction line reduces the capacity of the compressor as well as increases the horsepower per ton of refrigeration, and reduces the volumetric efficiency. The design of the suction piping should be for velocities ranging from 2,000 to 5,000 feet per minute, depending on the length of the line.

Liquid Line.—The liquid line generally is not covered but in many cases it may be beneficial to do so. The advisability of having the liquid refrigerant as cool as possible has already been shown, and for this reason some plants have been equipped with special liquid coolers.

The size of the liquid line depends on its length. A velocity of about 3 to 6 feet per minute can be used.

Pressure Drop in Ammonia Pipe Lines.—The drop in pressure in pounds per square inch ($P_1 - P_2$) due to friction between the two ends of an ammonia pipe line may be found by the use of the following equation,

$$P_1 - P_2 = \frac{V^2\left(1 + \frac{3.6}{d}\right)LD}{144 \times 454 \times d}$$

where V is the velocity in feet per *second*, L is the length of the pipe in feet, d is the diameter of the pipe in inches, and D is the density of the ammonia vapor in pounds per cubic foot.

Amount of Pipe for Cooling Coils.—In the indirect system of refrigeration, there are evaporator coils for cooling the brine and, also, brine coils for cooling the cold-storage compartments. If the brine is cooled in a tank, usually 120 to 150 running feet of $1\frac{1}{4}$ inch pipe are provided for each ton of refrigeration capacity. A double-pipe brine-cooling coil of the following dimensions has a rated refrigerating capacity of 15 tons every 24 hours: inner pipe, 2 inches in diameter; outer pipe, 3 inches in diameter; the pipes are 18 feet long, and the brine-cooling coils are 12 pipes high.

The refrigeration load of the cooling coils is the heat units (B.t.u.) to be removed from the walls of the building and from the goods stored. The amount of cooling surface may then be calculated by assuming that each square foot of cooling surface will pass about 3 B.t.u. per hour for each degree difference in temperature between the surfaces of the pipe.

The following tables have given ample refrigerating capacity in actual practice:

TABLE VI.—NUMBER OF CUBIC FEET OF WELL-INSULATED SPACE THAT CAN BE COOLED BY 1 RUNNING FOOT OF BRINE PIPE

For small rooms up to 1,000 cubic-foot capacity

Temperature held in rooms, degrees Fahrenheit	Diameter of pipe in coils			
	1 inch, cubic feet	1¼ inches, cubic feet	1½ inches, cubic feet	2 inches, cubic feet
0	½	⅝	¾	1
5	1	1¼	1½	2
10	2	2½	3	4
20	3	3¾	4½	6
32	4	5	6	8
36	5	6¼	7	10

For rooms from 1,000 to 10,000 cubic-feet capacity

Temperature held in rooms, degrees Fahrenheit	Diameter of pipe in coils			
	1 inch, cubic feet	1¼ inches, cubic feet	1½ inches, cubic feet	2 inches, cubic feet
0	1	1¼	1½	2
5	2	2½	3	4
10	3	3¾	4½	6
20	5	6¼	7½	10
32	7	8¾	10½	14
36	8	10	12	16

For rooms over 10,000 cubic-feet capacity

Temperature held in rooms, degrees Fahrenheit	Diameter of pipe in coils			
	1 inch, cubic feet	1¼ inches, cubic feet	1½ inches, cubic feet	2 inches, cubic feet
0	1½	2⅞	2¼	3
5	3	3¾	4½	6
10	4½	5⅝	6¾	9
20	6	7½	9	12
32	8	10	12	16
36	10	12½	15	20

TABLE VII.—NUMBER OF CUBIC FEET OF WELL-INSULATED SPACE THAT CAN BE COOLED BY 1 RUNNING FOOT OF DIRECT EXPANSION PIPE

For small rooms up to 1,000 cubic-foot capacity

Temperature held in rooms, degrees Fahrenheit	Diameter of pipe in coils			
	1 inch, cubic feet	1¼ inches, cubic feet	1½ inches, cubic feet	2 inches, cubic feet
0	½	⅝	¾	1
5	1	1¼	1½	2
10	2½	3⅛	3¾	5
20	4	5	6	8
32	6	7½	9	12
36	7	8⅜	10½	14

For rooms from 1,000 to 10,000 cubic-feet capacity

Temperature held in rooms, degrees Fahrenheit	Diameter of pipe in coils			
	1 inch, cubic feet	1¼ inches, cubic feet	1½ inches, cubic feet	2 inches, cubic feet
0	1	1¼	1½	2
5	2	2½	3	4
10	4	5	6	8
20	6	7½	9	12
32	8	10	12	16
36	10	12½	15	20

For rooms over 10,000 cubic-feet capacity

Temperature held in rooms, degrees Fahrenheit	Diameter of pipe in coils			
	1 inch, cubic feet	1¼ inches, cubic feet	1½ inches, cubic feet	2 inches, cubic feet
0	1½	2	2½	3
5	3	3¾	4½	6
10	6	7½	9	12
20	10	12½	15	20
32	12	15	18	24
36	15	18¾	22½	30

In connection with the above tabulations, the following table shows the amount of cooling space that is provided in well-insulated refrigerator compartments per ton of refrigeration in 24 hours.

Temperature held in rooms, degrees Fahrenheit	Size of room		
	Up to 1,000 cubic feet, cubic feet per ton	From 1,000 to 10,000 cubic feet, cubic feet per ton	Over 10,000 cubic feet, cubic feet per ton
0	200	600	1,000
5	400	1,200	2,000
10	800	2,500	4,000
20	1,400	4,500	6,000
32	2,000	6,000	8,000
36	2,500	8,000	10,000

When the indirect system is used, a pump is needed to keep the brine in circulation. A centrifugal pump is adaptable for this service. It should be located near the expansion coils or brine cooler, and a bypass pipe should be connected to the discharge and suction ends of the pump. By regulating a suitable valve in the bypass pipe, the flow of the brine may be regulated when the pump operates at a constant speed.

All of the pipes that make up the brine-cooling coils are generally connected to a header. The brine then flows through all of the pipes in the same direction. This method of connecting the pipes decreases the resistance to flow and reduces the work of the pump. The velocity of the brine should be about 60 feet per minute.

Length of Pipe for the Direct System.—In the direct system the size of the pipe will depend upon the conditions in the plant, such as the size of the rooms. Generally large pipes are used in large rooms while small pipes are used in small rooms. The length of the individual coils must be such as to allow the vapor to free itself from the pipe without too large a drop in pressure.

The maximum lengths for various sizes of pipe are shown in the following table:

Size of Pipe, Inches	Maximum Length for Direct System, Feet
¾	900
1	1,100
1¼	1,300
1½	1,500
2	1,900
2½	2,300

Length of Pipe for Indirect System.—Brine coils are in general, arranged like the coils in the direct system. The length of the individual coils varies with the velocity of the circulating brine. For low temperature work a coil having 100 to 120 feet of pipe is fed by one regulating valve, while for high temperature work a coil having 400 to 440 feet of pipe is fed by one regulating valve. In general the size of pipe varies from $1\frac{1}{4}$ inches to $2\frac{1}{2}$ inches and the larger sizes are used for the larger rooms.

Heat Transfer Coefficients for Apparatus.—The following table gives the heat transfer coefficients for various refrigerating apparatus in B.t.u. per square foot of surface per hr. per deg. F. difference of temperature.

TABLE VIIA.—HEAT TRANSFER COEFFICIENTS FOR REFRIGERATING APPARATUS

B.t.u. per sq. ft. per hr. per deg. F.

	B.t.u.
Can-ice-making piping:	
Old-style feed, nonflooded	15
Flooded	25
Ammonia condensers:	
Submerged (obsolete except for CO_2)	35
Atmospheric, gas entering at top	60
Atmospheric, drip or bleeder	125 to 200
Flooded	125 to 150
Shell and tube	150 to 300
Double pipe	150 to 250
Baudalot coolers, counterflow, atmospheric type:	
Milk coolers	75
Cream coolers	60
Oil coolers	10
Water for direct expansion	60
Water for flooded	80
Brine coolers:	
Shell and tube	80 to 100
Double pipe	150 to 300
Cooling coils:	
Brine to unagitated air	2 to $2\frac{1}{2}$
Direct expansion	$1\frac{1}{2}$ to 2
Water cooler:	
Shell and coil	30
Liquid ammonia cooler:	
Shell-and-coil accumulator	45 to 50
Air dehydrator:	
First coil, shell and coil (brine in coil)	5.0
Second coil, shell and coil (brine in coil)	3.0
Double pipe	6 to 7

Salt Brines.—Water could be used in the cooling coils of the refrigerator in the indirect system if it were not for the fact that it freezes at 32° F. As it is often necessary to use cooling coil temperatures below this value, salt is dissolved in the water in order to reduce the freezing point. Common salt (sodium chloride) or calcium chloride may be used. Calcium-chloride brine has the advantage that it has a lower freezing point than common-salt brine, and it will not corrode the pipes, as common salt will. In time, a brine of common salt will destroy the piping system. This corrosion can be greatly reduced, however, by adding soda to the common-salt solution. Because of the above-mentioned disadvantages in the use of common salt, calcium-chloride brine is the one more extensively used, even though it is the more expensive.

A strong solution of brine can be subjected to a lower temperature without freezing than can a weak solution. If the solution of brine is weak, it is likely to freeze to the cooling coil of the evaporator, thus reducing the heat transfer through the coils and, possibly, even stopping the circulation in the brine pipes. The brine solution should not be stronger than is necessary, since the specific heat of the brine is reduced as the density of the solution is increased. A very strong solution of brine requires a greater quantity to be circulated than does a weak solution, in order to absorb a given quantity of heat.

Different strengths of brine may be compared by their specific gravities. By *specific gravity* is meant the ratio of the weight of a given volume of brine to the weight of the same volume of water. For determining the specific gravities of brine a hydrometer called a *salinometer* marked with special calibrations for different strengths of brine is used. A salinometer is calibrated from 0 to 100°. The 0° corresponds to the specific gravity of water at 60° F., which is taken as the basis of measurement.[1] The 100° is taken as the specific gravity of a 25 per cent solution of salt brine at 60° F.

The properties of common-salt and calcium-chloride brine are shown in the following tables. From these tables one can also find the freezing points and the specific heats at 60° F. for different strengths of solutions.

---

[1] This is an arbitrary scale. A more logical one would, for example, have 100° corresponding to a saturated solution of salt at 60° F., as no more salt could be held in solution at this temperature.

TABLE VIII.—PROPERTIES OF SALT BRINE
Solution of sodium chloride in water

Per cent of salt by weight	Degrees on salinometer at 60° F.	Specific gravity at 60° F.	Specific heat	Pounds of salt in one gallon	Freezing point, degrees Fahrenheit
0	0	1.000	1.000	0.000	32.00
1	4	1.007	0.992	0.084	31.80
5	20	1.037	0.960	0.432	25.40
10	40	1.073	0.892	0.895	18.60
15	60	1.115	0.855	1.395	12.20
20	80	1.150	0.829	1.920	6.86
25	100	1.191	0.783	2.485	1.00

Commercial calcium chloride contains about 20 per cent by weight of water, so that approximately 20 per cent more calcium chloride (by weight) than tabulated above is required for solutions having the specific gravities given.

Saturated brine is a solution which cannot hold any more common salt or calcium chloride. If a solution is even nearly saturated, it is likely to deposit its salt in the pipes, thus interfering with the circulation and also insulating the pipes. Because of this, the usual "strength" of *common-salt* brine is 40 to 90° on the salinometer. Its lowest temperature is about 6° F. If lower temperatures are desired, calcium-chloride brine should be used.

Preparation of Brine.—A brine solution may be prepared in a barrel with a false bottom which is usually about 6 or 8 inches above the actual bottom. The false bottom is made up of strips of wood about 1 inch square in cross-section and placed about ½ inch apart. The strips are supported by two boards, 6 inches wide, placed edgewise, and nailed to the bottom. Over the false bottom, burlap is placed and tacked to the sides of the barrel. This keeps the smaller particles of salt from dropping into the space below the false bottom. It also prevents any foreign matter contained in the water from getting into the brine. A 1¼-inch pipe, which is to serve as the inlet pipe for water, is connected to the barrel below the false bottom. The outlet pipe is placed about 6 inches below the top of the barrel and is about 1½ inches in diameter. It should be provided with a strainer. A piece of wire gauze placed over it will serve this

TABLE IX.—PROPERTIES OF CALCIUM BRINE

Solution of calcium chloride in water

Degrees on salinometer, 60° F.	Specific gravity at 60° F.	Percentage of chloride calcium by weight	Freezing point, degrees Fahrenheit	Specific heat	Ammonia suction-gage pressure, pounds per square inch
4	1.007	1	+31.10	0.996	46.0
8	1.015	2	+30.33	0.988	45.0
12	1.024	3	+29.48	0.980	44.0
16	1.032	4	+28.58	0.972	43.0
22	1.041	5	+27.68	0.964	41.5
26	1.049	6	+26.60	0.960	39.5
32	1.058	7	+25.32	0.930	38.0
36	1.067	8	+24.26	0.925	37.0
40	1.076	9	+23.80	0.911	35.5
44	1.085	10	+21.30	0.896	34.0
48	1.094	11	+19.70	0.890	32.5
52	1.103	12	+18.10	0.884	30.5
58	1.112	13	+16.30	0.876	28.0
62	1.121	14	+14.30	0.868	26.0
68	1.131	15	+12.20	0.860	23.5
72	1.140	16	+10.00	0.854	21.5
76	1.150	17	+ 7.50	0.849	20.0
80	1.159	18	+ 4.60	0.844	18.0
84	1.169	19	+ 1.70	0.839	15.0
88	1.179	20	− 1.40	0.834	12.3
92	1.189	21	− 4.90	0.825	10.5
96	1.199	22	− 8.60	0.817	8.0
100	1.209	23	−11.60	0.808	6.0
104	1.219	24	−17.10	0.799	4.0
108	1.229	25	−21.80	0.790	1.5
112	1.240	26	−27.00	0.778	1.0-inch vacuum
116	1.250	27	−32.60	0.769	5.0-inch vacuum
120	1.261	28	−39.20	0.757	8.5-inch vacuum

purpose. The brine is made by filling the barrel with salt up to a point just below the outlet pipe. The water is then turned on and, in rising, dissolves some of the salt. The brine formed passes off through the overflow pipe. Gradually, the salt is dissolved, and more should be added to keep the barrel well filled.

A barrel like the one described can be connected to the brine system at its highest point. The strength of the brine can be varied by passing it through the barrel, adding salt to it to increase its strength, and adding water to weaken it. When the barrel is connected into the system, a bypass pipe with valves should be provided, so that the brine can be forced through or around the barrel. Considerable time is required to dissolve the common salt in making brine, and an even greater length of time is required with calcium chloride.

Calcium chloride comes fused in a solid mass, in sheet-iron drums containing about 640 pounds, and requires breaking up into lumps by hammering the outside of the drum before it is opened.

Piping and Fittings for Refrigerating Systems.—The joints in an ammonia system are quite different from those ordinarily used for other purposes. The ordinary pipe joints cannot be

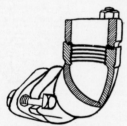

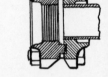

Fig. 132.—Flanged elbow for ammonia piping.　　　Fig. 133.—Flanges for piping joints.

made tight enough for most refrigerants. There are two forms suited to ammonia piping: (1) the gland joint and (2) the flange joint.

The *gland joint*, shown in Fig. 132, is simply a fitting which is threaded and has a recess filled with packing. A stuffing box is placed over the end of each pipe and is made tight against the packing by means of bolts. The end of the gland of the stuffing box which is next to the packing is beveled, so that the packing is forced against the end of the pipe, thus preventing leakage. If the pipes are free from expansion and vibration, the packing may be a lead gasket; otherwise, a rubber gasket should be used.

The *flange joint* (Fig. 133) is made up of two flanges, one having a "tongue," and the other a groove, which fit together. Each flange is threaded to receive the end of a pipe. A lead or rubber gasket is inserted in the groove. The gasket is compressed when the flanges are drawn together by bolts, thus preventing leakage. There is a recess in the backs of the flanges next to the pipe, and this recess is filled with solder which prevents leakage along the pipe.

A *branch tee* or *manifold* of the kind used in refrigerating systems is marked (7) in Fig. 134. Other kinds of fittings are shown in the figure and explained by reference to numbers.

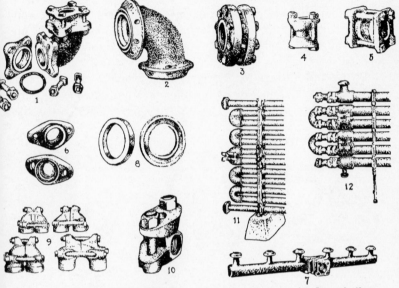

FIG. 134.—Typical pipe fittings for ammonia refrigerant: (1) flanged elbow; (2) ground-joint bolted elbow; (3) bolted pipe flanges; (4 and 5) ground-joint union; (6) oval flanges; (7) branch tee or header; (8) joint rings; (9) split return bends; (10) oval flanged elbow; (11) solid and flanged return bends; (12) double-pipe connections for brine cooler.

Working Temperatures in Ammonia Plants.—The temperature differences between the various elements of a refrigerating plant depend upon economic considerations. The cost of power, together with the cost of the pipe coil, determines, to a large extent, the magnitude of the temperature differences carried.

In general, it may be said that the larger the amount of coil surface the more economical the operating conditions will be, due to the fact that the suction pressure may be carried at a higher point. This is for the reason that the larger the coil surface for given conditions the smaller the temperature difference can be. The suction pressure should be carried as high as possible and still maintain the desired temperatures. The principal advantage of using a high suction pressure is that it requires less power per ton of refrigeration than do lower suction pressures. An additional advantage of higher suction is that the tonnage capacity of the compressor per cubic foot of displacement increases as the suction pressure is increased, since the ammonia weighs more per cubic foot.

In order to give an idea of the magnitude of these temperature differences, the following tables have been prepared, and these temperature differences should be maintained to insure economical operation:

DIRECT EXPANSION, DEGREES FAHRENHEIT

Room temperature	−10	0	10	20	30	40	50	60
Ammonia temperature	−25	−15	−5	3	10	16	22	26
Temperature difference	15	15	15	17	20	24	28	34

BRINE SYSTEM, DEGREES FAHRENHEIT

Room temperature	−10	0	10	20	30	40	50
Brine temperature	−20	−12	−4	4	12	20	28
Temperature difference	10	12	14	16	18	20	22

Room temperature	−10	0	10	20	30	40	50
Ammonia temperature	−28	−20	−13	−6	1	8	13
Temperature difference	18	20	23	26	20	32	37

Brine temperature	−20	−12	−4	4	12	20	28
Ammonia temperature	−28	−20	−13	−6	1	8	13
Temperature difference	8	8	9	10	11	12	15

Suction Pressure Required.—In order to operate a system at its maximum efficiency, the suction pressure should be as high as possible without failing to maintain the desired temperature. If different compartments are to be at different temperatures, the suction pressure must be of such value as to give the lowest temperature required. A compartment of the refrigerator which is held at a higher temperature than other compartments must be operated at a lower suction pressure than would otherwise be necessary.

CHAPTER VII

THERMODYNAMICS OF REFRIGERATING SYSTEMS

Refrigerating Machines Operating as "Heat Pumps."—A refrigerating machine is a mechanical device or "heat pump," which will transfer heat from a cold to a hotter body. This heat transfer, as stated by the second law of thermodynamics,[1] cannot take place of itself, but it can be effected by the expenditure of *mechanical work*. A steam, gas, or oil engine will serve as the heat pump of a refrigerating system if the engine is made to

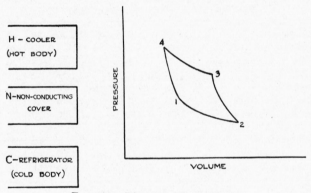

Fig. 136.—Diagram of Carnot cycle.

operate backward, so that the area of the indicator diagram taken on the cylinder of the engine represents work spent on, instead of done by, the gas or vapor which is used as the working substance.

A Carnot cycle in which *air is the working substance* may be used, as shown by the diagram in Fig. 136, to illustrate the "backward" operation of an engine, so that the cycle will be performed in the order indicated by the numbers 1-2-3-4.[2] Then, obviously, the area of the indicator diagram will have a

[1] For an explanation of thermodynamic principles, the reader is referred to Moyer, Calderwood, and Potter, "Elements of Engineering Thermodynamics," 3d Ed. This chapter uses the notation in that book.

[2] In the normal operation of a Carnot-cycle engine, the cycle is performed in the order 1-4-3-2, and then the area 1, 4, 3, 2 represents the work done by the air.

negative value and represents work spent upon the air. In the expansion 1-2, which is *isothermal*, meaning an expansion without change of temperature, the air is in contact with the *cold body C*, and it takes in a quantity of heat from the cold body equal to $wRT_2 \log_e r$,[1] where w is the weight of gas in pounds; T_2 is the constant absolute lowest temperature of the cycle in degrees Fahrenheit at which the expansion 1-2 takes place; T_1 is the constant absolute highest temperature in degrees Fahrenheit at which the isothermal compression 3-4 occurs; r is the ratio of expansion $(V_2 \div V_1)$; and R is a constant depending for its value on the kind of gas. In the following compression 3-4, the air gives out to the hot body H a quantity of heat equal to $wRT_3 \log_e r$. There is no transfer of heat along the adiabatic lines 2-3 and 4-1. Thus, the cold body C is constantly being drawn upon for heat and can, therefore, be maintained at a lower temperature than its surroundings. At the lower temperature T_2, the amount of heat taken up by the air from the cold body C is $wRT_2 \log_e r$, and at the higher temperature T_3, the amount of heat given out by the air to the hot body H is $wRT_3 \log_e r$. In an actual *refrigerating machine operating with air*, the cold body C may consist of a coil of pipe through which brine circulates, and the cold refrigerated air is brought into contact with the outside of the coil. The brine may be kept, by the action of the refrigerating machine, at a temperature below 32° F., and this brine may be used to remove heat by conduction from water which is to be frozen to make ice. The hot body H or "cooler," which is only relatively hot with respect to the cold body C, is kept at a temperature as low as possible by circulating cool water around it. This circulating water absorbs the heat rejected to the hot body H by the "working" air in the system.

In another class of refrigerating machines, the working substance or refrigerant, instead of being air, is the vapor of a liquid, and the action proceeds by alternate evaporation at a low pressure of the liquid refrigerant to a vapor and then the condensation of this vapor at a high pressure. A refrigerant must be chosen which evaporates at the lower limit of temperature at a pressure not so low as to make the bulk of the compressor excessive.

The Air System of Refrigeration.—The dense- or closed-air system is illustrated in Fig. 137, in which air from which the

[1] $2.3 \times \log$ base 10 $=$ log base e (Naperian or natural logarithms).

moisture has previously been removed is continuously circulated. The engine E furnishes power[1] to drive the compressor F.

The cylinder of the compressor delivers hot compressed air into a cooler A, where it is cooled and then passes on to the expansion cylinder G (connected mechanically to the compressor F and to the engine cylinder E which supplies the motive power). From the expander, the cold low-pressure air passes on, first, through the cooling coils of the brine cooler in the tank B and then back to the compressor cylinder F; thus, the air cycle is

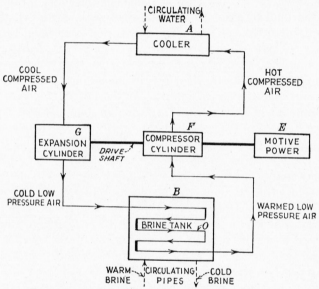

FIG. 137.—Outline of dense-air system of refrigeration.

completed. The course of the circulating water and also of the brine is shown by the dotted lines with accompanying arrows.

The work performed in the cylinder of a compressor can best be studied by means of an *indicator diagram*. If the compression is performed very slowly in a cylinder which is a good conductor of heat, so that the air within may lose heat by conduction to the atmosphere as rapidly as heat is generated by compression, the compression is *isothermal*, meaning that it takes place at the

[1] Since the work done by the expansion of the cool compressed air is less than that necessary for compressing the air taken from the cooling coils of the evaporator for the same range of pressures, a means must be employed to make up for this difference; and for this purpose, a prime mover is used.

constant temperature of the atmosphere. Now, if compressed air is distributed and used to do work in a compressed-air motor or "expander" without change of temperature, and the process of expansion in the compressed-air motor or expander is also very slow and consequently isothermal, then (neglecting losses due to friction in pipes, etc.) there will be no waste of power in the whole process including compression of the air and its expansion. The indicator diagram would be the same per pound of air in the air compressor as in the compressed-air motor or expander, although, of course, the cycle of the compressed-air motor would be the reverse of that of the air compressor.

Adiabatic compression and expansion take place approximately if the compression and expansion are performed very

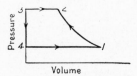

Fig. 138.—Compression diagram.   Fig. 139.—Expansion diagram.

quickly or when the air is not cooled during compression. In this case, the temperature of the air increases. The theoretical indicator diagram for adiabatic compression, as in Fig. 138, is 4-1-2-3, and that of the compressed air motor or expander, in Fig. 139, is 3-6-5-4. The compression 1-2 and the expansion

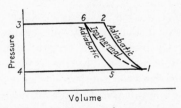

Fig. 140.—Superimposed diagram of compressor and expander.

6–5 (Figs. 138 and 139) are both adiabatic lines. As the result of the cooling of the compressed air between the compressor and the expander, the line 3-6 is shorter than the line 3-2.

If the indicator diagrams of the compressor and the expander are superposed, as in Fig. 140, and then an imaginary isothermal line is drawn between the points 6 and 1, it will be easily seen that adiabatic compression causes waste of power, as indicated by the area 6-2-1, while adiabatic expansion in the compressed-air motor causes a further waste, as shown by the area 5-1-6.

Work of Compression.—Assuming no clearance in the compressor and that the compression is isothermal, the pressure-volume diagram of the compression is shown in Fig. 138; and the work W done in the cycle of compression in foot-pounds is represented by the following equations, where P_1 and P_2 are the absolute initial and final pressures in pounds per square foot, and V_1 and V_2 are the initial and final volumes in cubic feet:

$$W = P_1V_1 - P_1V_1 \log_e^* \frac{V_1}{V_2} - P_2V_2$$

which becomes, since $P_1V_1 = P_2V_2$,

$$W = -P_1V_1 \log_e \frac{V_1}{V_2} = P_1V_1 \log_e \frac{V_2}{V_1}$$

In practice, a compression cannot be made entirely isothermal. The difference between isothermal and adiabatic compression is

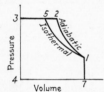

Fig. 141.—Diagram showing compression lines.

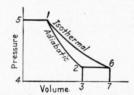

Fig. 142.—Diagram showing expansion lines.

shown graphically in Fig. 141 and between isothermal and adiabatic expansion in Fig. 142. In these examples, the terminal points are correctly placed for a certain definite ratio for both compression and expansion. In the compression diagram in Fig. 141, the area between the two curves 1-2-5 represents the work lost in the compression because of heating, and the area between the two curves 1-6-7-3-2[1] (in Fig. 142) shows the work lost by cooling during the expansion. The isothermal curve 6-1 is the same in the two cases.

---

* $2.3 \times \log$ base $10 = \log$ base e. Tables of natural logarithms are given in Moyer, Calderwood, and Potter, "Elements of Engineering Thermodynamics," 3d Ed., p. 214.

[1] The loss of work due to adiabatic expansion would be 1-6-7-3-2, if the isothermal and adiabatic expansions were interrupted at the points 6 and 2, respectively, and a further expansion were performed at constant volume to the level 4-7.

Increase in the temperature of the air is, in a measure, prevented during the compression by cooling the cylinder of the compressor. This cooling of the cylinder has the effect of changing the compression curve. The curves, which would have been PV = a constant, if isothermal, and $PV^{1.4}$ = a constant, if adiabatic, will be very much modified. In *perfectly* adiabatic conditions, the exponent n is 1.40 for air, but, in practice, the compressor cylinders are water jacketed, and thereby part of the heat of compression is conducted away, so that n becomes less than 1.40. This value of n varies with conditions and has generally a value between 1.2 and 1.3.

When the compression curve follows the law, PV^n equals a constant, and the work of compression (W) as in Fig. 138 is

$$W = P_1 V_1 - \frac{P_2 V_2 - P_1 V_1}{n - 1} - P_2 V_2$$

$$W = \frac{n}{n - 1}(P_1 V_1 - P_2 V_2) = \frac{n}{n - 1} \times wR \left[T_1 - T_2 \right]$$

where w is the weight of the gas or vapor in pounds.

The above formula when corrected for the friction loss may be written as follows:

$$W = \frac{n}{n - 1} wR \left[T_1 - T_2 \right] \frac{1}{1 - f}$$

where f is the friction loss. Substituting the thermodynamic relation

$$R = \frac{K - 1^*}{K} C_p,$$

the formula becomes

$$W = \left(\frac{K - 1}{K} \right)\left(\frac{n}{n - 1} \right) wC_p \left[T_2 - T_1 \right]\left(\frac{1}{1 - f} \right)$$

In the case of the expander the work done by the air in the cylinder can be obtained from this equation, providing the value of n for the expansion line is known and the proper correction is made for the friction loss. The work done by the expander is then

$$W = \left(\frac{K - 1}{K} \right)\left(\frac{n}{n - 1} \right) wC_p \left[T_6 - T_5 \right]\left(1 - f \right)$$

* The ratio of the specific heat of a gas at constant pressure (C_p) and the specific heat at constant volume (C_v) is K.

It should be noted that the effect of friction here is to reduce the energy delivered to the shaft of the expander (acting as a motor).

If the value of n for the expansion line is 1.4 and the value of K is 1.4, the quantity $\left(\dfrac{K-1}{K}\right)\left(\dfrac{n}{n-1}\right)$ becomes unity.

The work done by the expander is then

$$W = wC_p \left[T_2 - T_1 \right]\left(1 - f \right)$$

The net work or the energy supplied from the driving unit is then equal to the difference of the work done by compressing the air and the work done during expansion. The net work supplied is then,

$$\text{Net work} = wC_p \left[\left(\frac{K-1}{K}\right)\left(\frac{n}{n-1}\right)\left(\frac{1}{1-f}\right)\left(T_2 - T_1\right) - \left(1 - f\right)\left(T_6 - T_5\right) \right].$$

Since the lines of compression and expansion are not isothermal, and therefore have values of n other than unity, it is often necessary to determine an unknown temperature. When two pressures and one temperature are known, the other temperature can be found by the use of the following equation:

$$T_2 = T_1 \left(\frac{P_2}{P_1}\right)^{\frac{n-1*}{n}}$$

where T_1 and P_1 are the initial temperature and pressure, P_2 the final pressure and n the exponential value for the line or path.

The Effect of Clearance upon Volumetric Efficiency.—It is impossible to construct a compressor without clearance; consequently, the indicator diagram of an operating compressor differs from the ideal. At the end of the discharge stroke, the clearance volume is filled with compressed vapor or gas of the refrigerant.

When the piston moves on its outward stroke, the vapor or gas of the refrigerant expands, and the suction valves of the compressor will be closed until the piston has moved a sufficient

---

* The derivation of this equation may be found in Moyer, Calderwood, and Potter, "Elements of Engineering Thermodynamics," 3d Ed., p. 36.

distance to permit the trapped vapor or gas of the refrigerant to expand slightly below the suction pressure. When, in the expansion, the pressure reaches this value, any further movement of the piston opens the suction valves, and the vapor or gas of the refrigerant is drawn into the cylinder during the remainder of the stroke. Thus, the entire stroke of the compressor piston is not effective in pumping in a new supply of gas or vapor. The ratio of the apparent volume of vapor or gas drawn in, as shown by the indicator diagram, to the volume swept by the piston, or piston displacement of the cylinder, is termed *apparent volumetric efficiency*. *True volumetric efficiency* is the ratio of the volume of gas or vapor actually drawn in to the piston displacement.

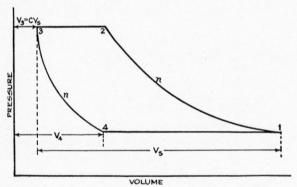

FIG 143.—Diagram of ideal air compressor with clearance.

Figure 143 illustrates an ideal compressor diagram with clearance. The gas or vapor of the refrigerant which remains in the clearance space is

$$V_3 = CV_s,$$

where V_s = volume swept or piston displacement of the cylinder
C = percentage of clearance

When the vapor or gas of the refrigerant expands to V_4, as shown in Fig. 143, the suction valves of the compressor are open and vapor or gas of the refrigerant is drawn into the cylinder as represented by the difference in volume between V_1 and V_4. This gas or vapor, as well as the clearance gas or vapor, is compressed to point 2, while the compressed gas or vapor is discharged from points 2 to 3. Knowing the percentage of clearance, the volume swept by the piston (V_s), and the initial and final pressure, the volumetric efficiency due to clearance E_v may be determined from the following equations:

$$E_v = \frac{V_1 - V_4}{V_s}$$

$$P_3(CV_s)^n = P_4 V_4{}^n$$

$$V_4 = \left(\frac{P_3}{P_4}\right)^{\frac{1}{n}} CV_s,$$

since

$$V_1 = V_s + CV_s,$$

$$V_1 - V_4 = V_s + CV_s - \left(\frac{P_3}{P_4}\right)^{\frac{1}{n}} CV_s$$

$$= \left[1 + C\left(1 - \left(\frac{P_3}{P_4}\right)^{\frac{1}{n}}\right) \right] V_s.$$

Therefore, volumetric efficiency is

$$E_v = \frac{\left[1 + C\left(1 - \left(\frac{P_3}{P_4}\right)^{\frac{1}{n}}\right) \right] V_s}{V_s}$$

$$= 1 + C\left[1 - \left(\frac{P_3}{P_4}\right)^{\frac{1}{n}} \right]$$

The volumetric efficiency E_v is less at low suction pressures, because the weight of a cubic foot of vapor of the refrigerant decreases.

The *true volumetric efficiency* may be expressed as the ratio of the capacity of the compressor to the piston displacement. The capacity is the actual amount of the vapor compressed and delivered, expressed in cubic feet per minute at intake temperature and pressure. The true volumetric efficiency is not easy to obtain as it requires the measurement of the refrigerant passing through the compressor, and takes into consideration the superheating of the suction vapor resulting from contact with the cylinder walls, piston and valves, which are always at a temperature above the suction vapor temperature. This effect cannot be shown by an indicator diagram. The superheating of the vapor causes a loss and, therefore, requires more work to be done on the vapor and also reduces the capacity of the compressor. A compressor of the uniflow type (Fig. 46) is designed to reduce this loss.

The actual piston displacement can be determined if the volumetric efficiencies due to (1) clearance and (2) superheating effect are known. This can be expressed as

$$Actual\ Piston\ Displacement = D_c \div (E_v \times E_s)$$

where E_v is the volumetric efficiency due to clearance, E_s the volumetric efficiency due to superheating, and D_c is the theoretical piston displacement.

The theoretical piston displacement per minute per ton of refrigeration D_{cmr} is expressed by the following equation

$$D_{cmr} = \frac{200V}{H_1 - h_3}$$

where H_1 is the total heat of vapor entering the compressor, h_3 the heat of the liquid of the refrigerant at the temperature it enters the expansion valve and V the specific volume of vapor for the conditions at the suction pressure.

The York Manufacturing Company use the following empirical formula based on tests, for the volumetric efficiency due to superheating:

$$E_s = 1 - \frac{t_2 - t_1}{1,330}$$

where $t_2 - t_1$ is the rise of temperature during the compression stroke (see Fig. 145).

When dealing with vertical single-acting compressors in which the clearance has been made very small, the chief loss then becomes that due to superheating. For standard conditions, the volumetric efficiency of vertical single-acting compressors will be about 85 per cent.

The piston displacement for the air system of refrigeration may be calculated for the compressor from the following equation,

$$D_c = \frac{wRT_1}{P_1\left[1 + C\left(1 - \left(\frac{P_2}{P_1}\right)^{\frac{1}{n}}\right)\right]}$$

and for the expander D_e,

$$D_e = \frac{wRT_5}{P_1\left[1 + C\left(1 - \left(\frac{P_2}{P_4}\right)^{\frac{1}{n}}\right)\right]}$$

where P_1 is the absolute suction pressure, P_2 is the pressure at the end of compression, w is the weight of air supplied per minute in pounds, C is the assumed ratio of the clearance to the piston displacement, R is the "gas constant" (53.3 for air), n is a thermodynamic exponent which is equal to 1.4 for adiabatic compression of air, T_1 is the temperature of the air at the beginning of compression, and T_5 is the temperature of the air at the end of the expansion (in the expander).

Problem.—A dense-air machine operates between the pressures of 65 pounds per square inch and 230 pounds per square inch absolute. The compressor receives air at a temperature of 10° F., and it is discharged from the *water cooler* at 95° F. The value for n for the compression line is 1.3; and for the expansion line, 1.4 (see Fig. 144).

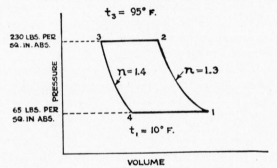

Fig. 144.—Graphical statement of problem.

Find (a) the weight of air per minute per ton of refrigeration; (b) net work per minute per ton of refrigeration; (c) weight of cooling water per minute per ton of refrigeration; (d) horsepower per ton of refrigeration; (e) displacement per minute per ton of refrigeration for the compressor, assuming 2 per cent clearance; (f) displacement per minute per ton of refrigeration for the cooling coils or expander, assuming 2 per cent clearance; (g) coefficient of performance.

Assume the friction loss to be 15 per cent, and also assume the initial temperature of the cooling water to be 65° F. and the final temperature 75° F.

Solution.

(a) $\dfrac{T_2}{T_1} = \left(\dfrac{P_2}{P_1}\right)^{\frac{n-1}{n}}$, $T_2 = 470\left(\dfrac{230}{65}\right)^{0.231} = 630°$ F. Abs. or 170° F.

$$T_4 = 555 \left(\dfrac{65}{230}\right)^{0.286} = 387° \text{ F. Abs. or } -73° \text{ F.}$$

Weight of air per minute per ton of refrigeration

$$= \frac{200}{0.24(10 - (-73))} = 10.0 \text{ pounds}$$

(b) Net work per minute per ton of refrigeration

$$= 10 \times 0.24\left[\left(\frac{1.4 - 1}{1.4}\right)\left(\frac{1.3}{1.3 - 1}\right)\left(\frac{1}{1.00 - 0.15}\right)(630 - 470)\right.$$
$$\left. - (1.00 - 0.15)(555 - 387)\right]$$

$$= 216 \text{ B.t.u.}$$

(c) Weight of cooling water per minute per ton of refrigeration

$$= \frac{0.24 \times 10(630 - 555)}{75 - 65} = 18 \text{ pounds}$$

(d) Horsepower per ton of refrigeration

$$= \frac{216 \times 778}{33,000} = 5.10$$

(e) Displacement per minute per ton of refrigeration for compressor

$$= \frac{10 \times 53.34 \times 470}{144 \times 65\left[1 + 0.02\left\{1 - \left(\frac{230}{65}\right)^{\frac{1}{1.3}}\right\}\right]}$$

$$= 22.7 \text{ cubic feet}$$

(f) Displacement per minute per ton of refrigeration for cooling coils or expander

$$= \frac{10 \times 53.34 \times 387}{144 \times 65\left[1 + 0.02\left\{1 - \left(\frac{230}{65}\right)^{\frac{1}{1.4}}\right\}\right]}$$

$$= 27.5 \text{ cubic feet}$$

(g) Coefficient of performance

$$= \frac{10 \times 0.24(470 - 387)}{216} = 0.923$$

Action of Refrigerant in Evaporator.—It will be remembered that when a liquid evaporates, as in the cooling coils of the evaporator in a refrigerating system, it takes up heat. This heat is the latent heat of evaporation. Not all of this heat, however, is available for cooling purposes, because the temperature of the liquid on entering the expansion valve is at a higher temperature than that within the cooling coils of the evaporator. Some of the liquid must, therefore, be evaporated in order to lower its temperature. The evaporation necessary for this lowering of temperature of the refrigerant is a loss in the total available heat for refrigerating purposes and is explained more in detail on page 179.

When flowing through the expansion valve, the liquid ammonia at the higher pressure p_2 (Fig. 145) is converted into moist vapor at the pressure p_1 and quality x_4, with a reduction in temperature from the saturation temperature t_2 (corresponding to the pressure p_2) to the saturation temperature t_1 (corresponding to the pressure p_1). The moist vapor of the refrigerant absorbs heat from the substance which is being cooled, and all the liquid refrigerant carried in the vapor is evaporated. The amount of heat absorbed per pound of the refrigerant is $L_1(1 - x_4)$,[1] where x_4 is the quality of the ammonia vapor just after passing through the expansion valve and L_1 is the latent heat of evaporation at the pressure p_1.

Since the total heat of the liquid ammonia at the pressure p_2 equals the total heat of moist vapor of quality x_4 at the pressure p_1,

$$h_2 = h_1 + x_4 L_1.$$

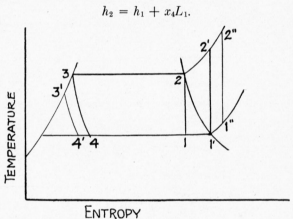

FIG. 145.—Entropy-temperature diagram showing effects of superheating and aftercooling.

where h_2 is the heat of liquid at the pressure p_2, and h_1 is the heat of liquid at the pressure p_1. From which the initial quality x_4 just after the expansion valve is

$$x_4 = \frac{h_2 - h_1}{L_1}$$

The theoretical pressure-volume (p.-v.) diagram for a refrigerating system, neglecting clearance and the effect of the expansion of the liquid in passing through the expansion valve, are shown by Fig. 146.

The vapor of the refrigerant is drawn into the compressor along the line 4-1 and is compressed adiabatically along the line

---

[1] This statement applies only when the vapor leaving the evaporator is dry and saturated.

1-2. In compressing the vapor, the pressure and, also, the temperature increase. This puts the vapor into a suitable condition to be liquefied in the condenser by the cooling water. It is discharged from the compressor into the condenser along the line 2-3. After the liquid refrigerant passes through the expansion valve, as indicated by the line 3-4, it evaporates in the cooling coils of the evaporator, where it absorbs heat from the substances to be cooled. During this heat exchange, the refrigerant again becomes a vapor at the lower pressure p_1. At this pressure, there is, also, a correspondingly lower temperature at which the liquid refrigerant boils. This evaporation in the cooling coils of the evaporator causes a change in volume of the refriger-

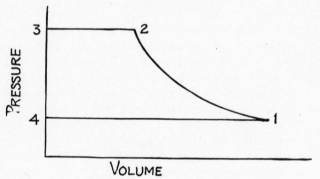

Fig. 146.—Typical pressure-volume diagram of compressor.

ant, as shown by the line 4-1. This cycle appears in a temperature-entropy diagram, in Fig. 145.

Analysis of Wet Compression and Aftercooling.—When the refrigerant has some liquid mixed with the vapor at the beginning of the compression stroke, the condition is called *wet compression*. On the indicator diagram, this kind of compression is shown by the line 1-2, in Fig. 145. When there is no liquid present; that is, when there is dry compression, the line showing compression is 1'-2'. On the other hand, when the vapor of the refrigerant is returned to the compressor with a small amount of superheat, the compression is 1''-2'', and the vapor is then discharged along 2'-3 or 2''-3 into the condenser, where it is changed to a liquid. The liquid refrigerant passes through the expansion valve, as indicated by the line 3-4, where the pressure and temperature are reduced. There is no loss or gain in heat along the 3-4 expansion line, so that this part of the refrigerating cycle is a constant-heat process. The refrigerant then takes up heat in the cooling coils of the evaporator when expanding along the line 4-1.

In some refrigerating machines, the cooling water of the condenser frequently cools the liquid refrigerant to a temperature lower than the temperature corresponding to the pressure This *aftercooling* is shown in Fig. 145 by the lines 3-3'. It can be seen that this aftercooling of the liquid increases the available amount of refrigerating effect. A similar cycle can be shown on a *total heat-pressure* diagram (p. 248).

From the diagram in Fig. 146, it can be shown that the work done is the area 4-1-2-3. The following notation may be used to determine the work in this compression and expansion: I_1 and I_2 are the internal energies (B.t.u. per pound), respectively, of the refrigerant entering and leaving the compressor; v_1 and v_2 are the specific volumes of the vapor of the refrigerant (cubic feet per pound), neglecting, as being very small, the volumes occupied by the liquid particles of the refrigerant; p_1 and p_2 are the absolute suction and discharge pressures at the compressor (pounds per square foot); A is the heat equivalent of mechanical energy or $\frac{1}{778}$ (B.t.u. per foot pound). Then, as shown in Fig. 146, the work performed by the refrigerant under the line 1-2 is $I_2 - I_1$; the work performed under the line 2-3 is $A p_2 v_2$; the work done by the refrigerant under the line 4-1 is $A p_1 v_1$. The *net work* of compression is therefore, $I_2 - I_1 + A p_2 v_2 - A p_1 v_1 = (I_2 + A p_2 v_2) - (I_1 + A p_1 v_1)$. But, since $I_2 + A p_2 v_2 = H_2$, the total heat (B.t.u. per pound) of the refrigerant at 2 and $I_1 + A p_1 v_1 = H_1$, the total heat (B.t.u. per pound) at 1, it follows that the work of compression is simply the difference between the total heats of the refrigerant at the points 2 and 1, or

Work of compression per cycle = $H_2 - H_1$ (B.t.u. per pound) The operation of the compressor is, theoretically, a reversed Rankine cycle.

The vapor discharged by the compressor may be *superheated*, having a temperature t_s at a pressure P_2. The condition of the discharged vapor is determined by equating the entropies at the inlet and discharge pressures. The total heat (H_2) of the discharged vapor will be

$$H_2 = [h_2 + L_2 + C_p(t_s - t_2)]$$

where C_p is the specific heat at constant pressure.

The *theoretical* horsepower of the compressor is, if w pounds of vapor of the refrigerant is circulated per minute;

$$\text{Hp.} = \frac{w(H_2 - H_1)778}{33,000} *$$

Heat Absorbed by Vapor in Evaporator.—The heat absorbed per minute by w pounds of vapor passing through the cooling coils of the evaporator will be

$$Q_r = w(1 - x_4)L_1 \text{ (B.t.u. per pound)}$$

when the refrigerant leaves the evaporator as a dry and saturated vapor, or is expressed by

$$Q_r = w[(1 - x_4)L_1 + C_p(t_1'' - t_1)] \text{ (B.t.u. per pound)}$$

when the compression is "dry"; that is, the refrigerant leaving the evaporator is *superheated* to the temperature t_1''. For the case of "*wet*" compression, that is when the refrigerant entering the compressor is a moist vapor of quality x_1, the heat absorbed in the evaporation is given by

$$Q_r = w(x_1 - x_4)L_1$$

and in general,

$$Q_r = w(H_1 - h_4) \text{ (B.t.u. per pound)}$$

Heat Absorbed by Cooling Water in Condenser.—The heat given to the cooling water in the condenser is, in general, as indicated in Fig. 145.

$$Q_c = w(H_2 - h_3) \text{ (B.t.u. per pound)}$$

where h_3 is the heat of the liquid at point 3 (temperature t_2). If the vapor leaving the compressor is superheated to the temperature t_2;

$$Q_c = w[C_p(t_2'' - t_2) + L_2 + (h_3 - h_3')] \text{ (B.t.u. per pound)}.$$

In this equation, L_2 is the latent heat of evaporation at the pressure p_2 and h_3' is the heat of the liquid due to aftercooling in condenser.

* In the case of fluids of which there are no published tables and charts, the theoretical horsepower can be calculated (if the compression is assumed to be adiabatic) from the following formula:

$$\text{Hp.} = \frac{144n}{33,000\,(n-1)} \times P_1 V_1 \left[\left(\frac{P_2}{P_1}\right)^{\frac{n-1}{n}} - 1 \right]$$

where V_1 = volume compressed per minute, cubic feet; P_1 = absolute intake pressure, pounds per square inch; P_2 = absolute discharge pressure, pounds per square inch; and n = exponent of PV^n = constant.

Heat Balance of the Compression System.—The general formula for the heat balance is as follows:

$$H_e + H_w = H_1 + H_3$$

where H_e = heat absorbed by evaporating refrigerant; H_w = heat equivalent of work in compressor; H_1 = heat rejected in condenser; H_3 = heat rejected or radiated in addition to H_1.

For purposes of illustration, the following list of quantities involved in the computation of the heat balances of compound compression systems is given:

HEAT ABSORBED (B.T.U. PER HOUR)

a. Heat absorbed in evaporator.

b. Heat entering evaporator insulation.

c. Heat absorbed in low-pressure suction main.

d. Heat absorbed in low-pressure suction trap.

e. Heat equivalent of work done in compressor.

f. Heat absorbed from engine room through cold surface of low-pressure compressor.

g. Heat absorbed through surface of intermediate liquid receiver.

h. Heat absorbed through surface of intermediate-pressure liquid line.

i. Heat absorbed from engine room through surface of high-pressure suction main.

j. Heat absorbed through cold surfaces of high-pressure compressor.

k. Heat absorbed or rejected through condenser shells.

l. Heat absorbed or rejected through receivers.

m. Heat absorbed or rejected in high-pressure liquid line.

HEAT REJECTED (B.T.U. PER HOUR)

n. Heat rejected by hot surface of low-pressure compressor.

o. Heat rejected from low-pressure discharge main between low-pressure compressor and intermediate vapor cooler.

p. Heat rejected in intermediate vapor cooler.

q. Heat rejected to engine room by intermediate vapor cooler.

r. Heat rejected in discharge main from intermediate vapor cooler to intermediate liquid receiver.

s. Heat rejected by hot surfaces of high-pressure compressor.

t. Heat rejected by high-pressure discharge main and oil separator between machine and condensers.

u. Heat rejected in ammonia condensers.

v. Heat rejected in liquid cooler.

w. Heat rejected or absorbed through condenser shells.

x. Heat rejected or absorbed through receivers.

y. Heat rejected or absorbed in high-pressure liquid line.

The heat absorbed by the condenser is theoretically equal to the sum of the heat absorbed in the refrigerator and the heat equivalent of the work of compression.

The volume of the ammonia vapor delivered to the compressor can be readily found from the weight of the refrigerant which circulates in the system and the specific volume of the vapor when it enters the compressor. The actual displacement of the compressor can then be ascertained if the volumetric efficiency is known.

Problem.—An ammonia compressor operates with dry compression under standard conditions. If the vapor is superheated to a *temperature of* 20° F. when it enters the compressor, determine the following, assuming the liquid ammonia at the throttling valve to be 80° F. with a 10° F. rise in temperature of the cooling water. Also, assume an overall efficiency of 75 per cent and a volumetric efficiency of 70 per cent:

Find (*a*) weight of ammonia per minute per ton of refrigeration; (*b*) horsepower required by compressor per ton of refrigeration; (*c*) gallons of cooling water per minute per ton of refrigeration; (*d*) piston displacement per minute per ton of refrigeration; (*e*) coefficient of performance.

Solution:

(*a*) Weight of ammonia per minute per ton of refrigeration

$$= \frac{200}{622.2 - 132}$$

$$= 0.408$$

(*b*) Horsepower per ton of refrigeration

$$= \frac{0.408[726 - 622]778}{33,000 \times 0.75}$$

$$= 1.33$$

(*c*) Gallons of cooling water per minute per ton of refrigeration

$$= \frac{0.408[726 - 132]}{8.33 \times 10}$$

$$= 2.91$$

(*d*) Piston displacement per minute per ton of refrigeration

$$= \frac{0.408 \times 8.473}{0.70}$$

= 4.94 cubic feet or 8,530 cubic inches.

(*e*) Coefficient of performance

$$= \frac{200}{0.408[726 - 622] \div 0.75}$$

= 3.54

Ammonia Absorption System of Refrigeration.—The absorption system of refrigeration depends on the fact that anhydrous ammonia has the property of forming aqua ammonia. The amount of ammonia which can be absorbed by water depends on the temperature of the water; the colder the water the greater its absorption of ammonia.

Heat Properties of Ammonia Solutions.—From the above discussion, it is apparent that an understanding of the thermodynamic properties of ammonia solutions is necessary in order thoroughly to understand the principles of the absorption system.

It has long been known that anhydrous ammonia has a great affinity for water, and a solution thus formed is said to have a "concentration of 30 per cent" if the solution contains 30 per cent ammonia and 70 per cent water by weight.

The temperature at which an ammonia solution will boil when under pressure and of a definite concentration has been studied by Mollier. Macintire has given the following equation from which the boiling temperature can be determined:

$$\frac{T_1}{T_2} = 0.00471Z + 0.655$$

where T_1 = temperature of saturated ammonia corresponding to the pressure, degrees Fahrenheit, absolute

T_2 = boiling temperature, degrees Fahrenheit, absolute

Z = per cent concentration

A family of curves, as shown in Fig. 148, has been arranged to simplify the use of the above equation.[1]

It has been previously stated that in the generator there is a mixture of water and ammonia vapor. The total pressure in the generator is the sum of the partial pressures of ammonia and water vapor. The partial pressure of the water vapor has been taken by Professor Spangler to be the steam pressure at the

[1] See MARK, "Handbook of Mechanical Engineering," Fig. 2, p. 1823.

temperature considered multiplied by the ratio of the number of molecules of water in a certain amount of solution to the total number of molecules of the solution. Hence, it follows that

$$\frac{x}{17} = \text{relative number of molecules}$$

$$\frac{100 - x}{18} = \text{relative number of water molecules}$$

For which the partial steam pressure p_a, in pounds per square inch absolute, is

$$p_a = p\frac{\dfrac{100 - x}{18}}{\dfrac{x}{17} + \dfrac{100 - x}{18}} = p\frac{1,700 - 17x}{1,700 + x}$$

where p equals the absolute steam pressure at the given temperature in pounds per square inch.

When 1 pound of ammonia vapor is absorbed by 200 pounds of water, about 893 B.t.u. of heat are developed. If a greater weight of water is used, the number of absorbed heat units is the same. For this reason, this value (in B.t.u.) is called the *heat of complete dilution*. On the other hand, if a smaller weight of water is used, less heat is developed. This latter case is called the *heat of partial absorption*, because, if more water is added to produce a dilution of 1 in 200, the remaining heat (to make the total 893 B.t.u.) would be generated.

It was found by Berthelot that the heat of complete dilution (H_d) expressed is 142.5 times the weight of the ammonia (in pounds) in the solution per pound of water. This value is expressed by the equation

$$H_d = 142.5\ \frac{z}{100 - z}$$

in B.t.u. per pound of ammonia solution having a concentration of z per cent
where z is the percentage of concentration of the solution which is formed.

The partial heat of absorption (H_a) is, then,

$$H_a = 893 - 142.5\ \frac{z}{100 - z}$$

in B. t.u. per pound of ammonia solution having a concentration of z per cent.

If w pounds of ammonia are absorbed, the partial heat of absorption for this amount is

$$H_a' = w\left[893 - 142.5 \frac{z}{100 - z} \right]$$

in B.t.u. per pound of ammonia solution having a concentration of z.

In the absorber, heat is generated by the addition of ammonia to the ammonia solution. If the strength of an ammonia solution is changed from z to z', this heat which is generated is given by the following equation:

$$H_{z-z'} = 893 - 142.5 \left[\frac{z'}{100 - z'} + \frac{z}{100 - z} \right]$$

in B.t.u. per pound of ammonia vapor which is added.

According to the experiments of Mollier, the heat developed in changing a weak solution having a concentration of z per cent to one having a concentration of z' per cent depends upon the mean concentration $x = \dfrac{z + z'}{2}$. The heat generated then is given by the equation $H_{z-z'} = 345\,(1 - x) - 400x^2$ in B.t.u. per pound of ammonia which is added.

In analyzing the operation of the absorption machine, it is customary to determine the amount of strong-ammonia solution in circulation per pound of anhydrous ammonia. If the following symbols are used, suitable equations for this determination can be found: W_w = weight of weak ammonia solution per pound of anhydrous ammonia, pounds; W_s = weight of strong ammonia solution per pound of anhydrous ammonia, pounds; Z_s = percentage of concentration of strong ammonia solution; Z_w = percentage of concentration of weak ammonia solution.

By equating the total weight of aqua ammonia entering the generator to the total weight leaving it,

$$W_s = W_w + 1$$

Again, by equating the weight of anhydrous ammonia entering the generator to the weight of anhydrous ammonia leaving it,

$$Z_s \times W_s = 1 + Z_w \times W_w$$

Solving the two equations above for the weight of strong ammonia solution,

$$W_w = \frac{1 - Z_s}{Z_s - Z_w}$$

The calculations may be simplified by reference to the table on page 237. From a thermodynamic viewpoint, it is interesting to calculate the heat balance of the absorption system, but since little is known as to all of the thermodynamic properties of ammonia solutions, it is difficult to make these calculations with much accuracy.

The following equation expresses the *heat balance* for the absorption system:

$$H_g + H_2 + H_5 = H_3 + H_4 + H_6$$

where

H_g = heat imparted to the fluid in the generator per pound of anhydrous ammonia passing through the expansion valve, B.t.u. per pound.

H_2 = heat absorbed in the cooling coils of the evaporator, B.t.u. per pound of anhydrous ammonia.

H_3 = heat rejected to the cooling water of the condenser, B.t.u. per pound of anhydrous ammonia.

H_4 = heat withdrawn from the absorber, B.t.u. per pound of anhydrous ammonia.

H_5 = heat equivalent of work of the pump, B.t.u. per pound of anhydrous ammonia.

H_6 = heat loss of radiation, etc., B.t.u. per pound of ammonia.

The heat H_2 absorbed in the coils of the evaporator can be calculated from the equation $H_2 = H_1'' - h_2$, where H_1'' is the heat content in B.t.u. per pound of the ammonia vapor corresponding to the pressure in the cooling coils or evaporator and h_2 is the heat content of the liquid ammonia in B.t.u. per pound corresponding to the temperature of the liquid ammonia entering the expansion valve.

The heat rejected to the cooling water by the condenser can be obtained if the temperature and pressure of ammonia vapor entering and the temperature of the liquid ammonia leaving the condenser are known. Then, $H_3 = H_2'' - h_2$, where H_2'' is the heat content in B.t.u. per pound in the ammonia vapor entering the condenser and h_2 is the heat of the liquid in B.t.u. per pound of the liquid ammonia leaving the condenser.

The heat withdrawn from the absorber H_4 can be found from the following: let t_1 represent the temperature of the ammonia vapor in coils in degrees Fahrenheit; t_0, the temperature of the ammonia solution in the absorber in degrees Fahrenheit; and t', the temperature of the weak ammonia solution entering the absorber in degrees Fahrenheit.

TABLE X.—POUNDS OF STRONG AQUA AMMONIA REQUIRED PER POUND OF AMMONIA EVAPORATED

Concentration of weak aqua ammonia, per cent	Concentration of strong aqua ammonia, per cent								
	20	22	24	26	28	30	32	34	36
18	41	20½	13⅔	10¼	8.2	6.84	5.86	5.12	4.55
20	..	40	20	13⅓	10	8.0	6.67	5.71	5.0
22	..	....	39	19½	13	9.75	7.8	6.5	5.57
24	..	....	....	38	19	12⅔	9½	7⅔	6.33
26	..	....	....	....	37	18½	12⅓	9.25	7.4
28	..	....	....	....	....	36	18	12.0	9.0
30	..	....	....	....	....	....	35	17.5	11.67

The ammonia vapor, when it enters the absorber, receives heat equal to $0.6(t_0 - t_1)$ in B.t.u. per pound of vapor, where 0.6 is the specific heat of ammonia vapor. The entering weak solution gives up the heat $W_w C'(t' - t_0)$ where C' represents the specific heat of the weak aqua ammonia (generally taken as unity) and W_w is the weight in pounds of the weak solution. When ammonia vapor is absorbed by a weak ammonia solution, heat is developed. This heat of absorption H_a, as has already been shown (on p. 235), can be obtained from the equation

$$H_a = 345(1 - x) - 400x^2$$

Hence,

$$H_4 = H_a + W_w(t' - t_0) - 0.6(t_0 - t_1)$$

The pump transfers W_s pounds of strong aqua ammonia at the pressure P_1 in the absorber to the pressure P_2 in the generator. If V is the volume of 1 pound of strong aqua ammonia, then

$$H_5 = \frac{(W_s)V(P_2 - P_1)}{778}.$$

The heat loss by radiation H_6 will be about 5 to 10 per cent of the heat supplied to the generator H_g.

Heat of Liquid for Mixtures of Ammonia and Water.—The heat added to 1 pound of an ammonia solution can be determined by assuming that the heat capacity of a solution of ammonia and water is the sum of the heat of liquid of the constituents

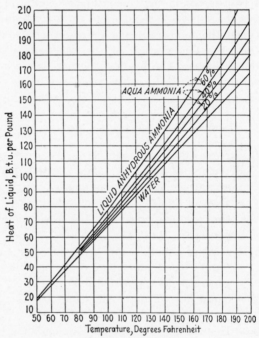

Fig. 149.—Heat of liquid for water and anhydrous ammonia and aqua ammonia of various concentrations.

according to their proportions in the solution. If h_a and h_w are the heat of liquid (as found in the ammonia and steam tables) and z is the per cent of concentration, the weight of water is $\dfrac{1-z}{100}$ per pound of solution, and the heat of the liquid of an ammonia solution is then equal to

$$h_a z + h_w \frac{(1-z)}{100}$$

Values of the heat of liquid for ammonia solution for various temperatures and concentration can be found graphically[1] from Fig. 149.

Heat Supplied to Generator.—The heat supplied to the generator may be found from the heat balance by assuming the radiation loss, or an approximation can be made by considering that the generator is an absorber operating in a reverse process. The heat transferred in the generator per pound of anhydrous ammonia is the sum of heat added to the strong-ammonia solutions between the temperature of the entering strong-ammonia solution and the temperature of the weak-ammonia solution leaving the generator, the heat of solution, and the ammonia vapor from the liquid to the superheated condition. Expressing this statement in the form of an equation,[2] we have the following:

$$H_g = W_w(h_2' - h_1') + h_{sol.} + (H_1 - h_0)$$

where H_g = Heat supplied by generator, B.t.u. per pound

W_w = Weight of weak ammonia solution per pound of anhydrous ammonia pounds

h_2' = Heat of liquid of ammonia solution of z concentration for temperature of the weak solution leaving generator, B.t.u. per pound

h_1' = Heat of liquid of ammonia solution of z' concentration for the temperature of strong solution entering generator, B.t.u. per pound

H_1 = Total heat of ammonia vapor in generator, B.t.u. per pound

h_0 = Heat of liquid ammonia corresponding to temperature of strong-ammonia solution, B.t.u. per pound

Values for the heat of solution h_{sol} of liquid ammonia may be taken from the following table:

[1] See POWER, "Practical Refrigeration," Fig. 101.
[2] The equation does not consider the effect of the water vapor in the generator.

TABLE XI.—HEAT OF SOLUTION OF LIQUID AMMONIA
B.t.u. given up per pound of ammonia dissolved

Concentration[1]	Heat of solution, B.t.u. per pound	Concentration[1]	Heat of solution, B.t.u. per pound	Concentration[1]	Heat of solution, B.t.u. per pound	Concentration[1]	Heat of solution, B.t.u. per pound	Concentration[1]	Heat of solution, B.t.u. per pound	Concentration[1]	Heat of solution, B.t.u. per pound
0	347.4	11	302.8	21	253.8	31	197.6	41	135.0	51	63.0
1	343.8	12	298.2	22	248.4	32	191.9	42	127.8	52	55.8
2	340.2	13	293.6	23	243.0	33	186.1	43	120.6	53	48.6
3	336.6	14	289.0	24	237.6	34	180.4	44	113.4	54	41.4
4	333.0	15	284.4	25	232.2	35	174.6	45	106.2	55	34.2
5	329.4	16	279.4	26	226.4	36	168.1	46	99.0	56	27.4
6	325.0	17	274.3	27	220.7	37	161.6	47	91.8	57	20.5
7	320.6	18	269.2	28	214.9	38	155.2	48	84.6	58	13.7
8	316.2	19	264.2	29	209.2	39	148.7	49	77.4	59	6.8
9	311.8	20	259.2	30	203.4	40	142.2	50	70.2	60	0.0
10	307.4										

[1] Average concentration, per cent of ammonia by weight.

Density and Specific Gravity of Ammonia Solutions.—In order to determine the horsepower developed by the strong aqua-ammonia pump, it is necessary to know the density of the solution. This is determined from its specific gravity, and the relationship is shown graphically[1] in Fig. 150. The specific gravity is fixed at a temperature of 60° F. At other temperatures, the solution will occupy a different volume, and, therefore, the specific gravity will change even when the concentration remains the same.

If the temperature is within 5 to 10° F. of 60° F., the percentage of concentration can be taken from the curve when the specific gravity has been found. For the high temperatures found in an absorption system, there is usually difficulty in obtaining the concentration by testing. This is due to the volatility of the sample of the ammonia solution because of its high temperature and low pressure when it is removed from the system. In order to take a sample for testing, it is customary to have suitable outlets arranged at points where the temperatures are comparatively low, as on the discharge side of the pump for the strong-ammonia solution and between the absorber and weak-liquid cooler for the weak-ammonia solution. A glass graduate and hydrometer are

[1] See POWER, "Practical Refrigeration," Fig. 99.

needed for testing. The graduate should be half filled with water cooled to about 32° F. The tube for obtaining the samples of the ammonia solutions should be placed so that its outlet is below the surface of the water in the graduate. The ammonia solution to be tested should be discharged into the graduate

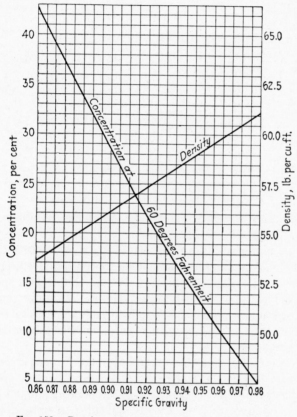

Fig. 150.—Density and specific gravity of aqua ammonia.

until the temperature of the mixture rises to 60° F. The specific gravity then can be found by means of the hydrometer. Since it is the concentration of the sample that is desired, one can then calculate the concentration by equating the weight of ammonia in the solution to the total weight of ammonia in the final mixture of ammonia and water, as follows:

$$S_p \times Z(1 - R) = 1 \times S_{pm} \times Z_m$$

or

$$Z = Z_m \left(\frac{S_{pm}}{S_p} \times \frac{1}{1 - R} \right) \tag{1}$$

Equating the weight of the mixture to the sum of the weights of the ammonia solution and water, the following relation is obtained:

$$1 \times S_{pm} = (R \times 1) + (1 - R)S_p \tag{2}$$

Eliminating S_p (which is not known) between equations (1) and (2) the following expression is obtained for the desired concentration Z.

$$Z = Z_m \div \left(1 - \frac{R}{S_{pm}} \right)$$

where Z = concentration of ammonia solution, per cent

Z_m = concentration of ammonia and water mixture, per cent

R = ratio of the volume of cold water before mixing with sample to the volume of the ammonia and water mixture.

S_p = specific gravity of the ammonia solution tested.

S_{pm} = specific gravity of the ammonia and water mixture.

If the temperature is higher than 60° F., the specific gravity will be somewhat lower, between about 0.001 and 0.005 for each 10° F. of temperature difference, depending on the concentration. The strong solutions have a higher coefficient of expansion and, therefore, need a greater correction factor than the weak solutions. The specific gravity at 60° F. can then be found from the following formula:

$$S_{p60} = S_{pt} + 0.003(t - 60)(1 - S_{pt})$$

where S_{p60} = specific gravity at 60° F.

S_{pt} = specific gravity at the temperature t

The *approximate* specific gravity of an ammonia solution S_{pa}, taking the specific gravity of water as unity, can be found from the following formula:

$$S_{pa} = 1 - \frac{4.3}{1,000} \left(Z - \frac{Z^2}{100} + \frac{Z^3}{1,000} \right)$$

where Z is the percentage of concentration of the ammonia solution.

Related Physical Properties of Refrigerants.—There are five important properties applying particularly to vapors and gases that have important related characteristics. These are (1) pressure, (2) temperature, (3) volume, (4) total contained heat, and (5) entropy. These determine the characteristics of a vapor or gas of a refrigerant in any given state; and when any two of the five properties are known, the others may be obtained. Thus, if the pressure and temperature of a refrigerant are known, the three missing quantities (volume, total contained heat, and entropy) may be calculated or may be taken directly from suitable tables, as given in this book.

Example of Ammonia as Refrigerant.—The absolute pressure of ammonia vapor at a given condition is 170 pounds per square inch, and the temperature is 86.3° F. Now, if the temperature of this vapor is increased to 240° F. without changing the pressure, the other properties will be varied, as indicated in the following table:

	Case 1	Case 2
Pressure, pounds per square inch absolute...	170	170
Temperature, degrees Fahrenheit..........	86.3	240
Specific volume, cubic feet per pound.......	1.76	2.47
Total contained heat, B.t.u. per pound.....	631.6	730.9
Entropy................................	1.19	1.351

The properties of saturated ammonia vapor are shown in Table I, (pp. 386 to 389 inclusive in the Appendix). The properties of ammonia vapor are given with the temperature as the independent variable upon which the other properties depend. They have been determined by the U. S. Bureau of Standards.[1]

In this table, the first column contains the even degrees of temperature in Fahrenheit. The second column contains the *absolute pressure* in pounds per square inch. And the third column contains the *gage pressure* in pounds per square inch.[2]

The pressures in the third column, which are below atmospheric, are given in inches of mercury below the standard atmospheric pressure (29.92 inches of mercury). It will be noted that the pressure increases gradually as the temperature is

[1] *Bur. Standards, Bull.* 142, Table of Thermodynamic Properties of Ammonia.

[2] Gage pressure has been obtained from the absolute pressures in column 2 by subtracting a normal atmospheric pressure (14.7 pounds per square inch absolute) and dropping the last decimal place.

increased. The fourth column contains the volume of the saturated ammonia vapor in cubic feet per pound. The table shows that the specific volume increases rapidly as the temperature is lowered below 0° F. This fact is important in determining the size of the cylinder of a compressor, which is required to operate at very low temperatures. The fifth, sixth, and seventh columns show, respectively, the weight of the ammonia vapor in pounds per cubic foot, the total heat content of the liquid ammonia in B.t.u. per pound, and the total heat content of the ammonia vapor in B.t.u. per pound. These last two properties are useful for calculating the refrigerating effect of ammonia under different operating conditions. The latent heat of evaporation is shown by the eighth column and is given in B.t.u. per pound of ammonia. The latent heat of evaporation as shown in this last column represents the refrigerating effect which would be produced by the evaporation of 1 pound of liquid ammonia, provided that the liquid ammonia were initially at the saturation point. Under actual practical conditions, however, the temperature of liquid ammonia in a refrigerating system is invariably several degrees Fahrenheit above the saturation temperature, so that part of the latent heat of evaporation is unavoidably lost in cooling the remainder of the liquid ammonia to the temperature corresponding to the saturation point.

The ninth column gives the entropy of liquid ammonia in B.t.u. per pound per degree Fahrenheit absolute, and the tenth column gives the entropy of the ammonia vapor in the same units. It will be observed, in these last two columns, that the entropy of the liquid gradually increases as the temperature is increased, while the entropy of the ammonia *vapor* gradually decreases as the temperature is increased. It has already been explained that entropy is a mathematical ratio representing no physical condition of the substance and is used merely as a short-cut device in heat calculations.

Table II[1] is also a table of the properties of saturated ammonia, but, in this case, the absolute pressure in pounds per square inch is taken as the independent variable. The columns in this table are similar in Table I[1] with the exception that the eighth column has the heading Entropy of Evaporation. This column gives the entropy of evaporation expressed in B.t.u. per pound per degree Fahrenheit of *absolute temperature*.

[1] Tables are given in the Appendix, pp. 386 to 406.

Table III[1] gives the properties of saturated ammonia with the gage pressure as the independent variable. In all these tables, −40° F. has been adopted as a reference point for calculating the total heat contents. All heat contents above −40° F. are, therefore, in positive units. This use of a reference point eliminates minus quantities, which are sometimes awkward and lead to errors. In most of the calculations in refrigerating engineering, the temperatures are above −40° F., so that there is not likely to be occasion for the use of negative quantities for temperature conditions below −40° F.

Tables.—At the end of the book will be found tables of the properties of carbon dioxide and ammonia, giving, for certain temperatures and the corresponding pressures, the latent heats of evaporation and the specific volumes in cubic feet per pound. These tables are for 1 pound of vapor, and the pressures are in absolute units; that is, the pressures are measured above a perfect vacuum. The ordinary gage indicates pressures above the atmospheric pressure. The absolute pressure, then, is the gage pressure plus the atmospheric pressure. The normal or average atmospheric pressure at sea level is 14.7 pounds per square inch. The values given in tables for latent heat are based on 1 pound of vapor; if more or less than a pound is used, these values must be multiplied by the actual weight of the vapor of the refrigerant in order to find the actual latent heat.

Entropy Table.—The theoretical condition of the vapor of a refrigerant during and after compression can be conveniently shown by means of entropy[2] calculations. The use of entropy for the calculation of refrigeration problems may be simply illustrated by the following example, which refers to an ammonia compression system. In this case, the ammonia vapor is assumed to be at the so-called *standard conditions;* that is the condensing temperature in the condenser is 86° F. and in the evaporator, 5° F. By reference to the tables on page 400, the various properties of ammonia for the conditions of dry and

[1] Tables are given in the Appendix, pp. 386 to 406.

[2] *Entropy* is a mathematical ratio obtained by dividing the total amount of heat in 1 pound of a substance by the absolute temperature. Entropy will remain constant during an *adiabatic compression*, because, by definition, there is no heat transferred during a compression of this kind. The entropy of the gas or vapor of a refrigerant at the beginning of a compression stroke is the same as the entropy of the superheated gas or vapor at the end of an adiabatic compression.

saturated vapor before compression and superheated vapor after compression are given in the following items:

PROPERTIES OF SATURATED AMMONIA VAPOR BEFORE COMPRESSION AT 5° F.

Pressure of saturated ammonia vapor, pounds per
　square inch absolute............................　34.2
Specific volume per pound........................　8.15　　cubic feet
Total heat of saturated vapor per pound............　613.3　　B.t.u.
Entropy of dry saturated vapor....................　1.3252

PROPERTIES OF SATURATED AMMONIA VAPOR AFTER COMPRESSION AT 86° F.

Pressure of saturated vapor, pounds per square inch
　absolute......................................　170
Specific volume per pound........................　2.346　　cubic feet
Total heat of superheated vapor per pound..........　712.9　　B.t.u.
Temperature of saturated vapor, degrees Fahrenheit..　86
Temperature of superheated vapor, degrees Fahren-
　heit..　210
Degrees of superheat of vapor, degrees Fahrenheit....　124
Entropy of superheated vapor.....................　1.3252

Theoretical Horsepower Required for Adiabatic Compression of Ammonia.—In the above table, the total amount of heat in the ammonia vapor before compression is 613.3 B.t.u. per pound. After adiabatic compression, the total heat in the superheated ammonia vapor is 712.9 B.t.u. per pound. There is, therefore, an increase of 99.6 B.t.u. per pound of ammonia during the adiabatic compression.

There is a definite mechanical equivalent for every heat unit expended in compression or any other kind of work, the heat equivalent of 1 horsepower being 42.42 B.t.u. per minute.[1]

The expenditure of 99.6 B.t.u. per pound of circulated ammonia vapor is equivalent, therefore, to 99.6 ÷ 42.42 or 2.35 horse-power per pound of ammonia. In the refrigerating system which is the basis of the example on page 251, it is found that 0.42 pound of ammonia is required to be circulated per minute per ton of refrigeration, and, therefore, the horsepower required per unit of refrigeration is 2.35 times 0.42 or 0.99 horsepower per ton of refrigeration. In the calculation of this *theoretical horsepower*, it is assumed that the cylinder of the compressor is filled completely at each suction stroke of the piston.

Theoretical Horsepower Required for Compressors When Corrected for Volumetric Efficiency.—The horsepower required

---

[1] One horsepower is defined as 33,000 foot-pounds per minute; similarly, 1 B.t.u. has the mechanical equivalent of 778 foot-pounds. One horsepower, therefore, in heat units is 33,000 ÷ 778 or 42.42 B.t.u. per minute.

to drive a compressor per ton of refrigeration may be approximately calculated by correcting the theoretical horsepower requirement, as determined in the last paragraph for the volumetric efficiency, which, in the case of a *vertical single-acting compressor* with practically no clearance, may be assumed to be 84 per cent. The theoretical power requirement in the preceding example, for an ammonia compressor, as thus corrected, is 0.99 ÷ 0.84 or nearly 1.2 horsepower per ton of refrigeration.

On the other hand, if the compressor is *double-acting* or is a vertical type with about the same amount of clearance provided in a *horizontal compressor*, the volumetric efficiency would be about 80 per cent, and the actual indicated horsepower would probably be about 0.99 ÷ 0.80 or nearly 1.25 horsepower per ton of refrigeration.

Actual Horsepower Required to Drive Compressor.—There are various losses in the compressor, such as friction, windage, etc., that increase the power actually required to drive a compressor. These losses are about 20 per cent of the actual horsepower. In the two cases above, the actual horsepower required to drive the vertical single-acting compressor is 1.2 ÷ 0.80 or 1.5 horsepower per ton of refrigeration, and in the case of the double-acting compressor, it is 1.25 ÷ 0.80 or 1.6 horsepower per ton of refrigeration.

Kilowatts Required to Drive Compressor.—In cases where compressors are to be driven by electric motors, it is necessary to compute the electric power required. This transposition of power units can be made by dividing actual horsepower by 0.746. This may be done in the two cases of the ammonia compressors under discussion, (1) for the vertical single-acting compressor with small clearance, for which the electric power required is 1.44 × 0.746 or 1.07 kilowatts per ton of refrigeration; and (2) in the case of the double-acting compressor with normal clearance, for which the electric power required is 1.5 × 0.746 or 1.12 kilowatts per ton of refrigeration.

Pressure-total Heat Chart of Ammonia.—A useful chart for refrigerating calculations when ammonia is used has been prepared by the U. S. Bureau of Standards. In it, the absolute pressure of the ammonia is taken as the scale of ordinates, and the total heat in B.t.u. per pound is the scale of abscissas. A chart of this kind is shown in Fig. 185. A simplified diagram is shown in Fig. 152. For the diagram enclosed by heavy lines, the temperatures of saturated ammonia are taken at the so-called *standard* values of 86 and 5° F., respectively, in the condenser and the cooling coils of the evaporator. The intersections of the constant-temperature lines in the diagram with the *saturated-liquid* line (shown by the very heavy line on the chart) show on the scale of ordinates the *absolute* pressure in pounds per square inch corresponding to the temperature of the saturated condition of the ammonia vapor. Using this method of determining pressures, it will be found by interpolation that the constant-temperature line for the standard condition of 86° F. intersects the saturated-liquid line at approximately 169 pounds per square inch absolute pressure; and, similarly, that the 5° F.

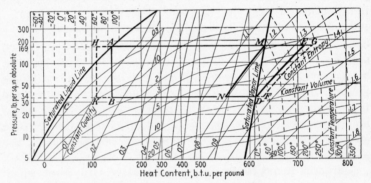

FIG. 152.—Simplified total heat content-pressure diagram for ammonia.

constant-temperature line intersects the saturated-liquid line at 34 pounds per square inch absolute pressure. The point corresponding to 86° F. on the saturated-liquid line is marked *A* in the figure. The first process to be represented in the figure is, of course, the expansion through the expansion valve from the higher to the lower pressure, that is, from 169 pounds per square inch absolute to 34 pounds per square inch absolute. Since the expansion is adiabatic, that is, without any change in the total amount of heat per pound of ammonia, a vertical line on the chart will represent the expansion. This vertical line is, of course, drawn through the point marked *A* to intersect the pressure line corresponding to the pressure in the cooling coils of the evaporator, that is, 34 pounds per square inch absolute. The intersection of the vertical line through *A* with the pressure line corresponding to 34 pounds per square inch absolute is marked *B*.[1] The diagram also shows curved lines marked "constant quality."[2] The point *B* is between the constant-quality line 0.15 and the line 0.20. By interpolation, the condition of the ammonia at the point *B*, as determined by the "quality" lines, is about 0.16, meaning that 16 per cent of the liquid ammonia has been evaporated when it passes through the expansion valve. In the cooling coils of the evaporator, the mixture of liquid ammonia and ammonia vapor absorbs heat from the substance being cooled in the refrigerator and, in thus taking up or absorbing heat, becomes completely vaporized, so that when it passes out of the cooling coils or evaporator, its condition is represented on the chart in Fig. 152 by the point *D*. It is interesting to calculate now from the chart how much heat has been lost by the ammonia mixture in being vaporized. The amount is, of course, approximately equivalent to the amount given up by the substance being cooled in the refrigerator. On the scale of abscissas, it will be found that the total heat of the ammonia mixture at the point *B* is 139 B.t.u. per pound and that the total heat at the point *D*, which represents total vaporization of ammonia, is 613 B.t.u. per pound. The heat transfer in the cooling coils of the evaporator during the vaporization of the ammonia mixture from the quality of 0.16 to complete vaporization is 613 − 139 or 474 B.t.u. per pound of ammonia.

In the next step of the compression refrigerating cycle, the ammonia vapor is taken from the cooling coils of the evaporator through the suction pipe into the cylinder of the compressor where the ammonia vapor is compressed approximately adiabatically, without much gain or loss of heat to the higher pressure of the system or 169 pounds per square inch absolute. The line on the chart representing this adiabatic compression must, of course, be parallel to the constant-entropy lines shown in the

---

[1] It will be noticed that the point *B* is on a horizontal line through the point where the 5° F. constant temperature line intersects the saturated liquid line is marked *C*.

[2] If the horizontal line through the point *B* is extended to the point *D* on the saturated vapor line, the condition of the ammonia as represented by the point *D* will be shown by the constant quality lines to be 1.00 meaning that at this point, the ammonia is 100 per cent vaporized. It is interesting to note that the quality of the ammonia at any point in a chart of this kind can be determined as at *B*, by measuring the distances *CD* and *CB* and then calculating the ratio, or *CB* ÷ *CD* is the quality of the ammonia.

right-hand portion of the chart and is represented by the line *DE*. The point *E* is naturally found at the intersection of the constant-entropy line through *D* with a horizontal constant-pressure line through the point *A*. The point *E* represents the condition of the ammonia vapor after being compressed adiabatically in the compressor. The heat equivalent of the work done in the compressor per pound of ammonia vapor handled is, of course, the difference between the total heats measured on the scale of abscissas at the points *D* and *E*. These values are, respectively, 613 and 713, the difference being 100 B.t.u. per pound of ammonia (see pages 89 and 246).

The condition of the ammonia vapor, as represented by any points in that portion of the chart to the right of the saturated-vapor line, is superheated, meaning the temperature is higher than the saturation temperature corresponding to the pressure. In Fig. 152, the point *D* is on the saturated-vapor line indicating that its condition is dry and saturated. The point *E* is in the region to the right of the saturated-vapor line and is, therefore, *superheated*. The amount of superheat is indicated by the lines of constant temperature, which show that at the point *E* the superheat is a little more than 210° F.

In the compression system, after the superheated vapor is discharged from the compressor it passes into the condenser, where heat is removed by cold water used for cooling. In this cooling process, all the ammonia vapor is condensed; in other words, the ammonia vapor changes from the superheated condition at the point *E* in the chart to the condition at *A* at the same pressure (169 pounds per square inch absolute), where it is all liquid. The heat removed in the condenser from the ammonia vapor is 713 − 139 or 574 B.t.u. per pound of ammonia.

The lines *AB*, *BD*, *DE*, and *EA* represent, as laid out in Fig. 152, the *dry-compression system* of refrigeration for the so-called *standard conditions* of 86° F. for the upper and 5° F. for the lower limit of temperature of the ammonia.

Ammonia Chart.—Another kind of ammonia chart, which was also prepared by the Bureau of Standards in Washington, is shown in Fig. 185. It shows graphically the various heat quantities, volumes, pressures, and temperatures of ammonia. These properties may be read from the chart with sufficient accuracy for all practical purposes. The ordinates of the chart are laid off in proportion to the *logarithms* of the pressures. The abscissas are heat units in B.t.u. per pound above a "reference point," which is − 40° F. A curve called the *saturated-liquid line* is shown in the chart extending from left to right, beginning at the lower left-hand corner. Extending across the right-hand side of the chart is the *saturated-vapor line*. The part of the chart to the left of the *saturated-vapor line* represents mixtures of saturated vapor and liquid ammonia, while the points on the saturated-vapor line represent saturated-ammonia vapor, which contains no liquid. The region between the saturated-liquid line and the saturated-vapor line represents mixtures of liquid ammonia and vapor of varying quality. In the space near the saturated-liquid line, the mixtures are almost entirely liquid ammonia; and in the space near the saturated-vapor line, the mixtures are almost entirely ammonia vapor. Points having the same percentages of liquid ammonia in a liquid and vapor mixture are shown, by lines marked "constant quality," in the space between the saturated-liquid line and the saturated-vapor line.

The region in the diagram to the right of the saturated-vapor line represents *superheated* ammonia vapor. Small amounts of superheat are near the saturated-vapor line, and, as the amount of superheat in the ammonia vapor increases, the space from this line increases toward the right. The chart shows, also, constant-volume, constant-entropy, and constant-temperature lines.

Pressure-total Heat Chart to Calculate Amount of Refrigerant Circulated.—The amount by weight of refrigerant that must be circulated in an ammonia refrigerating system per ton or refrigeration for the standard conditions of temperature (86 and 5° F.) can be calculated from the data of the preceding paragraphs. The amount of heat removed from the substance in the refrigerator by the refrigerant as it condenses in the cooling coils of the evaporator for these temperature conditions was found to be 474 B.t.u. per pound of ammonia. One ton of refrigeration has a cooling effect at the rate of 200 B.t.u. per minute. The amount of refrigerant that must be circulated per minute per ton of refrigeration at these standard conditions is, therefore, 200 ÷ 474 or 0.42 pound.

Calculation of Theoretical Piston Displacements and Horsepower.—In the preceding calculation, it was found that 0.42 pound per minute of refrigerant must be circulated in an ammonia system per ton of refrigeration for standard temperature conditions. At the absolute pressure of 34.3 pounds per square inch in the evaporator, the volume of 1 pound of dry saturated ammonia vapor, as read at the point *D*, in Fig. 152, is approximately 8 cubic feet per pound. The volume of refrigerant which is now drawn into the compressor cylinder is, therefore, 8 × 0.42 or 3.36 cubic feet per minute. If the volumetric efficiency were 100 per cent, this volume of ammonia vapor would be equivalent to the piston displacement per minute. On the other hand, if the volumetric efficiency of the compressor is, say, 80 per cent, the actual displacement of the cylinder of the ammonia compressor is 3.36 ÷ 0.80 or 4.2 cubic feet per minute.

The theoretical power required to drive an ammonia compressor when 0.42 pound of ammonia vapor is circulated per minute is found by the method of first computing the heat unit (B.t.u.) equivalent to the work done in compression per pound of ammonia vapor. For the standard conditions of the preceding calculations, it was found that 100 *B.t.u. per pound of refrigerant were required for compression.* In the case now being considered, the weight of refrigerant circulated is 0.42 pound, so that the heat equivalent of the work done per minute is 100 × 0.42 pound or 42 B.t.u. per minute; and this can be expressed in terms of theoretical horsepower by remembering that 42.42 B.t.u. per minute are equivalent to 1 horsepower (see p. 246). The theoretical horsepower required to drive the ammonia compressor operating under the so-called *standard* conditions of temperature is, then, 100 × 0.42 ÷ 42.42, or approximately 1 horsepower.

Theoretical Coefficient of Performance.—The theoretical coefficient of performance is the rate at which heat is absorbed by the refrigerant in the cooling coils of the evaporator to the heat equivalent of the work done by the compressor in the same time. The theoretical amount of heat resulting from adiabatic compression per ton of refrigeration per minute is 100 × 0.42 B.t.u. The heat equivalent of 1 ton of refrigeration is 200 B.t.u. per minute. The coefficient of performance is, therefore, 200 ÷ (100 × 0.42) or 4.77.

Pressure-total Heat Chart for Superheating and Aftercooling.—The pressure-total heat chart, as used in Fig. 152, shows a cycle of refrigeration for dry compression with no superheating or aftercooling. The same chart can be used to show, also, refrigerating cycles in which there is superheating of the ammonia vapor between the cooling coils of the evaporator and the suction valve of the compressor and cycles in which the liquid ammonia from the condenser is aftercooled before expansion takes place in the expansion valve.

Superheating of the ammonia vapor which comes from the cooling coils of the evaporator before it reaches the suction side of the compressor makes some modification of the simple refrigerating diagram as shown in Fig. 152. The dotted lines at the right-hand side of the figure show the modification resulting from superheating the ammonia vapor before it enters the suction side of the compressor. These dotted lines join the points A, B, F, and G. In this "vapor mixture" region, the line AB represents, as before, a constant heat line of the ammonia through the expansion valve; the line BD represents the evaporation of the ammonia liquid in the cooling coils of the evaporator as it absorbs heat from the substance cooled in the refrigerator; the line DF represents the heat added to the dry and saturated ammonia vapor so that, because of superheating, its temperature is above 5° F.; the line FG indicates the adiabatic compression of the superheated ammonia vapor in the compressor; the line GA shows the loss of heat by the ammonia vapor cooling in the condenser, reducing the temperature of the superheated ammonia vapor from 240° F. to a completely liquefied state at the point A.

Aftercooling is illustrated in the same figure by the addition of the dotted lines AH, HK, and KB to the refrigerating cycle. The line AH shows the cooling (aftercooling) of the *liquid ammonia* at the pressure corresponding to the standard temperature of 86° F. at which it leaves the condenser to the temperature of 60° F. (represented by point H). Constant heat expansion through the expansion valve is shown by the vertical line drawn through H to intersect the extension of the line BD at the point K.

The refrigerating cycle for dry compression with no superheating of the ammonia vapor as it leaves the compressor, but with aftercooling by which the temperature of the liquid ammonia is reduced from 86 to 60° F., is shown by the lines joining the points H, K, D, E, and H.

Wet-compression Cycle.—When enough liquid ammonia is taken into the compressor through the suction pipe to absorb all the heat generated by the compression of the ammonia vapor, the refrigerating cycle is called *wet compression*. *Theoretically*, enough liquid ammonia should be mixed with the ammonia vapor which enters the compressor so that the latter will be dry and saturated at the end of compression. This means that if, for example, the refrigerating cycle begins at the point A (Fig. 152), with liquid ammonia (without aftercooling), and has constant heat expansion along the vertical line from A to B and further evaporation at constant pressure due to the absorption of heat along the horizontal line through B, the cycle of refrigeration must pass through the point M located on the horizontal line through A, in order that the ammonia vapor may be dry and saturated at the end of the adiabatic compression. Now, if the end of the adiabatic compression is at M, the beginning of the compression must be at some point on the horizontal line through B. *Adiabatic compression* means, of course, a compression that is represented on a line of constant entropy. Such a line is shown by MN.

A cycle of wet compression may be shown by the lines joining the points A, B, M, and N, where the evaporation in the cooling coils of the evaporator is indicated by BN; adiabatic compression in the compressor, by NM; and condensation of the ammonia vapor in the condenser, by MA; so that the ammonia vapor will be dry and saturated at the end of the compression. For practical reasons, however, it is not desirable in a wet compression system to have so much liquid ammonia in the mixture as would be required for this theoretical condition, so that, as a general rule in practical work, the ammonia vapor at the end of compression will be slightly superheated at the end of compression instead of being dry and saturated, a practice considered much better. All the refrigerating cycles which have been illustrated on the pressure-total heat diagram have been based on the *standard* conditions of operating pressures corresponding to the saturation temperatures of 86° F. in the condenser and 5° F. in the cooling coil of the evaporator. Methods of representation on such charts would be similar, however, for other temperature or pressure conditions.

CHAPTER VIII

REFRIGERATION ECONOMICS AND PLANT TESTING

Economics in Refrigeration.—This chapter is devoted to the application of the general principles that give the most economical operation of refrigerating plants. The study must include a comparison of actual operating results with ideal performance. Obviously, it is the duty of those in charge of refrigerating plants to produce the maximum amount of refrigeration with a minimum expenditure of labor, materials, and mechanical or electrical energy. In the final analysis, the economics of any engineering process is concerned with the conditions of value, price, cost, and profit.[1]

Refrigeration Costs.—A number of factors must be considered in estimates of the cost of refrigeration, because the estimates will depend on such items as the geographical location; the cost of fuel, labor, and supplies; the size of the plant; and the efficiency of the mechanical equipment. These general items may be divided into classifications under the general headings of

a. Fixed Charges.—These are independent of the refrigeration output of the plant and go on whether or not the plant is operated.

b. Operating Expenses.—These expenses depend on the amount of output; in other words, they increase, in some measure, in proportion to the increase in the tons of refrigeration of the plant.

Somewhat in detail, the classifications may be tabulated as follows:

Fixed Charges	Operating Expenses
Interest	Power
Depreciation	Labor
Repairs	Ammonia or other refrigerant
Taxes	Oil
Insurance	General supplies
Incidentals	

[1] *Value* is the exchangeable worth of property or service. *Price* is the money given for property or service. *Cost* is the actual money expended for property or service. It includes not only the price paid at the time a property is acquired but also the other items of expenditure which are chargeable in determining the present value of the property. Profit is the difference between the selling price and the cost.

Fixed charges and operating expenses will vary considerably with the operating conditions. By keeping the mechanical equipment of the plant in good condition, its depreciation may be reduced a great deal, and, at the same time, there will be a saving in the operating expenses for such items as repairs, maintenance, etc. A refrigerating plant which is operated on a commercial basis should, of course, have sufficient profits for the depreciation charges, so that when the equipment is no longer serviceable, it may be replaced with new machinery.

Fixed charges do not vary a great deal in different parts of the country, except, of course, that the total of interest charges is very much larger where expensive land must be purchased than where relatively cheap land is available. Interest and other fixed charges will be about as follows:

Fixed Charges	Per Cent
Interest	6 to 7
Depreciation	5 to 6
Repairs	3 to 5
Taxes and insurance	2 to 4
Total	16 to 22

It will be noted that the total amount of interest and other fixed charges varies from 16 to 22 per cent of the original investment, which includes the total cost of the plant and all the items of labor, material, interest, engineering, and overhead charges during construction. In the sample calculations that follow, the *average total* fixed charge of 19 per cent will be used for purposes of comparison.

Cost of Power.—Until recent years, nearly all refrigerating plants were operated by steam engines, simple non-condensing, slow-speed Corliss engines being used for plants having capacities of 20 to 200 tons of refrigeration per day. Larger plants having capacities up to 1,000 tons of refrigeration per day are operated with compound condensing steam engines which receive their steam from boilers equipped with automatic stokers. In some modern plants, electric motors are used to drive the mechanical equipment, the electricity being purchased from a company distributing and selling electric power.

Small refrigerating plants operated by steam will produce only about 10 tons of refrigeration per ton of coal, while some of the largest plants will produce about twice as much per ton. The cost of coal varies, of course, a great deal with the location of the plant, particularly as the distance varies for the transportation of the coal from the mines. The cost of electric current for refrigerating plants is not nearly so variable as that of steam power. The average rate charged by large electric companies for electric current in ice-making and refrigerating plants varies from 0.7 cent to 1.4 cents per kilowatt-hour. The average is, therefore, approximately 1 cent per kilowatt-hour.

Comparative Manufacturing Costs.—The various manufacturing costs, including interest and other fixed charges, will be calculated for an ice-making plant operating 7 months in the year at full load and having a capacity of 100 tons of ice per day. The plant is operated by electric motors, and its total cost is $100,000.

The ratio of the actual yearly output of a refrigerating plant to its full load is called the *yearly load factor*. This is simply the ratio of the actual output of the plant during the year to the total output which the plant would have if operated at its full-load capacity throughout the year, or for 365 days of 24 hours each (8,760 hours). In the case of the plant to be studied, there is full-load operation for 7 months or 213 days in the year, so that the yearly load factor is 213 ÷ 365, which is 0.584 or 58.4 per cent.

Interest and Other Fixed Charges.—Assuming that the average fixed charges for this plant are 19 per cent, these charges for a $100,000 plant are $19,000 per year, or approximately $52 per day.

Cost of Electric Current for Plant.—An economically operated ice-making plant of 100 tons capacity will use about 53 kilowatt-hours per day per ton of ice. A smaller plant of about 50 tons of ice-making capacity will use about 55 kilowatt-hours per ton, and plants of over 500 tons of ice-making capacity will use about 51 kilowatt-hours per ton of ice. The average price to be paid by a 100-ton refrigerating plant to large electric companies is about 1 cent per kilowatt-hour. Assuming the power consumption to be 53 kilowatt-hours per ton of ice per day, the cost of electric current for the plant is 100 × 53 × 0.01 or $53 per day. The expense for incidental items such as ammonia, oil, and supplies is obtained from the following table at about $15 per day:

Cost of Incidental Items Including Ammonia, Oil, and Supplies

Ice-making Capacity per Day, Tons	Incidental Costs, Dollars per Day
10	3
50	9
100	15
200	23
500	43

The cost of labor in a refrigerating plant is likely to vary considerably. For example, in a plant where the labor turnover is not large from year to year, and where there are a number of employees who have grown up in the business, the labor charge is likely to be greater than in a company which has been operated for only a few years. Average labor charges in an economically operated plant may be taken from the following table:

Cost of Labor in Ice-making Plants

Ice-making Capacity per Day, Tons	Cost of Labor, Dollars per Day
10	20
50	30
100	45
200	65
500	125

The total cost of operation, including interest and other fixed charges, is 52 + \$53 + \$15 + \$45 or \$165 per day. The total manufacturing charges including interest of the plant for the whole period of annual operation is 213 times \$165 or \$35,145. There will necessarily be some charge for the labor of keeping the plant in repair during the remainder of the year when it is not operating. It may be assumed that the same total labor expenses per day will be incurred during the remainder of the year and that the expenses for labor in addition to the interest charge of \$52 per day will be additional daily expense of \$52 + \$45 or \$97. The total additional expense for the 152 days when the plant is not operating is 152 times \$97 or \$14,744. The total yearly expense including the labor and interest charges during the time the plant is shut down is, therefore, \$35,145 + \$14,744 or \$49,889.

The total amount of ice manufactured during 213 days of operation at the rate of 100 tons per day is 21,300 tons, so that the operating and fixed charge per ton of ice is, therefore, \$49,889 ÷

21,300 or \$2.34 per ton of ice. W. H. Motz has calculated the total cost of manufacturing ice by a method similar to the one given in the preceding example and has obtained the data given in the following table:

TOTAL COST OF MANUFACTURING ICE AVERAGE ELECTRICALLY OPERATED PLANT, 60 PER CENT YEARLY LOAD FACTOR

Ice-making Capacity per Day, Tons	Cost per Ton of Ice, Dollars
10	4.00
50	2.50
100	2.25
200	1.85
500	1.60

The cost of making ice in a small steam-driven plant is considerably greater than the costs given in the above table for electrically operated plants. For example, the cost of making 1 ton of ice in a plant having a capacity of 10 tons of ice is about \$6 per ton. The considerably increased cost of the engine-operated plant over the one which is electrically operated is due to the greater cost of labor. Ice can probably be made more cheaply in a small plant operated by an oil engine rather than a steam engine except, of course, where coal is unusually cheap. It is stated that in many 500-ton refrigerating plants, a ton of "raw water" ice can be made for \$1 per ton.

Yearly Load Factor.—The effect of yearly load factor on the cost of making ice in a 100-ton electrically operated plant is shown in the following table:

EFFECT OF YEARLY LOAD FACTOR ON COST OF MAKING ICE

Yearly Load Factor, Per Cent	Cost per Ton of Ice, Dollars
50	2.60
60	2.25
70	1.90
80	1.75
90	1.65
100	1.60

The method of calculation, as indicated in the preceding example and the data given in the tables, must necessarily be used with judgment, as the values which are given are not intended to be exact and will not apply accurately in all cases. The object has been to show the general relation between the factors in calculations of this kind.   Every engineer must study his plant, particularly as to costs of power, labor, and yearly load factor, in order to determine the actual costs.

The Cost of Harvesting Natural Ice.—The average cost of cutting thick ice on a pond or river is about 25 cents per ton, and the average cost of loading, hauling, and packing is about $1.25 per ton, when the ice house is near the pond or river.   When it is at a considerable distance from the pond or river, the cost of hauling is greatly increased, so that the total cost of cutting, loading, hauling, and storing natural ice is, in many cases, as much as from $3 to $4 per ton.

Instruments for Refrigeration-plant Testing.—Thermometers and pressure gages must be installed at points where it is desirable to determine the conditions of pressures and temperatures. These instruments are very helpful in maintaining the system in proper operation.   Gage glasses should be provided at all points of the system where it is desirable to ascertain the level of the working liquids.   Suitable connections for testing aqua ammonia or anhydrous liquid into the system should be provided. Likewise, suitable connections should be provided for withdrawing strong and weak liquor for testing purposes.

Use of the Indicator.—In making a test on a compressor, it is necessary to determine the amount of power required to compress the ammonia vapor.   At the same time, it is often necessary to find the amount of power developed in the cylinder of the steam or gas engine which drives the compressor.   These measurements are most conveniently obtained with an instrument called an *indicator*, which gives also a means of finding out the action of the compressor valves and the manner in which the vapor of the refrigerant is being compressed.   The indicator serves as a means to draw on a card of paper attached to the instrument a diagram representing the pressure in the cylinder for every position of the piston for both the compression and suction strokes.   Such an indicator diagram shows a complete record of what takes place in the cylinder for one or more revolutions.

Figure 153 shows the construction of an outside spring indicator.   It consists of a cylinder *C* containing a nicely fitted piston *B*, which is free to move up and down without appreciable friction.   To the piston is connected a piston rod *R* having a double coil spring *S* connected to its upper end.   The piston rod is also connected to the pencil mechanism, which consists of levers and a pencil arm L the right-hand end of which carries a pencil or a brass stylus, moving vertically parallel to the axis of the indicator drum D. The drum is given a to-and-fro rotary motion, coincident with, and bearing a constant ratio to, the motion of the piston of the engine or compressor. It is moved in one direction by means of a cord attached indirectly to the crosshead of the engine and wound around the base of the drum. Inside the drum is a coil spring, which is wound up when the cord

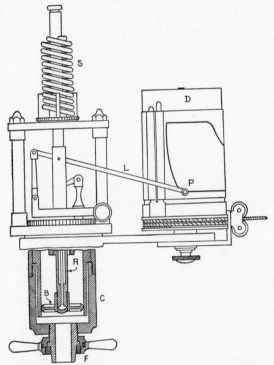

Fig. 153.—Typical indicator for testing ammonia compressors.

is pulled out and, in unwinding, when the pull on the cord is removed, turns the drum in the opposite direction. The cylinder C is connected to the clearance space of the compressor cylinder by means of a union F and a short piece of pipe containing an indicator cock. The varying pressure of the ammonia vapor in the cylinder of the compressor acts against the underside of the piston of the indicator and pushes it up against the action of the spring S.

The springs used with indicators are made in different sizes. In order to obtain a correct diagram, the movement of the pencil point must exactly represent a certain pressure. Springs are marked according to the movement of the pencil point; *i.e.*, a No. 60 spring will produce a pencil movement of 1 inch when a pressure of 60 pounds per square inch acts against the piston. A pressure of 90 pounds per square inch will cause a pencil movement of $1\frac{1}{2}$ inches.

The back-and-forth motion of the indicator drum D is in unison with the motion of the piston of the compressor. Also, the pencil point P moves up and down with the varying pressure in the cylinder of the compressor. The combining of these two motions gives the indicator diagram traced by the pencil P, which shows what is taking place inside the cylinder of the compressor. The diagram traced by the pencil is an area representing the work being developed in the cylinder of the compressor. This area represents work, because the pressure exerted on the piston varies with that in the compressor cylinder, and the back-and-forth motion of the drum is proportional to the piston travel. When using an indicator attached to the cylinder of a steam engine, the indicated horsepower developed by the engine can be calculated. This is the power which is being developed in the cylinder of the steam engine.

Indicator Diagram.—An indicator diagram obtained from an ammonia compressor is shown in Fig. 154. The length of the diagram A represents the stroke of the compressor according to some scale. At the end of the suction stroke or the point E, the cylinder is filled with ammonia vapor; when the piston of the compressor starts on its compression stroke, the ammonia vapor in the cylinder is compressed along the line EG. At the point G, the ammonia vapor has been compressed above the pressure which opens the discharge valves and is then forced out of the cylinder during the remainder of the stroke GJ.

As already mentioned, the ammonia vapor is compressed somewhat above the discharge pressure before the discharge valve opens, due to the fact that the discharge valve is conical in shape and that the side next to the discharge chamber is somewhat larger than the side next to the cylinder. The discharge valve is forced to its seat by the tension of a spring and must be opened against this spring but only when the pressure is great enough.

In Fig. 154, the ammonia vapor is compressed along the line *EF*, which is for dry compression. If the compressor is operating with wet compression, the ammonia vapor would be compressed along the line *EH*. Since the area of an indicator diagram represents work expended in compressing the ammonia vapor, it can be seen that more work is required to compress the ammonia vapor for dry than for wet compression.

After the compressed vapor is forced out of the cylinder, the discharge valve closes, and the piston starts back on its suction stroke. At the beginning of the suction stroke, there is left in the clearance space some ammonia vapor which expands along the line *JM* until the pressure falls slightly below the suction

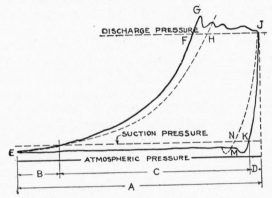

Fig. 154.—Typical indicator diagram of ammonia compressor.

pressure. The suction valve opens at the point *M*, and new vapor is drawn into the cylinder during the remaining portion of the suction stroke *ME*. The dip in the reexpansion line *JK* is due to the fact that the inner face of the suction valve is larger than the outer face and, also, because of the tension of the spring on the valve stem.

As seen from Fig. 154, the piston must move a distance *B* on the compression stroke before the pressure rises above the suction pressure. Also, the piston must move a distance *D* on the suction stroke before the ammonia vapor left in the clearance space expands to the suction pressure. It can now be seen that, instead of a cylinder full of new vapor being drawn in during each suction stroke, there is only a volume equal to *C*, measured at the suction pressure. The actual capacity of the compressor is, then, only *C*, while the theoretical capacity is the full piston displacement

A. The loss of capacity *B* is due to the action of the suction valve, while that of *D* is due to the clearance space. If the clearance space had been larger, the reexpansion line would have been along some line, as *JN*. The effect of a larger clearance space would be to reduce the actual capacity of the compressor still more. The ratio of the length *C* on the diagram to the length *A*, or $C \div A$, is called the apparent *volumetric efficiency* of the compressor. This is the ratio which the actual useful volume of vapor taken into the cylinder bears to the full piston displacement. The heavy, full lines are drawn by the indicator and also the atmospheric line. The latter, representing the atmospheric pressure, is drawn by placing the pencil to the indicator card after the indicator cock is closed. It is useful as a reference line by which other pressures may be measured.

Mean Effective Pressure.—To find the horsepower required to compress the ammonia, it will be necessary to obtain the

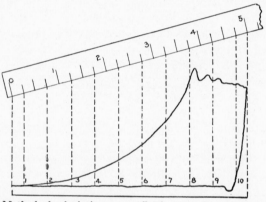

Fig. 155.—Method of calculating mean effective pressure of indicator diagram.

average pressure during a complete revolution of the compressor. This is obtained from the indicator diagram. The average pressure is equal to the average height of the diagram between the suction line and the compression and discharge lines times the scale of the spring. The average pressure is called the *mean effective pressure (or m.e.p.)*. The mean effective pressure can be found from the indicator diagram by dividing it into 10 equal parts and measuring the height of the diagram at these divisions. The sum of these different heights divided by 10 gives the mean height. This value multiplied by the scale of the spring gives the mean effective pressure. A very easy way to divide the diagram into 10 equal parts is shown in Fig. 155. To do this, draw two lines perpendicular to the atmospheric line and through the extreme points of the diagram. Now lay an ordinary rule in such a position that the zero mark is on the left-hand perpendicular line. Place the 5-inch mark on the perpendicular at the right-hand end of the diagram. From the first ¼-inch mark, draw through the diagram a perpendicular line to the atmospheric line, and draw lines from each ¾- and ¼-inch mark to the 5-inch mark. The reason for dividing the diagram at the ¼-inch mark is to prevent the first and last divisions from coming at the ends of the diagram, for here the pressure is varying rapidly.

Another way of obtaining the mean effective pressure is by the use of a planimeter, an instrument which measures an area directly in square inches. Obtain the area of the indicator diagram and divide this area by the length of the diagram in inches, giving the mean height in inches, which, multiplied by the scale of the spring, gives the mean effective pressure.

Indicated Horsepower.—The indicated horsepower (or i.h.p.) can be found from the following formula:

$$\text{Indicated horsepower} = \frac{p \times l \times a \times n}{33,000}$$

where p = mean effective pressure, pounds per square inch
l = length of the stroke, feet
a = area of the piston, square inches
n = number of revolutions per minute

When using the above formula, the m. e. p. is measured from the indicator diagram as obtained from one end of the cylinder. Where the compressor is double-acting, a diagram should be taken for each end. The indicated horsepower should be calculated for each end independently, and the total indicated horsepower of the compressor is obtained by adding these values.

With double-acting compressors, the entire piston area of the crank end is not subjected to the full pressure, because the piston rod reduces the effective area.

To illustrate the method of calculating the indicated horsepower of a compressor, suppose the combined heights of the 10 divisions of the indicator diagram to be 7.0 inches, and the diagram to have been drawn with a No. 80 spring. The average height of the diagram is $7.0 \div 10$ or 0.70 inches. The mean effective pressure is, then, 0.7×80 or 56 pound per square inch. Suppose that the compressor cylinder has a diameter of 10 inches, length of stroke 24 inches, and speed 80 revolutions per minute.

The area of the piston is $0.785 \times 10^2 = 78.5$ square inches, and the length of the strike is $24 \div 12 = 2$ feet.

$$\text{The indicated horsepower} = \frac{p \times l \times a \times n}{33,000}$$

$$= \frac{56 \times 2 \times 78.5 \times 80}{33,000} = 21.7 \text{ horsepower}$$

To find the indicated horsepower of the steam engine which drives the compressor, it is necessary to proceed exactly in the same manner as for obtaining the horsepower of the compressor. The indicated horsepower of the steam engine will always be larger than the indicated horsepower obtained from the compressor. This is due to the fact that in transferring energy from the engine to the compressor there is a loss, as the friction of the moving parts of the engine and the compressor must be overcome. The ratio of the indicated horsepower of the compressor to the indicated horsepower of the steam engine is called the overall *mechanical efficiency* and is

$$\text{Mechanical efficiency} = \frac{\text{indicated horsepower of compressor}}{\text{indicated horsepower of engine}}.$$

Dimensions and Capacity of Compressor and Engine.—Because the indicated horsepower developed by the steam engine is greater than that developed by the compressor, the size of the steam engine is somewhat larger than the size of the compressor. Also, it often happens that the ammonia vapor is compressed to a higher pressure than the steam pressure at the throttle of the engine. This would naturally require a smaller compressor cylinder.

Referring to the table (p. 414) showing the dimensions of compressors, it will be found that the diameter of the compressor cylinder is usually slightly less than the diameter of the engine cylinder; and the stroke of the compressor is much less than the stroke of the engine. In large machines, the speed of the compressor will be the same as that of the engine, for the compressor is directly connected with the engine. The mean effective pressure of the compressor can be about the same as or even greater than the mean effective pressure of the engine, but the product of the piston area and the length of stroke of the compressor will be less than those of the engine; for, as has been shown, the indicated horsepower of the compressor is less than the indicated horsepower of the steam engine.

Refrigerating machines of the horizontal type have the engine connected to one end of the shaft and the other end connected to the compressor. A flywheel is placed between the two cranks. Because the stroke of the compressor is less than the stroke of the engine, the crank of the compressor is made shorter than the crank of the engine. There is an unfavorable distribution of the pressures in the two cylinders. The steam engine has a maximum pressure which occurs at the beginning of the stroke, whereas the compressor has a maximum pressure at the end of the stroke. This is unfavorable, since the maximum steam pressure occurs at a time when it is least needed. In order partly to overcome this difficulty, the cranks of the compressor and of the engine are generally set 90 degrees apart. Another way to produce the same result is to place the compressor cylinder in a vertical position and the steam-engine cylinder in a horizontal position. In this case, both compressor and engine act on the same crank. A flywheel is added to produce a smoothly running machine. The former stores up energy when the steam pressure is highest and returns it again when the pressure in the compressor is greatest.

TABLE XII.—DIMENSIONS AND CAPACITIES OF AMMONIA COMPRESSORS AND STEAM ENGINES

Ammonia compressor (double-acting)					Steam engine	
Refrigerating capacity, tons in 24 hours	Diameter of cylinder, inches	Stroke, inches	Horse-power required	Revolutions per minute	Diameter of cylinder, inches	Stroke, inches
5	5⅞	12⅝	10	75	9	14
15	8¼	15	23	70	11	16
20	9½	15	30	70	10	30
50	12¹³⁄₁₆	21¼	63	66	16	36
75	14	30	94	60	18	42
100	18½	27⁹⁄₁₆	125	50	22	42

Testing Refrigerating Plants.—It is sometimes desired to test a refrigerating plant in order to determine its capacity or efficiency under certain operating conditions. It is, therefore, useful to know how to make such tests and how to work out results from the data or readings obtained during the test. In order to show how this is done, data are given from a typical test of a refrigerating plant with a double-acting compressor.

The following is a brief description of the refrigerating system and of the conditions under which the tests were made: they were made with a double-acting, horizontal compressor directly connected to a horizontal Corliss engine, the plant having a rated refrigerating capacity of 15 tons in 24 hours. The steam cylinder was 9 inches in diameter and had a 24-inch stroke, and the piston rod was 1.68 inches in diameter. The ammonia cylinder was 8 inches in diameter and had a 16-inch stroke. The diameter of the piston rod was 1.68 inches. The ammonia condenser had two vertical tiers of 8 pipes each and was 17 feet in length. The condenser was a double-pipe type, the outer pipe being 2 and the inner pipe being 1¼ inches in diameter. The brine cooler was made of double pipes and had one vertical tier of 15 pipes 17 feet long. The inner or brine pipe was 2, whereas the outer pipe was 3 inches in diameter. The cooling surface was approximately 158 square feet. The ammonia leaving the compressor passed to the oil trap, then to the condenser, and from the condenser to the liquid receiver; from the liquid receiver, it passed to the brine cooler and again returned to the compressor. Between the liquid receiver and the brine cooler, there were installed two weighing drums for the purpose of weighing the ammonia, the latter being discharged from one drum during the time that the second drum was being filled. These drum rested upon scales, so that the ammonia could be weighed, and valves were provided, so that the drums could be alternately filled with ammonia.

The brine was pumped through the brine cooler by means of a centrifugal pump provided with a bypass, so that the quantity of brine passing through could be regulated. From the brine cooler, it passed through a double-pipe reheater and, passing through the inner pipe, was heated by steam introduced between the inner and the outer pipes. By regulating the amount of steam, the temperature at which the brine entered the brine cooler could be kept constant. From the reheater, the brine passed to a tank from which it was allowed to flow into two measuring tanks. These were graduated to pounds at a temperature of 70° F. and for brine having 25 per cent calcium chloride. From these tanks, the brine was again pumped through the brine cooler by means of the brine pump, so that the operation was continuous. The condensing water was taken from the mains and, after passing through the ammonia condenser, was allowed to flow into two graduated tanks, one of which could be filled while the other was being emptied, so that the weight of the cooling water could be determined. During the time of the tests, indicator diagrams were taken from the steam cylinder and also, from the compressor at 10-minute intervals. The exhaust from the engine was condensed and weighed. Pressures of ammonia and of steam were taken at regular intervals by means of gages which had previously been tested. Thermometer wells were inserted in the different pipes for the purpose of determining the temperature of the ammonia, brine, and cooling water. Knowing the differences of temperature and the amount of brine, ammonia, and water used per hour, the transfer of heat in the different parts of the system could be determined.

Method of Making the Tests.—The tests were two in number, a different back pressure being used in each. Each test was made in the following manner: the engine and compressor were started and allowed to operate at the pressure decided upon until the conditions became constant. After all temperatures became constant, the test was started. All temperature readings and indicator cards from engine and compressor were taken at 10-minute intervals. The ammonia, brine, condensing water, and condensed steam were collected and weighed on scales or measured in graduated tanks, as before described. The tests proper were of from 1 to 2 hours' duration.

TEST OF DOUBLE-ACTING 15-TON REFRIGERATING PLANT

Item
1. Duration of test, hours.. 2
2. Suction pressure (by gage), pounds per square inch.................. 21
3. Condenser pressure (by gage), pounds per square inch............... 117.1
4. Revolutions per minute... 70.7
5. Temperature of brine, inlet, degrees Fahrenheit.................... 47.0
6. Temperature of brine, outlet, degrees Fahrenheit.................. 17.9
7. Difference, inlet and outlet temperature, degrees Fahrenheit.......... 29.1
8. Specific heat of brine, degrees Fahrenheit......................... 0.757
9. Weight of brine circulated, pounds............................... 16,300
10. Weight of brine circulated per hour, pounds...................... 8,150
11. Cold produced, B.t.u. per hour.................................. 179,533
12. Tons capacity in 24 hours....................................... 14.96

Test of Double-acting 15-ton Refrigerating Plant.—(*Continued*)

Item

13.	Temperatures of condensing water, degrees Fahrenheit.	Outlet to condenser	66.75
14.		Inlet to condenser	52.00
15.		Difference, outlet and inlet	14.75
16.	Weight of cooling water used, pounds		28,630
17.	Weight of cooling water used per hour, pounds		14,315
18.	B.t.u. absorbed per hour by cooling water		211,146
19.	Temperatures of ammonia, degrees Fahrenheit.	At condenser inlet	71.9
20.		At condenser outlet	54.5
21.		Difference, inlet and outlet of condenser	17.4
22.		At cooler inlet	61.1
23.		At cooler outlet	7.8
24.		Difference cooler inlet and outlet	53.3
25.	Weight of ammonia used, pounds		710.5
26.	Weight of ammonia used per hour, pounds		355.25
27.	Weight of dry steam used, pounds		1,416
28.	Weight of dry steam used per hour, pounds		708
29.	Mean effective pressures	Head end, steam cylinder, pounds per square inch	36
30.		Crank end, steam cylinder, pounds per square inch	31.5
31.		Head end, ammonia cylinder, pounds per square inch	53.7
32.		Crank end, ammonia cylinder, pounds per square inch	52.6
33.	Indicated horsepower	Head end, steam cylinder	9.82
34.		Crank end, steam cylinder	8.29
35.		Total, steam cylinder	18.11
36.		Head end, ammonia cylinder	7.72
37		Crank end, ammonia cylinder	7.22
38.		Total, ammonia cylinder	14.94
39.	Mechanical efficiency, per cent		82.5
40.	Weight of dry steam per indicated horse power per hour, steam cylinder, pounds		39.1
41.	Weight of dry steam per hour per ton of refrigeration in 24 hours, pounds		47.3

Method of Calculating Test

Item

$7 =$ item 5 — item 6

  $= 47.0 - 17.9 = 29.1$

$10 =$ item 9 ÷ item 1

  $= 16,300 ÷ 2 = 8,150$

$11 =$ item 10 × item 8 × item 7

  $= 8,150 × 0.757 × 29.1 = 179,533$

$12 = \dfrac{\text{item } 11 \times 24}{288,000} = \dfrac{179,533 \times 24}{288,000} = 14.96$

$15 =$ item 13 — item 14

  $= 66.75 - 52.00 = 14.75$

$17 =$ item 16 ÷ item 1

  $= 28,630 ÷ 2 = 14,315$

$18 =$ item 17 × item 15

  $= 14,315 × 14.75 = 211,146$

$21 =$ item 19 — item 20

  $= 71.9 - 54.5 = 17.4$

METHOD OF CALCULATING TEST.—(*Continued*)

Item

24 = item 22 − item 23
= 61.1 − 7.8 = 53.3

26 = item 25 ÷ item 1
= 710.50 ÷ 2 = 355.25

28 = item 27 ÷ item 1
= 1,416 ÷ 2 = 708

$$33 = \frac{\text{item } 29 \times 2 \times 63.62^* \times \text{item } 4}{33,000}$$

$$= \frac{36 \times 2 \times 63.62 \times 70.7}{33,000} = 9.82$$

$$34 = \frac{\text{item } 30 \times 2 \times 61.4^* \times \text{item } 4}{33,000}$$

$$= \frac{31.5 \times 2 \times 61.4 \times 70.7}{33,000} = 8.29$$

35 = item 33 + item 34
= 9.82 + 8.29 = 18.11

$$36 = \frac{\text{item } 31 \times 16 \times 50.27^* \times \text{item } 4}{33,000 \times 12}$$

$$= \frac{53.7 \times 16 \times 50.27 \times 70.7}{33,000 \times 12} = 7.72$$

$$37 = \frac{\text{item } 32 \times 16 \times 48.05^* \times \text{item } 4}{33,000 \times 12}$$

$$= \frac{52.6 \times 16 \times 48.05 \times 70.7}{33,000 \times 12} = 7.22$$

NOTE.—In practice, the indicated horse power would be calculated from each indicator diagram separately and the average of the indicated horse powers taken, instead of using the average mean effective pressure and average revolutions per minute, as is done here.

38 = item 36 + item 37
= 7.72 + 7.22 = 14.94

39 = item 38 ÷ item 35
= 14.94 ÷ 18.11 = .825

40 = item 28 ÷ item 35
= 708 ÷ 18.11 = 39.4

41 = item 28 ÷ item 12
= 708 ÷ 14.96 = 47.3

Heat Balance.—The ammonia travels through a complete circuit, taking up heat at some points and giving it out at others. These amounts should balance, since the ammonia always returns to the condition in which it started. The heat balance serves to show this balance and also tells where and in what quantities the heat is transferred.

* Effective area of piston in square inches.

The method of calculating the quantities given in the heat balance follows:

Heat Discharged from Compressor.—Ammonia at the rate of 355.25 pounds per hour enters the compressor cylinder at a gage pressure of 21 pounds per square inch and 7.8° F.; 21 pounds per square inch gage pressure corresponds to (21 + 14.7 =) 35.7 pounds per square inch absolute pressure.

From the table of properties of saturated ammonia (p. 386) the temperature of saturated ammonia at 35.7 pounds per square inch absolute pressure is 6.73° F.; the ammonia vapor entering the cylinder is, therefore, superheated

$$7.8 - 6.73 = 1.07° \text{ F.}$$

The amount of heat in 1 pound of the ammonia vapor above the heat in the liquid ammonia at −40° F. is equal to heat of the liquid + latent heat + superheat.

Work of compression per pound of ammonia

$$= \frac{14.94 \times 2,545}{355.25} = \frac{38,022}{355.25} = 107$$

Note.—14.94 is the indicated horsepower of the ammonia cylinder and 2,545 is the number of B.t.u. equivalent to indicated horsepower acting for 1 hour.

355.25 is the weight of ammonia used per hour.

Heat in 1 pound of ammonia discharged from compressor = 721 B.t.u.

Heat in 355.25 pounds of ammonia discharged from compressor

$$= 355.25 \times 721 = 256,135 \text{ B.t.u.}$$

Heat Lost between Compressor and Condenser.—The heat leaving the compressor in 1 pound of ammonia vapor is 721 B.t.u., being made up of

Heat of liquid + latent heat + superheat

The heat of the liquid and latent heat being taken at discharge pressure = 117.1 + 14.7 or 131.8 pounds per square inch absolute pressure.

From the table of properties of saturated ammonia, the temperature corresponding to 131.8 pounds per square inch absolute pressure is 71.3° F.

The latent heat corresponding to 131.8 pounds per square inch absolute pressure is 507.3 B.t.u.

The superheat is $(t - 71.3) \times 0.60$.

NOTE.—0.60 is the specific heat of ammonia vapor.

The heat of the liquid per pound of ammonia = 122.0 B.t.u., and the latent heat per pound = 507.3 B.t.u. Therefore,

$$721 = 122 + 507.3 + (t - 71.3) \times 0.60,$$

or

$$t - 71.3 = \frac{721 - 629.3}{0.60} = \frac{91.7}{0.60} = 152.8$$

and

$$t = 152.8 + 71.3 = 224.1° \text{ F.}$$

This is the temperature of the ammonia vapor leaving the compressor.

Temperature of ammonia vapor entering condenser = 71.9° F.

Heat lost per pound of ammonia between compressor and condenser = $0.60(224.1 - 71.9) = 0.60 \times 152.2 = 91.3$ B.t.u.

Total heat lost per hour between compressor and condenser = $355.25 \times 91.3 = 32,442$ B.t.u.

Heat Lost in the Condenser.—Temperature of ammonia vapor entering condenser = 71.9° F.

Temperature of ammonia vapor corresponding to pressure = 71.3° F.

Degrees of superheat of ammonia vapor entering condenser 0.6° F.

Total heat in 1 pound of ammonia vapor entering condenser is 630.0 B.t.u.

Temperature of ammonia leaving condenser is 54.5° F.

Heat in 1 pound of ammonia leaving the condenser = 104.0 B.t.u.

Heat removed in condenser

$$= (630 - 104) \, 355.25 \text{ B.t.u.}$$
$$= 526 \times 355.25 = 186,862 \text{ B.t.u.}$$

NOTE.—The "heat lost between compressor and condenser" might have been calculated more easily by subtracting the "heat lost in the condenser" from the "heat discharged from the compressor." The calculations have been made in the way shown here in order to show how the temperature of the ammonia vapor leaving the compressor may be calculated.

Heat Gained between Condenser and Cooler.—Temperature of ammonia at inlet of brine cooler = 61.1° F.

Temperature of ammonia at outlet of condenser = 54.5° F.
Heat gained per pound of ammonia between condenser and brine cooler = 109.3 − 104.0 = 5.3 B.t.u.
Total gain of heat between condenser and brine cooler = 5.3 × 355.25 = 1,883 B.t.u.

Heat Gained in Cooler.—The heat gained in the brine cooler is equal to the heat in the ammonia vapor leaving the brine cooler minus the heat in the ammonia entering the cooler.

The temperature of the liquid ammonia entering the cooler is 61.1° F. The heat per pound of liquid above −40° F. in the liquid entering the brine cooler is 109.30 B.t.u.

The heat per pound in the ammonia vapor leaving the brine cooler is made up of the heat above −40° of the liquid, the latent heat of evaporation at 35.7 pounds per square inch absolute pressure, and the heat necessary to superheat the vapor is 1.07 deg. F., which is the amount of superheat in the ammonia vapor as it entered the compressor.

The heat in the ammonia vapor per pound = 614.0

Therefore, the heat gained per pound of ammonia in the brine cooler

$$= 614.0 − 109.3 = 504.7 \text{ B.t.u.}$$

Total heat gained in the brine cooler

$$= 504.7 × 355.25 = 179,295 \text{ B.t.u.}$$

Summary of Heat Cycle.

	Heat gained	Heat lost
Work of compression..........................	38,022	
Between compressor and condenser..............	....	33,442
To condensing water.........................	....	186,862
Between condenser and cooler.................	1,883	
In cooler....................................	179,295	
Total.......................................	219,200	220,304

The heat cycle should, of course, balance exactly. In this case, it is out of balance 220,304 − 219,200 = 1,104 B.t.u., an error of only

$$\frac{1,104}{219,200} = 0.005 \text{ or } \frac{1}{2} \text{ per cent.}$$

This small error is due to neglecting fractions and is so small as to be unimportant; so that, for all practical purposes, we may say that the heat summary balances.

A.S.R.E. TEST CODE (1925) FOR REFRIGERATING SYSTEMS

The Test Code for Refrigerating Systems is intended for use in the determination of the performance of compression systems in which compressors of the reciprocating type as well as absorption machines are used. In so far as the fundamental operations of all the systems are in common, general rules will be laid down, and where the systems differ separate rules will be given. For the test of the driving element in compression systems, the A.S.-R.E. Power Test Codes for Steam Engines, Steam Turbines, Internal-combustion Engines, etc. should be followed.

Measurements.—The principal measurements and quantities determined in a test are:

(a) The quantity of the refrigerant circulated; (b) the various temperatures of the refrigerant in the cycle; (c) the various pressures of the refrigerant in the cycle; (d) the energy required to operate the driving element and the various auxiliary apparatus; (e) the various temperatures of condensing and cooling water; (f) the quantity of condensing and cooling water; (g) quantity, quality, and pressure of steam used in the steam cylinder or generator; (h) quantity of oil passing through the compressor; (i) quantity, composition of and density of brine used; (j) temperature of brine entering and leaving the evaporator; (k) quality of liquor in absorption plants.

Instruments and apparatus necessary in carrying out the test are:

(a) Suitable meter for measuring liquid refrigerant on the high- or inter-mediate-pressure side where same passes to the expansion coils of the brine cooler or elsewhere; (b) platform scales and suitable tanks for measuring water and condensed steam; (c) water meters, calibrated tanks, or tank and platform scale for measuring condensing and cooling water; (d) pressure gages and vacuum manometers including a suitable U-tube for mercury column to be connected at the low-pressure suction of the compressor; it is recommended that this be used in all cases rather than a pressure or vacuum gage for suction pressures under 20 pounds' gage; (e) calibrated thermometers and thermometer mercury wells of sufficient lengths to extend beyond the centers of the pipes. Thermometers used for taking temperatures of brine shall be graduated in $\frac{1}{10}°$ F. and readings estimated for $\frac{1}{100}°$ F.; (f) barometer and psychrometer when necessary; (g) revolution counter or other accurate speed-measuring device; (h) graduated stroke indicator for direct-acting pumps; (i) picnometer, Mohr-Westphal balance.

or calibrated hydrometer for specific gravity of brine; (*j*) calorimeter for determining the quality of the steam; (*k*) steam and ammonia indicators; (*l*) planimeter; (*m*) deadweight gage tester; (*n*) appropriate instruments for measuring current consumption of motor-driven machines.

The *thermometer wells* should be of steel for ammonia lines, and bronze for brine lines, and should extend into the pipe a sufficient distance so that the bulb of the thermometer will extend at least to the center of the pipe. These wells should be filled with mercury to the point indicated on the stem of the thermometer. Insulation on the cold lines should extend even to the top of the well, and the thermometers pass through corks fitted to the wells and bored to accommodate the thermometers. The thermometer well must be placed at least 10 feet away from brine coolers or pumps so that the solution has uniform temperature where the readings are taken. Electric-resistance thermometers or thermocouples may be used in taking temperatures of brine as a check on mercury thermometers. In testing a plant where the load is light, a brine heater or a heater using waste condensing water flowing over the evaporating coils should be used.

For ammonia a special steel indicator must be provided which has steel indicator cocks with short separate connections to the ends. The indicator should be provided with a stop so that a light spring may be used for studying suction conditions.

In ammonia absorption systems the anhydrous ammonia should not contain over 3 per cent moisture. Samples should be drawn before and immediately after the test and determinations of moisture made.

Starting and Stopping.—The plant should be operated a sufficient length of time prior to the starting of the test to insure uniformity of conditions and, when these conditions are obtained, the test should be started and continued as stated in this code. It is essential to the accuracy of the test that all parts of the plant contain the same amount of heat estimated above some datum at the end as at the beginning of the test. To accomplish this, all vessels containing liquid refrigerant should be supplied with suitable gage glasses so that the same quantity of fluid may be distributed alike at the beginning and end of the test and the quantities and temperature of the fluids in the various parts maintained as uniform as possible.

The test should be continued over a period of time not less than 8 hours.

Fifteen-minute readings will be sufficient except where there is considerable fluctuation in the readings, in which case more frequent readings must be taken to insure good averages.

Each indicator card should be marked with the date, time of day, cylinder and end of cylinder, identification mark, and strength of indicator spring, as pointed out in the Test Code for Reciprocating Steam Engines. To assist in the uniformity of operation a chart should be plotted during the test of the principal quantities, including the estimated tonnage.

The data and results should be tabulated in accordance with the form shown in the following tables, adding items not provided for and omitting items not needed to conform to the object in view. Unless otherwise indicated, the items refer to the numerical readings which are recorded in the log.

Calculation of Results.—The now generally adopted recommendations of the Joint Committee of the A.S.M.E. and the American Society of Refrigerating Engineers on **Standard Tonnage Basis for Refrigeration** are as follows:

a. A standard ton of refrigeration is 288,000 B.t.u.

b. The standard commercial ton of refrigeration is at the rate of 200 B.t.u. per minute or 12,000 B.t.u. per hour.

c. The standard rating of a refrigerating machine[1] using liquefiable vapor is the number of standard commercial tons of refrigeration it performs under adopted refrigerant pressures.[2]

The **capacity** of the system shall be expressed in tons of refrigeration per 24 hours as calculated from the weight of liquid refrigerant and the amount of available cooling effect produced in the evaporator. This method shall be employed in the case of all refrigerants where the physical properties have been determined and where tables of such properties are recognized as sufficiently accurate.

The weight of refrigerant circulated shall be determined by a suitable liquid meter. As an alternate method the weight of

[1] A refrigerating machine is the compressor cylinder of the compression refrigerating system, or the absorber, liquor pump, and generator of the absorption refrigerating system.

[2] These pressures are measured outside and within 10 feet of the refrigerating machine, distances which are measured along the inlet and outlet pipes, respectively; (*a*) the inlet pressure being that which corresponds to a saturation temperature of 5° F. (−15° C.) and (*b*) the outlet pressure being that which corresponds to a saturation temperature of 86° F. (30° C.).

liquid refrigerant shall be calculated from the volume as obtained from a pair of calibrated receivers or by direct weighing.

The amount of available refrigerating effect shall be the weight of refrigerant circulated per hour multiplied by the difference in heat content on entering and leaving the evaporator. Where there is more than one evaporator in which different pressures exist, the weight of refrigerant to each evaporator and the total heat from the vapor must be determined separately and the total refrigerating effect may then be computed by the following formula:

$$Q_e = W_a(H_e - h_e),$$

where Q_e = total refrigerating effect per hour.

W_a = weight of anhydrous refrigerant circulated, in pounds per hour.

H_e = total heat in the vapor leaving the evaporator.

h_e = total heat in the liquid at the expansion valve.

The **refrigeration effect** (**R.E.**) expressed in standard commercial tons of refrigeration is

$$R.E. = \frac{Q_e}{12,000}.$$

Theoretical Horsepower Required to Compress Adiabatically.—The work done in the cylinder of the compressor per pound of ammonia circulated expressed in thermal units may be found by referring to either the Mollier chart or the tables adopted and published by the American Society of Refrigerating Engineers.

$$Hp. = \frac{(H_o - H_i) \times W_a \times 778}{33,000},$$

where H_o = heat content of vapor after adiabatic compression.

H_i = heat content at compressor inlet.

W_a = weight of ammonia circulated, in pounds per hour.

Gross or Brake Horsepower.—See Test Code for Displacement Compressors and Blowers.

Electrical Horsepower.—See Test Code for Displacement Compressors and Blowers.

Volumetric Efficiency.—See Test Code for Displacement Compressors and Blowers.

Mechanical Efficiency.—Mechanical efficiency is the ratio of the indicated horsepower in the compressor cylinders to the indicated horsepower in the power cylinders in the case of a steam-driven or internal-combustion-driven compressor, and to the brake horsepower delivered to the shaft in the case of a motor-driven machine.

Compression Efficiency.—Compression efficiency is the ratio of work required to compress adiabatically all the vapor delivered by the compressor to the work done within the compressor cylinder as shown by the indicator cards.

Overall Efficiency.—The method of computing the overall efficiency is described in the Test Code for Displacement Compressors and Blowers.

Condenser Performance.—The condenser is required to remove the total heat of the vapor drawn into the compressor plus the heat of compression. It is therefore incorrect to consider the removal of 12,000 B.t.u. per hour by the condensing water as equivalent to the standard commercial ton as produced in the evaporator. The total heat removed by the condensing water shall be calculated from the observed data when the enclosed type of condensers, either shell and tube or double pipe, is used. The total heat may also be calculated from the quantity of refrigerant circulated. In this case

$$Q_1 = W_a(H_c - h_c),$$

where Q_1 = heat removed per hour.

H_c = heat content of vapor entering condenser.

h_c = heat content of liquid leaving condenser.

W_a = weight of refrigerant condensed per hour.

Determination of Heat Transfer in Condensers.—The work done in the condenser may be divided into three stages: (1) the removal of superheat; (2) the liquefaction of the refrigerant; and (3) the subcooling of the condensed liquid. It is therefore to be expected that the rate of heat transfer is not the same in all parts of the condenser. The logarithmic mean difference is based upon a constant temperature of liquefaction throughout the condenser on the assumption that the heat transfer is uniform throughout the condenser. While the calculation of heat transfer per square foot of refrigerant surface per hour per degree of logarithmic mean difference does not give entirely satisfactory results, the determination of heat transfer shall be calculated in this manner.

$$\text{Logarithmic mean difference} = \frac{t_o - t_i}{\log_e \dfrac{t_e - t_i}{t_e - t_a}}$$

where t_e = temperature of liquefaction corresponding to condenser pressure.

t_i = temperature of incoming water.

t_o = temperature of outgoing water.

Evaporator Performance.—The evaporator performance shall be calculated from the observed data. In this case

$$Q_e = W_a(H_e - h_e),$$

in which Q_e = heat removed per hour.

H_e = heat content of vapor.

h_e = heat content of liquid entering expansion valve.

W_a = weight of refrigerant entering evaporator, in pounds per hour.

Determination of Heat Transfer in Evaporator.—(*a*) Brines coolers. Brine-cooler performance shall be expressed in terms of heat transfer per square foot of cooling surface per hour per degree of logarithmic mean difference.

$$\text{Logarithmic mean difference} = \frac{t_i - t_o}{\log_e \dfrac{t_i - t_v}{t_o - t_v}},$$

where t_o = temperature of brine out of evaporator.

t_i = temperature of brine to evaporator.

t_v = temperature of vaporization corresponding to evaporator pressure.

(*b*) The performance of ice tanks and all other forms of expansion coils or apparatus will not be specifically covered in this code, which is intended to include the main items of the refrigerating cycle rather than the products of the cycle.

Pump Horsepower.—The water-horsepower output at observed total suction and discharge pressure is

$$\text{w.hp.} = \frac{(\text{pounds of liquid per minute}) \times (\text{total head in feet})}{33,000}.$$

The gross or brake horsepower input shall be observed for all pump-driving elements and the efficiencies calculated.

Heat Balance.—A heat balance shall be made of the refrigerating cycle, of which the following is an illustration of all the items required in a compound-cycle compression system. As a heat balance is impossible unless extreme care has been taken in making the measurements, it will be found necessary to have most accurate thermometers for observing the temperature of water on and off condensers as well as for taking temperature of brine. It is also necessary to have indicator cards taken at uniform intervals, at least every 30 minutes, in order to determine the heat equivalent of work done in the compressor.

The general formulas for heat balance are as follows:

Compression cycle: $Q_e + Q_w = Q_1 + Q_3$

Absorption cycle: $Q_e + Q_s = Q_1 + Q_2 + Q_3$

where Q_e = heat absorbed by evaporating refrigerant.

Q_w = heat equivalent of work in compressor.

Q_s = heat imparted by steam in generator.

Q_1 = heat rejected in condenser.

Q_2 = heat rejected in absorber.

Q_3 = heat rejected or radiated in addition to Q_1 and Q_2.

For purposes of illustration the following list of quantities involved in the computation of the heat balances of compound compression systems is given.

Heat Absorbed   Heat Rejected
(B.t.u. per Hour)

a. Heat absorbed in evaporator

b. Heat entering evaporator insulation

c. Heat absorbed in low-pressure suction main

d. Heat absorbed in low-pressure suction trap

e. Heat equivalent of work done in compressor

f. Heat absorbed from engine room through cold surface of low-pressure compressor

g. Heat absorbed through surface of intermediate liquid receiver

h. Heat absorbed through surface of intermediate-pressure liquid line

i. Heat absorbed from engine room through surface of high-pressure suction main

j. Heat absorbed through cold surfaces of high-pressure compressor

k. Heat absorbed or rejected through condenser shells.

l. Heat absorbed or rejected through receivers.

m. Heat absorbed or rejected in high-pressure liquid line.

a. Heat rejected by hot surfaces of low-pressure compressor

b. Heat rejected from low-pressure discharge main between low-pressure compressor and intermediate vapor cooler

c. Heat rejected in intermediate vapor cooler

d. Heat rejected to engine room by intermediate vapor cooler

e. Heat rejected in discharge main from intermediate vapor cooler to intermediate liquid receiver

f. Heat rejected by hot surfaces of high-pressure compressor

g. Heat rejected by high-pressure discharge main and oil separator between machine and condensers

h. Heat rejected in ammonia condensers

i. Heat rejected in liquid cooler

TABLE 1.—DATA AND RESULTS OF TEST ON POWER-DRIVEN REFRIGERATING UNIT

General Information

(1) Date of test; (2) location; (3) owner; (4) builder; (5) test conducted by; (6) object of test.

Description, Dimensions, of Compresser, Condenser, Etc.

7. Type of compressor (single- or multiple-stage, and kind of refrigerant)..
8. Type of compressor valves..
9. Method of driving compressor.....................................
10. Method of volume control ....
11. Rated discharge pressure...........................lb. per sq. in.
12. Rated speed..r.p.m.
13. Rated displacement...............................cu. ft. per min.
14. Rated output expressed in standard tons of refrigeration............
15. Type of intercoolers..

	First Inter-cooler	Second Inter-cooler
16. Area of water-cooled surface................sq. ft.	......	....

	First Stage	Second Stage
17. Diameter of compressor cylinders..............in.	......	....
18. Stroke of pistons..............................ft.	......	....
19. Diameter of piston rods or tail rods............in.	......	....
20. Clearance in terms of piston displacement...per cent	......	....
(a) Clearance, head end...........................	......	....
(b) Clearance, crank end..........................	......	....
(c) Clearance, average............................	......	....
21. Cylinder ratio based on piston displacement		
(a) First stage to second stage....................	......	....
22. Horsepower constant, cylinder:		
(a) Head end (stroke × net piston area ÷ 33,000).	......	....
(b) Crank end (stroke × net piston area ÷ 33,000).	......	....
23. Area of compressor cylinder jacketed surface, sq. ft.	......	....
24. Length and cross-sectional area, intake pipe.....ft.	......	....
25. Diameter of final discharge pipe................in.	......	....

NOTE.—For description, dimensions, etc., of compressor-driving element, see Tables 2, 3, or 4.

26. Type of condenser...
27. Area of condenser surface on refrigerant side..................sq. ft.
28. Type of evaporator..
29. Area of evaporator surface on refrigerant side.................sq. ft.
30. Type of water pumps..
31. Size of water pumps, No. 1, No. 2......................gal. per min.
32. Type of brine pumps..
33. Size of brine pumps, Nos. 1, 2, 3......................gal. per min.
34. Type of cooling tower..

TABLE 1.—DATA AND RESULTS OF TEST ON POWER-DRIVEN REFRIGERATING
UNIT (*Continued*)

35. Rated capacity of cooling tower.................................
36. Type of liquid after cooler....................................
37. Cooling surface of liquid after cooler........................sq. ft.
38. Type of intermediate liquid cooler.............................
39. Size of intermediate liquid cooler.............diam.......height

General Data

40. Composition of brine..
41. Specific gravity of brine used at 68° F. compared with water at 39.1° F.[1]
42. Specific heat of brine used....................................
43. Specific gravity of liquid refrigerant as measured...................
44. Kind of cooling water used (well, salt, river)........................
45. Specific gravity of cooling water................................
46. Specific heat of cooling water..................................

Test Data and Results

61. Duration of test..hr.

Average Pressures

62. Barometric pressure..............................in. of mercury
   (a) Corresponding absolute pressure.................in. of mercury
63. Pressure by mercury manometer at intake near cylinder
   first stage.......................................in. of mercury
   (a) Corresponding absolute pressure.................lb. per sq. in.

First
Stage,
Etc.

64. Pressure by gage in discharge pipe near cylinder....................................lb. per sq. in. ....
   (a) Corresponding absolute pressure.........lb. per sq. in. ....
65. Pressure in intercooler by gage..............lb. per sq. in. ....
   (a) Corresponding absolute pressure.........lb. per sq. in. ....
66. Condenser pressure by gage..................lb. per sq. in. ....
   (a) Corresponding absolute pressure.........lb. per sq. in. ......
67. Pressure in evaporator, by gage..............lb. per sq. in. ....
   (a) Corresponding absolute pressure.........lb. per sq. in. ....
68. Pressure at inlet of cooling-water pumps, by
   gage...................................lb. per sq. in. ....
69. Pressure at outlet of cooling-water pumps, by
   gage...................................lb. per sq. in. ....
70. Pressure at inlet of brine pump, by gage.....lb. per sq. in. ....
71. Pressure at outlet of brine pump, by gage ....lb. per sq. in. ....

Average Temperatures..

76. Engine-room temperature ....deg. Fahr.
77. Condenser-room temperature ....deg. Fahr.
78. Temperature of outside air ....deg. Fahr.

  [1] Temperature of the maximum density of water.

Table 1.—Data and Results of Test on Power-driven Refrigerating Unit (*Continued*)

79. Temperature of wet bulb, outside air . . . . .deg. Fahr.
                                                                First
                                                                Stage,
80. Temperature of vapor near intake (to be measured   Etc.
    not more than two feet from the compressor inlet
    and should be between 6 and 12° F. of super-
    heat). . . . . deg. Fahr. . . . .
80a. Temperature of vapor from evaporator (to be
    measured not more than 2 feet from outlet). . . . deg. Fahr. . . . .
81. Temperature of vapor near discharge port. . . . . . . deg. Fahr. . . . .
82. Temperature of vapor at inlet to intermediate
    vapor cooler. . . . . deg. Fahr. . . . .
83. Temperature of vapor at outlet to intermediate
    vapor cooler. . . . . deg. Fahr. . . . .
84. Temperature of liquid from condensers . . . . deg. Fahr.
85. Temperature of liquid from liquid receivers . . . . deg. Fahr.
86. Temperature of liquid from liquid cooler . . . . deg. Fahr.
87. Temperature of liquid from intermediate liquid cooler . . . . . deg. Fahr.
88. Temperature of liquid at measuring point . . . . deg. Fahr.
89. Temperature of jacket cooling water, inlet . . . . deg. Fahr.
90. Temperature of jacket cooling water, outlet . . . . deg. Fahr.
91. Temperature of cooling water, intermediate vapor cooler
    inlet . . . . deg. Fahr.
92. Temperature of cooling water, intermediate vapor cooler
    outlet . . . . deg. Fahr.
93. Temperature of cooling water, liquid-cooler inlet . . . . deg. Fahr.
94. Temperature of cooling water, liquid-cooler outlet . . . . deg. Fahr.
95. Temperature of cooling water, condenser inlet . . . . deg. Fahr.
96. Temperature of cooling water, condenser outlet . . . . deg. Fahr.
97. Temperature of water to cooling tower . . . . deg. Fahr.
98. Temperature of water from cooling tower . . . . deg. Fahr.
99. Temperature of brine, brine-cooler inlet . . . . deg. Fahr.
100. Temperature of brine, brine-cooler outlet . . . . deg. Fahr.
101. Temperature range through brine coolers by electric-
    resistance thermometer . . . . deg. Fahr.

Total Quantities

107. Liquid delivered to evaporator. . . . . .lb.
108. Brine circulated. . . . . .gal.
Unit Quantities
115. Liquid delivered to evaporator (Item 107 ÷ Item 61). . . . .lb. per min.
116. Brine circulated (Item 108 ÷ Item 61 × 60). . . . . .gal. per min.
117. Cooling water supplied to condensers. . . . . .gal. per min.
                                                                First
                                                                Stage,
                                                                Etc.
118. Cooling water supplied to jackets. . . . . .gal. per min. . . . .

TABLE 1.—DATA AND RESULTS OF TEST ON POWER-DRIVEN REFRIGERATING
UNIT (*Continued*)

119. Cooling water supplied to intermediate vapor
cooler.....................................gal. per min. ....

120. Cooling water supplied to liquid cooler........gal. per min. ....

Refrigerating Output

121. Available cooling effect (Q_e)
122. (*a*) Tons of refrigeration produced (Item 121 ÷ 12,000).............
  (*b*) Tons of refrigeration, brine method as a check (Item 116 × Item
  101 × Item 41 × 8.33 × Item 42 ÷ 200).....................

Speed

126. Total number of revolutions as shown by compressor counter.........
127. Revolutions per minute Item 126 ÷ (Item 61 × 60),..........r.p.m.
128. Average piston speed................................ft. per min.

Power

129. Indicated horsepower of compressor cylinders, whole compressor..i.hp.
130. Low-pressure cylinder or cylinder if single-stage:
  Crank end..i.hp.
  Head end..i.hp
131. High-pressure cylinder:
  Crank end..i.hp
  Head end..i.hp.
132. Friction horsepower (Item 144 (Table 2), or Item 133 (Table
  3)—Item 129)...i.hp.

Power Input

See Tables 2, 3 or 4.

Economy Results

145. Gross or brake horsepower of compressor per ton of refrigeration..hp.
146. Electrical horsepower of compressor per ton of refrigeration.......hp.
147. Indicated horsepower of compressor per ton of refrigeration (Item
  129 ÷ Item 122a)..hp.

Efficiency Results

148. Theoretical horsepower calculation:

First
Stage,
Etc.

(*a*) Total heat contained in 1 pound vapor at suction..............B.t.u.
(*b*) Total heat contained in 1 pound liquid entering expansion valve...B.t.u.
(*c*) Available latent heat per pound of refrigerant (Item *a*—Item *b*).......
(*d*) Work required to compress 1 pound refrigerant adiabatically (see
  Mollier chart facing, p. 404)............................... B.t.u.
(*e*) Theoretical temperature of discharge vapor (see Mollier chart) deg. Fahr.
(*f*) Horsepower per ton for adiabatic compression...................i.hp.
152. Total horsepower for adiabatic compression........................
153. Volumetric efficiency...

TABLE 1.—DATA AND RESULTS OF TEST ON POWER-DRIVEN REFRIGERATING
UNIT (*Continued*)

154. Compression efficiency...

155. Mechanical efficiency...

156. Overall efficiency...

Condenser

157. Heat removed per minute by condensing water (Item 96—Item
95) × Item 117 × 8.33..................................B.t.u.

158. Heat removed as calculated from refrigerant condensed as a check....

159. Heat removed per hour (Item 157 × 60).....................B.t.u.

160. Logarithmic mean temperature difference in degrees Fahrenheit.......

161. Coefficient of heat transfer, K = (Item 159 ÷ Item 160 × Item 27)..

Evaporator

162. Heat removed per minute from brine.......................B.t.u.

163. Heat removed per hour (Item 162 × 60)...................B.t.u.

164. Logarithmic mean temperature difference = degree Fahrenheit.......

165. Coefficient of heat transfer, K = (Item 163 ÷ Item 164 × Item 29)..

Auxiliary pumps:

(*a*) *Brine pumps*

166. Gross or brake horsepower................................b.hp.

167. Water horsepower..hp.

168. Overall pump efficiency.................................per cent

(*b*) *Water pumps*...b.hp.

170. Water horsepower..hp.

171. Overall pump efficiency.................................per cent

TABLE 2.—ADDITIONAL ITEMS APPLYING ONLY WHEN THE DRIVING ELE-
MENT IS AN ELECTRIC MOTOR

Description, Dimensions, Etc., of Compressor Drive

47. Type of motor..

48. Rated power of motor...

49. Volts...

50. Amperes...

51. Phase...

52. Cycles..

53. Revolutions per minute......................................

54. Type and rating of exciter..................................

(*a*) Volts...

(*b*) Amperes...

Power Input

133. Volts...

134. Amperes per phase...

135. Power factor (from meter)...................................

136. Exciter:..

(*a*) Volts...

(*b*) Amperes...

TABLE 2.—ADDITIONAL ITEMS APPLYING ONLY WHEN THE DRIVING ELE-
MENT IS AN ELECTRIC MOTOR (*Continued*)

137. Efficiency of exciter (from builder's test)...........................
138. Horsepower input to driving motor (calculated from voltmeter,
ammeter, and power-factor meter)...........................hp.
139. Horsepower input to driving motor by precision wattmeter.......hp.
140. Efficiency of driving motor (from builder's test)................hp.
141. Net motor horsepower...hp.
142. Horsepower output for exciter.................................hp.
143. Net horsepower to drive exciter...............................hp.
144. Horsepower to drive compressor or blower.....................hp.

TABLE 3.—ADDITIONAL ITEMS APPLYING ONLY WHEN THE DRIVING
ELEMENT IS A STEAM ENGINE

Description, Dimensions, Etc., of Compressor Drive

47. Type of engine (simple or multiple-expansion or uniflow)............
48. Type of steam valves...
49. Auxiliaries (steam or electric drive)..............................
50. Type and make of condenser equipment..........................
51. Rated capacity of condenser equipment..........................
52. Type of air pump, jacket pump, and reheater pump (direct or
independently driven)..
53. Type of governing apparatus....................................
54. Diameter of steam cylinders...........................in.   ....
55. Stroke of pistons...................................ft.   ....
56. Clearance in terms of piston displacement.........per cent   ....
   (*c*) Clearance, crank end...............................   ....
   (*d*) Clearance, head end................................   ....
57. Horsepower constant, steam cylinder:
   (*a*) Head end..   ....
   (*b*) Crank end...   ....
58. Area of steam-cylinder jacketed surface.............sq. ft.   ....
59. Area of interior surface...........................sq. ft.   ....
60. Steam-cylinder ratio (overall):
   (*a*) First cylinder to second cylinder............................
   (*b*) Second cylinder to third cylinder............................

Average Pressures

72. Pressure above atmosphere in steam pipe near throttle by
   gage...lb. per sq. in.
   (*a*) Corresponding absolute pressure................lb. per sq. in.
   (*b*) Maximum pressure above atmosphere, steam-pipe
   diagram near throttle........................lb. per sq. in.
   (*c*) Minimum pressure above atmosphere, steam-pipe
   diagram near throttle........................lb. per sq. in.
73. Pressure in steam receiver by gage...................lb. per sq. in.
74. Pressure in exhaust pipe near engine by mercury column.in. of mercury
   (*a*) Corresponding absolute pressure................lb. per sq. in.
75. Pressure in jackets and reheater....................lb. per sq. in.

TABLE 3.—ADDITIONAL ITEMS APPLYING ONLY WHEN THE DRIVING
ELEMENT IS A STEAM ENGINE (*Continued*)

Average Temperatures

102. Temperature of steam near throttle.....................deg. Fahr.
103. Temperature of saturation at pressure near throttle........deg. Fahr.
104. Temperature of steam leaving steam receiver, if superheated..deg. Fahr.
105. Temperature of steam in exhaust pipe as observed.........deg. Fahr.
106. Temperature of saturated steam in exhaust pipe corresponding to pressure of exhaust in pipe.....................deg. Fahr.

Total Quantities

109. Superheat, at throttle.................................deg. Fahr.
110. Moisture in steam.......................................per cent
111. Total steam and water consumed by engine as measured..........lb.
112. Total steam less water consumed................................lb.
113. Correction factor conforming to conditions agreed upon...........lb.
114. Equivalent total steam consumed, conforming to conditions.......lb.

Unit Quantities

123. Steam and water (or superheated steam) consumed per hour as
measured..lb.
124. Steam less water (or superheated steam) consumed per hour.......lb.
125. Equivalent conforming to conditions consumed per hour..........lb.

Power Input

172. Steam cylinder—indicated horsepower developed, whole engine....i.hp.
173. High-pressure steam cylinder, crank end......................i.hp.
head end......................i.hp.
174. Low-pressure steam cylinder, crank end.....................i.hp.
head end......................i.hp.

Economy Results

175. Steam less water (or superheated steam) consumed per indicated
horsepower-hour (Item 124 ÷ Item 129).....................lb.
176. Equivalent steam consumed per indicated horsepower-hour (Item
125 ÷ Item 129)...lb.
177. Steam less water (or superheated steam) consumed per ton of
refrigeration at intake pressure and temperature (Item 112 ÷
Item 122a)..lb.
178. Equivalent steam consumed per ton of refrigeration at intake
pressure and temperature (Item 114 ÷ Item 122a).............lb.

A.S.R.E. TEST CODE (1924) FOR ABSORPTION REFRIGERATING
SYSTEMS

TABLE 5.—DATA AND RESULTS OF TEST ON ABSORPTION REFRIGERATING
SYSTEMS

General Information

(1) Date of test; (2) location; (3) owner; (4) builder; (5) test conducted by; (6) object of test.

Description, Dimensions, Etc.

7. Type of condenser...
8. Area of condenser surface on refrigerant side.................sq. ft.
9. Type of evaporator..
10. Area of evaporator surface on refrigerant side................sq. ft.
11. Type of water pumps..
12. Rated capacity of water pumps.......................gal. per min.
13. Type of brine pumps..
14. Rated capacity of brine pumps.......................gal. per min.
15. Type of cooling tower..
16. Rated capacity of cooling tower................................
17. Type of absorber..
18. Area of absorber surface on refrigerant side..................sq. ft.
19. Type of generator...
20. Area of heating surface in generator..........................sq. ft.
21. Type of strong-liquor pump....................................
22. Diameter of piston rod, liquor pump...........................in.
23. Stroke of liquor pump...in.
24. Piston displacement of liquor pump............................cu. ft.
25. Type of rectifier..
26. Cooling surface in rectifier..................................sq. ft.
27. Type of exchanger...
28. Cooling surface in exchanger.................................sq. ft.

General Data

29. Composition of brine..
30. Specific gravity of brine at 68° F. compared with water at 39.1° F....
31. Specific heat of brine...
32. Specific gravity of liquid refrigerant as measured.................
33. Concentration of strong liquor.................................
34. Concentration of weak liquor..................................
35. Quality of steam to generator.................................
36. Kind of cooling water used.....................................
37. Specific gravity of cooling water..............................
38. Specific heat of cooling water.................................

Test Data and Results

39. Duration of tests...hr.

Average Pressures

40. Barometric pressure...............................in. of mercury
    (a) Corresponding absolute pressure................in. of mercury

TABLE 5.—DATA AND RESULTS OF TEST ON ABSORPTION REFRIGERATING SYSTEMS (*Continued*)

41. Pressure in evaporator by gage.......................lb. per sq. in.
42. Steam pressure in generator, by gage..................lb. per sq. in.
43. Pressure in absorber, by gage........................lb. per sq. in.
44. Pressure in condenser, by gage.......................lb. per sq. in.

Average Temperatures

45. Engine-room temperature...............................deg. Fahr.
46. Condenser-room temperature...........................deg. Fahr.
47. Temperature of outside air.............................deg. Fahr.
48. Temperature of wet bulb...............................deg. Fahr.
49. Temperature of liquid from condensers...................deg. Fahr.
50. Temperature of liquid from liquid receivers...............deg. Fahr.
51. Temperature of liquid from liquid cooler..................deg. Fahr.
52. Temperature of liquid at measuring point.................deg. Fahr.
53. Temperature of water to cooling tower at measuring point..deg. Fahr.
54. Temperature of water from cooling tower at measuring point.deg. Fahr.
55. Temperature of brine, brine-cooler inlet at measuring point..deg. Fahr.
56. Temperature of brine, brine-cooler outlet at measuring point.deg. Fahr.
57. Temperature range through brine coolers by electric-resistance thermometer.....................................deg. Fahr.
58. Temperature of ammonia vapor, inlet to rectifier...........deg. Fahr.
59. Temperature of ammonia vapor, outlet from rectifier.......deg. Fahr.
60. Temperature of weak liquor to weak-liquor cooler..........deg. Fahr.
61. Temperature of weak liquor from weak-liquor cooler........deg. Fahr.
62. Temperature of water, inlet to weak-liquor cooler..........deg. Fahr.
63. Temperature of water, outlet from weak-liquor cooler.......deg. Fahr.
64. Temperature of weak liquor, inlet to absorber.............deg. Fahr.
65. Temperature of weak liquor, exit to generator.............deg. Fahr.
66. Temperature of strong liquor, inlet to exchanger...........deg. Fahr.
67. Temperature of strong liquor, outlet from exchanger........deg. Fahr.
68. Temperature of condenser cooling water, inlet.............deg. Fahr.
69. Temperature of condenser cooling water, outlet............deg. Fahr.
70. Temperature of steam to generator......................deg. Fahr.
71. Temperature of condensed steam from generator..........deg. Fahr.

Total Quantities

72. Liquid delivered to evaporator...............................lb.
73. Brine circulated...lb.
74. Strong liquor..lb.
75. Weak liquor...lb.
76. Steam condensed in generator..............................lb.

Unit Quantities

77. Liquid delivered to evaporator.......................lb. per min.
78. Brine circulated..................................gal. per min.
79. Cooling water supplied to condensers.................gal. per min.
80. Cooling water supplied to absorber....................gal. per min.
81. Cooling water supplied to rectifier....................gal. per min.
82. Cooling water supplied to weak-liquor cooler...........gal. per min.

TABLE 5.—DATA AND RESULTS OF TEST ON ABSORPTION REFRIGERATING SYSTEMS (*Continued*)

Refrigerating Output

83. Available cooling effect per hour (Q_e)..............................

84. Tons of refrigeration produced (Item 83 ÷ 12,000).................

85. Tons of refrigeration produced, brine method as a check:
    (Item 78 × Item 57 × Item 30 × 8.33 × Item 31 ÷ 200).........

Economy Results

86. Tons of refrigeration per pound steam used in generator.............

Generator

87. Heat imparted by steam per minute (Q_s).....................B.t.u.

88. Heat imparted by steam per hour (Item 87 × 60).............B.t.u.

89. Logarithmic mean temperature difference.................deg. Fahr.

90. Coefficient of heat transfer (K = (Item 88 ÷ Item 89 × Item 20))...B.t.u.

Condenser

91. Heat removed per minute by condensing water (Item 68 − Item 69 × Item 79 × 8.33).............................B.t.u.

92. Heat removed as calculated from refrigerant condenser as a check....

93. Heat removed per hour (Item 91 × 60).....................B.t.u.

94. Logarithmic mean temperature difference.................deg. Fahr.

95. Coefficient of heat transfer (K = (Item 93 ÷ Item 94 × Item 8))...B.t.u.

Evaporator

96. Heat removed per minute from brine.......................B.t.u.

97. Heat removed per hour (Item 96 × 60).....................B.t.u.

98. Logarithmic mean temperature difference................deg. Fahr.

99. Coefficient of heat transfer (K = (Item 97 ÷ Item 98 × Item 10))....

Absorber

100. Heat removed by water per minute (Q_2).....................B.t.u.

101. Heat removed by water per hour (Item 100 × 60).............B.t.u.

102. Logarithmic mean temperature difference.................deg. Fahr.

103. Coefficient of heat transfer (K = (Item 101 ÷ Item 102 × Item 18))...B.t.u.

Strong Liquor Pump

104. Indicated horsepower..i.hp.

105. Steam consumption....................................lb. per hr.

Brine Pumps

106. Gross or brake horsepower.................................b.hp.

107. Water horsepower...hp.

108. Overall efficiency..per cent

Water Pumps

109. Gross or brake horsepower.................................b.hp.

110. Water horsepower...hp.

111. Overall efficiency..per cent

CHAPTER IX

ICE MAKING

Ice-making Systems.—The present system of mechanical refrigeration owes its origin to the necessity for manufacturing ice. Mechanical refrigeration, although first used in making ice, now finds many other applications, as in cold storage, candy factories, sugar refineries, chemical works, and marine service. Since ice was first manufactured, methods have become more or less standardized, so that the present systems and apparatus employed are very much alike.

There are two systems of ice making in general use at the present time—the can and the plate. These two systems differ from each other in the relative location of the freezing medium and the water to be frozen.

In the *can system*, the water to be frozen is contained in metal cans placed in large tanks containing cold brine which circulates around the cans. In this process, the water begins to freeze from the outer walls of the can toward the center.

In the *plate system*, the water to be frozen surrounds the large metal plates, which contain coils or cells filled with expanding ammonia or cold brine. In this system, the water first begins to freeze on the outer walls of the plates.

Transparent Ice.—Ice which is not injurious to the health when taken internally by a person is said to be wholesome and sanitary and is called *hygienic ice*. Any suitable drinking water may be used for producing hygienic ice. Ice which is not transparent may be pure and wholesome. The presence of air in the water to be frozen makes the ice opaque and non-transparent. A cake of ice frozen by the can system may have a milky appearance at its center. This is due to the presence of air in the water and is not injurious. Transparent ice may be made by the can system through the use of properly distilled water.

In order to meet the public demand for clear and crystal ice, considerable ingenuity has been exercised, and complicated methods have been used, which, of course, add to the cost of production.

Analysis of Water.—Pure water is composed of hydrogen and oxygen, without even a trace of any other substance. As water forms, it seizes hold of various gases in the atmosphere. In this way, carbonic acid, ammonia, and nitrates are absorbed. Rain containing these chemicals falls to the earth where it reacts and forms different salts. A water containing large quantities of salts is said to be *hard,* and one containing few salts is said to be *soft.* To insure clear ice, an analysis of the water should be made, and if it shows large amounts of salts, it should be softened by chemical and mechanical means. The following is an analysis of a hard water, which shows the amounts of salts in solution:

Carbon carbonate.......... 34.4092 grains per U. S. gallon
Magnesium chloride........ 16.3755 grains per U. S. gallon
Magnesium sulphate........ 7.2917 grains per U. S. gallon

This water is heavily impregnated and is a very difficult water to handle for "raw"- or natural-water ice making.

In manufacturing ice, it is advisable, out of consideration for the public health, to make a bacterial and chemical examination of the water used. No water not suitable for drinking purposes should be used for ice making. All water filtered and softened should meet the requirements of the state Board of Health. This does not mean that all waters must be purified and treated, as any city drinking water, after proper filtering, is suitable for the manufacture of raw-water ice; but if water is taken from wells and rivers, it should always be tested and treated.

Purifying Water for Ice Making.—In the modern refrigerating plants using raw water for making ice, it is necessary, in practically all cases, to remove the organic matter, iron, clay, and sand, which may be in suspension in the water. For this purpose, special types of water filters have been designed. The filtering material is usually alternate layers of coarse and fine sand, crushed flint quartz being usually preferred. Such filtering devices are usually supplemented by charcoal filters provided to remove coloring matter, objectionable odors, and tastes. The filters can be used successfully for removing the organic matter and minerals held in suspension. Occasionally, however, a kind of water that has iron in *solution* is to be used in refrigerating plants; in this unusual circumstance, a special device must be designed which will pass compressed air in minute bubbles through the water. Mineral matter held in *solution* in water, making it *hard,* is ordinarily removed by processes included under the term *water softening.* There are no general rules to be laid down for the softening of natural or raw water, and in every plant the chemical treatment must be determined from a mechanical analysis of the water. Alum is often satisfactorily used, and some types of water filters are provided with a so-called *alum pot,* which is connected into the pipe supplying the raw water to the filter apparatus. Such an alum pot is shown in Fig. 156.

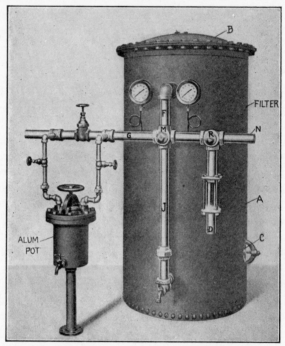

Fig. 156.—Pressure water filter and alum pot.

Operation of Alum Pot.—When alum is introduced into water with an alkaline reaction, a flaky precipitate (aluminum hydroxide) is formed, which is insoluble in water. This flaky precipitate binds together into bits of gravel the very fine particles of suspended organic and mineral matter which would otherwise pass through the sand. These bits of gravel collect on top of the sand in the filter, where they add to the deposit of filtering material. It is usually recommended that the operators of ice-making plants determine by trial how much alum is to be introduced into the water for softening. If too much alum is used, it has the same effect on the ice as any other soluble material. For making the core of the ice clear, best results are obtained by reducing the amount of alum introduced until the clearest core is obtained. Rock alum and not the powdered kind should be used, and the pot should be inspected frequently to see that it is kept well filled.

Pressure Type of Water Filter.—A typical water filter of the pressure type is shown in Fig. 156. It consists of a cylindrical steel shell *A* of which the flanged top can be removed for cleaning and repairing. There is also a hand hole at *C* near the bottom, to make it easy to remove the beds of filtered material. The raw water to be filtered enters near the top through the pipe *F*. The end of this pipe inside the shell is fitted with a galvanized distributing funnel located centrally over the filtering material. There is a branched outlet pipe in the bottom of the filter, and this is provided with so-called *umbrella nozzles*, designed to give a good distribution of the *wash water* through the filtering sand.

In the operation of this filtering device, water flows down through the beds of filtering sand and discharges from the bottom into the pipe *J*, which extends upward so that the filtered water passes through the four-way valve into the pipe *M*, shown extending to the right in the figure.

Pressure gages are placed in the water inlet and discharge pipes of the filter, to show the loss of pressure of the water in passing through the filtering beds. When this loss of pressure becomes excessive, it is an indication that the filter needs cleaning. The permissible pressure drop through the filter depends, of course, on the initial water pressure. For example, if the gage pressure of the water in the inlet pipe is 60 pounds per square inch, a pressure drop through the filter of 5 pounds per square inch is about average practice; and when the pressure drop becomes as much as 10 pounds per square inch, the filter needs cleaning. The filtering beds should not be washed oftener than is absolutely necessary, because the material which collects on top of the bed increases its efficiency. In order to wash the filtering sand, the four-way cock *M* should be turned so that the water will flow from the inlet pipe *G* downward through the pipe *J*, then upward through the layers of filtering sand inside the filter and discharge through the pipe *N*. The water used for washing cannot be used for ice making, so that it should be discharged into the drainpipe *D*. A sight glass is provided in a section of the pipe *D*, so that a person engaged in washing the filter may observe, from the appearance of the water discharged into the drain, when the washing has been carried far enough.

Distilled-water System.—If so-called *raw* or natural water, as taken from wells, rivers, or ponds is frozen by artificial means without being distilled before freezing and without agitation while freezing, the ice produced will have a whitish, marble-like appearance due to the air which is always present in natural water. This kind of ice is perfectly good, as far as any useful purpose is concerned, but most people, at least in America, do not like to use it for table or household purposes.[1]

The distilled-water system was one of the first successful devices for making clear artificial ice. Briefly, in this system, the exhaust steam from the steam engine is condensed at about atmospheric pressure in a condenser and then passes on to a reboiler, where the water is heated to a temperature at which it will boil again while exposed to the atmosphere, to permit the air in the condensed steam to be separated out and pass off from the surface of the liquid. This reboiler should have a skimmer or surface blowoff to remove any foreign matter which may accumulate on the surface of the condensed steam, especially the oil used for lubricating the engine. After the condensed steam is drawn off from the reboiler, it is passed through a set of water-cooled coils, where it is cooled to about 70 to 80° F., after which it goes through a sand filter and then a charcoal filter, the latter being especially useful in removing the last traces of any oil used in the engine. After being discharged from the two filters, the distilled water is ready to be frozen into cakes of ice, unless some system of precooling is used in the plant. The ice made from this distilled and filtered water will be entirely transparent if care is taken not to let air get into the water while it is freezing. Figure 157 shows the arrangement of water-distilling apparatus in an ice-making plant. As arranged here, the exhaust steam, after leaving the engines and

---

[1] Transparency in ice is not a requirement when the ice is to be used as the cooling medium in railroad refrigerator cars, in packing fish for transportation, and in ice-cream packing. For these purposes, it is unnecessary to go to the expense of either distilling the water used in making ice or providing mechanical means for removing the air in the water. At present, there are few distilled-water ice plants being installed.

pumps, passes through a feed-water heater, losing some of its heat and, at the same time, heating the boiler feed water. From the feed-water heater, the exhaust steam passes to an oil trap, where a large part of the oil is removed. It then passes to the condenser, where it is condensed by being brought in contact with water-cooled surfaces. The water, upon leaving the condenser, passes to a reboiler, where it is slowly boiled in order to remove the air. The rate of flow through the reboiler is such that any oil which may be present will rise to the surface and be

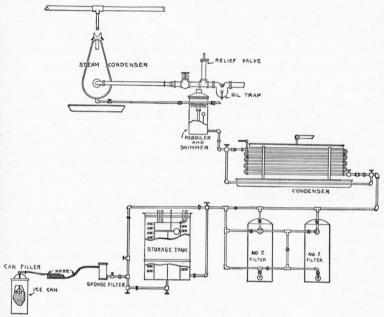

Fig. 157.—Water distilling system.

removed there by a skimming device. Any gases passing off are collected under a hood from which they escape to the atmosphere. From the reboiler, this purified water is passed to a forecooler, where its temperature is lowered by the removal of heat. The heat is removed by coils containing circulating cold water. The economy of the plant may be increased if the boiler feed water is utilized to perform this cooling before it reaches the feed-water heater.

After the water is filtered, it is chilled by brine or direct-expansion coils before being used to fill the ice cans. Before the chilled water enters the cans, it is usually passed through sponge filters, to insure absolute purity.

Where Distilled-water Ice-making Plants Must Be Used.— In some places, it is necessary to use a system of making ice from distilled water. Such places are usually where the natural water contains a large amount of mineral matter which cannot be readily precipitated—for example, sodium salts. In such places, there is still the possibility of using electric motors or oil engines for motive power by the application of a series of evaporating tanks[1] in case the cost of fuel and operation of a steam plant are excessive. For any set of conditions, it is necessary to work out the best method of removing insoluble mineral matter from the water, and cases of this kind can be decided only after careful study of all the conditions. While it is true that there are very few new plants now being equipped to use distilled water for ice making, one must realize that there are still a great many distilled-water plants in operation. Every year, however, there are a number of distilled-water steam-operated plants changing over to electric operation. One of the serious objections to the distilled-water system of ice making is that the distilling apparatus deteriorates very rapidly.

The Plate Raw-water System.—When raw or natural water was first used in ice-making plants, the ice was frozen in large slabs or plates. In this system, the refrigerant is circulated in expansion coils between large, flat metal plates so as to maintain the plate at a temperature of about 0° F. or lower while it is submerged in a tank of water which is to be frozen. The ice is formed on one side only on this plate, and the water near the freezing surface is kept in constant agitation. By this method, after somewhere between 5 and 7 days of freezing, a slab of ice will be formed on the refrigerated metal plate, the thickness of the ice slab being between 10 and 12 inches. When the required thickness of ice has been formed, the refrigerant is turned off from the coil adjacent to the plate on which the ice is being formed, and then hot ammonia vapor (in an ammonia plant) is discharged into the coil. This hot vapor melts the slab of ice from the metal plate to which it was attached. After the slab of ice is detached, it is lifted from the ice tank by a crane. Such a slab of ice usually weighs between 3 and 5 tons. After it is lifted

---

[1] See MACINTIRE, "*Handbook of Mechanical Refrigeration*," p. 378.

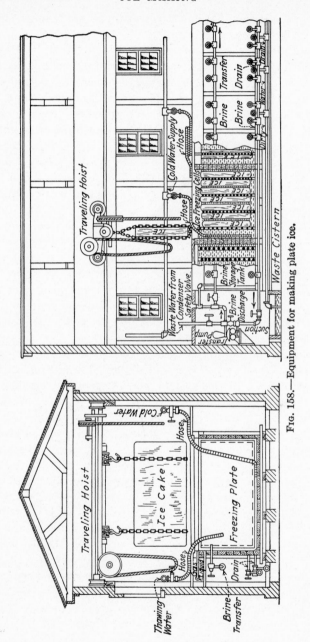

Fig. 158.—Equipment for making plate ice.

by the crane from the freezing tank, it is carried away to a suitable table, where it is sawed into cakes of ice.

By the plate method, a very good quality of ice can be made. It has, however, the disadvantage that the cakes of ice are not uniform in thickness, and this fact causes some objection from dealers. It must also be noted that the freezing tank for the plate system must be made deeper than the tank used for other systems of ice making, and, because of this greater depth, the headroom over the ice tank for the operation of the crane must also be greater. Another item of expense is the cost of power to operate the saw on the table where the slab of ice is cut up into cakes. Briefly, the disadvantages of the plate system as compared with the systems more generally used are (1) that the first cost is greater, (2) that there is trade resistance because of the non-uniform thickness of the cakes, and (3) that there is greater expense for operating the plant. Because of these items of greater initial costs, operating expenses, and trade resistance, very few ice-making plants are now being installed equipped for making ice in slabs or plates.

A general arrangement of the freezing tanks in a plate ice-making plant is shown in Fig. 158. The plates shown here are made up with freezing coils arranged so that brine may be circulated through them. An auxiliary brine pump is used to circulate the brine through the freezing coils. In order to prevent the pump from subjecting the freezing coils to undue pressure, a safety valve connected to the discharge of the pump conveys the brine back into the storage tank, when a pressure exceeding that of the setting of the safety valve occurs.

As shown in the figure, the cakes of ice are removed from the plates by means of warm water, which is allowed to pass either directly from a hose into the ice-freezing cells or into the freezing coils, melting the cakes free from the plates. The circulating water from the condenser furnishes warm water at a temperature sufficient to perform this operation.

The Can Raw-water System.—The method of making artificial ice in cans is very old; in fact, almost innumerable variations have been advocated and also practically applied for making ice in this way. The large problem to be met in any system of making artificial ice is, of course, the elimination in the water of air, which has the effect of making the ice white and marble-like in appearance. In some of the early plants for making can ice, paddles were provided in each can for the purpose of keeping the water in agitation and thus removing the air. The method

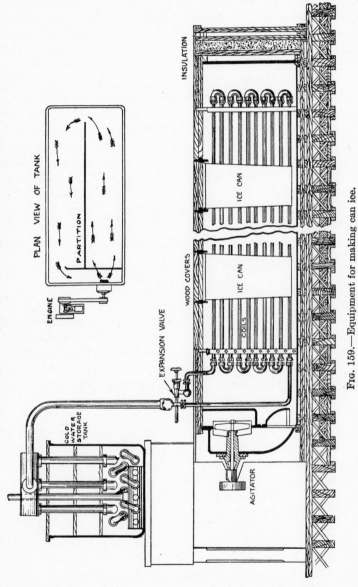

Fig. 159.—Equipment for making can ice.

has been tried of attaching short shafts to the sides of the can, so that it could be supported on bearings and rocked by a suitable mechanical device to keep the water in agitation. Methods have also been tried of avoiding any method of agitation by special treatment of the water. In one of these latest systems, the raw water for ice making is collected in a water-storage tank, and after chemical treatment and filtering it is heated to about 150° F. in a very high vacuum.

It is a general present practice to put raw water for ice making into the cans, which are then lowered into the freezing tank where cold brine circulates around them. The level of the brine is usually about the same as the level of the surface of water inside the cans, although there is an advantage in having the

Fig. 160.—Modern freezing tank for making can ice.

level of the former slightly above the level of the latter in order to shorten the time required for freezing. The temperature of the brine for making ice in cans is usually about 14 to 18° F. It is maintained either by means of direct-expansion piping in the freezing tank, as in Figs. 159 and 160, or by means of a shell-and-tube cooler which is submerged in the brine in the tank. In either case, the brine is kept in circulation by means of a suitable agitator driven by an electric motor. The horizontal type, shown in Fig. 161, is used in the freezing tank in Fig. 158. The vertical type of agitator, shown in Fig. 162, is more generally used.

In Fig. 159 is shown a general layout of a can system. In studying this figure, note that the cooling coils of the evaporator are submerged in the brine. An expansion valve is placed in the pipe line supplying the coils in order to regulate the flow of ammonia and thus control the temperature of the brine. At the left is shown the agitator. The plan view shows the method of partitioning off the tank in order to improve the circulation of the brine over its entire width. When the water in the cans is frozen, they are removed from the brine by an overhead crane. They should be wiped off or allowed to drip so as to prevent brine from entering the other cans. Then the traveling crane carries them to the thawing apparatus. In one type of thawing apparatus, the cans containing ice are brought to a horizontal position, and then warm water is sprayed on them, freeing the ice cakes from them. Another method is to

Fig. 161.—Horizontal brine agitator.

Fig. 162.—Vertical brine agitator.

immerse the cans containing the cakes of ice in a dipping tank containing water warm enough to detach the ice cakes. The ice cakes, after removal from the cans, are placed on a chute which discharges them into the ice-storage room.

In one system of making ice, the ice cans are always stationary in small freezing tanks as in Fig. 173, and have heavily insulated bottoms. The ice cakes are thawed from the sides of the cans in a freezing tank by the method of circulating around the cans brine which has been warmed by being pumped through the water storage tanks, instead of being circulated through the other freezing tanks in the plant. This use of stationary ice cans and warm brine circulation for thawing is called the *Arctic Pownall* system.

Air Agitation in Ice Cans.—One of the first systems used for agitating the water in ice cans for the removal of air required the use of a *drop pipe* into the center of each can about three-fourths of the way to the bottom of the can. Compressed air at a gage pressure of about 3 pounds per square inch was allowed to pass into this pipe and discharge from its lower end into the water. After a certain amount of freezing, the drop pipe was removed, and the freezing was continued without any agitation of the water. There is also another method by which the drop pipe is left in the core of the cake of ice somewhat longer than in the preceding method, and then, when it is removed, there is provision for adding distilled water into the space from which the drop pipe was removed. In either of these systems, however, it is necessary to remove the drop pipe at a somewhat definite time, as, otherwise, it will be frozen into the cake of ice, and, at any rate, the usefulness of the drop pipe ceases when it begins to freeze into the ice, because the pressure of the compressed air in such a system is not great enough to prevent the formation of ice at the end of the pipe. This ice formation at the end of the pipe, of course, closes it to the further distribution of compressed air.

A can system of making artificial ice from raw water, using compressed air for agitation at about the pressure stated in the last paragraph, will give satisfactory ice for marketing when fairly good natural water is used. In this method, there is, of course, always the expense of handling the drop pipes which must be removed from the cans at the proper time or from the cakes, of ice by some method of thawing.

One type of drop pipe for low-pressure agitation is placed in the center of the can and is intended to be frozen into the center of the cake of ice. In this method, the drop pipe is perforated with small holes at several places along its length to permit the escape of compressed air for agitating the water at the core of the cake of ice, especially after the end of the tube has been filled up by the ice's freezing at its end. The present tendency seems to be to use drop pipes which are intended to be frozen into the center of the cake of ice, because, by this method, it is possible to obtain more agitation than if the drop pipe has an opening only at the bottom. This agitation of the water, first mainly at the bottom of the pipe and then, later, through the holes along the length of the pipe, seems to have the effect of decreasing the amount of white core in the completely frozen cakes of ice.

The compressed air which is supplied for the agitation of the water in ice cans should preferably be taken from the air space in the freezing tank, that is, near the top of the tank, for the reason that the air in this space does not circulate much and is, therefore, cooled to a low temperature by the brine. This provision for obtaining cool air for water agitation in the cans is a worthwhile consideration for the best efficiency of an ice-making plant and is especially important in summer weather, when the air taken from the atmosphere for the same purpose would be at a very much higher temperature and would contain a great

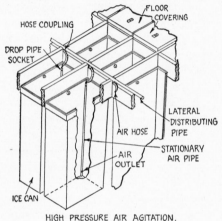

FIG. 163.—High-pressure air piping for ice cans.

deal more moisture. The effect of injecting warm air and warm-water vapor into the ice cans is to increase the refrigerating effect required and to increase also, the time required to freeze a cake of ice. The compressed air is usually delivered to the cans of ice by means of large distributing pipes with a great many outlets for the attachment of shorter lateral pipes. Each of the laterals has a number of outlets for the attachment of pieces of hose which run to the drop pipes in the individual cans. A typical arrangement of piping is shown in Fig. 163. Such an arrangement makes it possible to have a fairly uniform air pressure in all the cans of a freezing tank.

If the drop pipe is located in the center of the ice can, the temperature of the air in the pipe will be at 32° F. from the time that freezing begins until the water in the core is frozen. Under these conditions, with ordinary freezing temperatures in the drop pipe for practically the whole time that the ice can is in the freezing tank, no opportunity is given for the moisture in the air supplied for agitation to freeze in the drop pipe. When, however, the drop pipe is mechanically attached to the side of the ice can either by being soldered in the corner, as in Fig. 163, or fastened in some other way to the side of the can, it is in metallic contact with the side of the can during the whole period of freezing of the ice cake and is, therefore, for all this time, at a temperature between 14 and 18° F. The air supplied through the drop pipe for water agitation under these conditions requires a higher pressure than when the drop pipe extends down through the vertical axis or middle of the can. This compressed air at the higher pressure requires the removal of some of the moisture in order to prevent the freezing of the air in the drop pipe long before the ice cake is frozen. For this kind of air distribution for water agitation in the cans, it is customary to provide air in the lateral distributing pipes at somewhere between 10 and 20 pounds per square inch gage pressure, and, consequently, the compressor supplying this air will have to operate at a still higher pressure, usually from a few to 10 pounds more than the pressure in the laterals. All of these systems of water agitation by means of compressed air require the removal of the water vapor, with the exception of the systems using the low-pressure system. The apparatus used for removing the moisture from air is called a *dehumidifier*.

Dehumidifier.—One of the simplest and most easily explained devices for removing the moisture from the air used for agitating the water in ice-making plants utilizes sprays of cold water and brine to chill it, the moisture in the air, when sufficiently chilled, being easily deposited and removed. This apparatus, called a *dehumidifier*, consists of two vertical cylindrical shells, the air from which the moisture is to be removed passing first through one and then through the other. In other words, the moisture to be chilled passes through these two shells in series. The shell through which the air first passes is usually about half full of water, which is cooled by means of a brine coil; and the second shell is half full of brine, which is cooled by the use of direct-expansion piping connected to the evaporator of the refrigerating system. The pipe carrying the air from the dehumidifier to the piping system supplying air to the ice cans has, usually, a cartridge type of air filter which is replaced every few hours.

The cartridge filter is necessary to collect the mineral matter remaining in the air after the moisture has been removed. This mineral matter must be taken out of the air in order to prevent its closing the very small orifices in the needle valves at the drop pipes supplying the air to the ice cans.

Another device for removing the moisture from the air required for water agitation consists of two vertical cylindrical shells arranged in series in the same way as explained for the preceding method with a coil of pipe in each shell (Fig. 164). Each of the two shells is cooled by the circulation of brine through the coils.

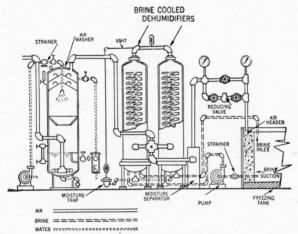

Fig. 164.—Brine-cooled dehumidifier.

The passage of the air through the first shell has merely the effect of reducing its temperature, and there is practically no frosting. In the passage of the air through the second shell, however, the moisture which is removed from the air collects as frost on the cooling surfaces of the coils and must be defrosted every 6 to 8 hours. This defrosting is accomplished by simply reversing a four-way valve. The advantage of this type of apparatus is that there is no dilution of the brine by the absorption of moisture, as in the first method. The accumulation of frost on the second coil assists in cooling the air by the amount of the latent heat of fusion of ice when defrosting the coil.

Power and Refrigeration Requirements for Air Agitation.—The amount of air required for the agitation of water in ice cans is quite large, so that air agitation in ice making involves a considerable operating expense. The first cost of the equipment for this service is also a large item. For the system of high-pressure air agitation in the ice cans, it is estimated that the usual power requirement is from 3 to 4 kilowatts[1] for every one-hundred 300-pound cans. In connection with air agitation, some refrigeration must be supplied to cool and remove the moisture from the air required for agitation. The low-pressure system requires usually only about 0.75 kilowatt per one-hundred 300-pound ice cans. In either system, about ½ kilowatt is required per one-hundred 300-pound cans for the operation of the core pump and the water and brine pumps. There seems to be a tendency, in the most recently constructed plants, to use a medium air pressure for water agitation in the cans, the gage pressure being about 10 pounds per square inch; and the drop pipe is then preferably in the vertical axis of the can, is made of brass, and extends nearly to the bottom of the can. In the low-pressure system, the drop pipe when centrally located, extends, usually, not nearly so near the bottom of the can and, in most cases, has its lower end about 9 inches from the bottom.

The medium-pressure system produces cakes of ice with very small cores, requires considerably less labor in the operations connected with the freezing tank, and does not require much more power than the old-fashioned low-pressure systems.

Removal of Core Water from Ice Cans.—There are not many kinds of natural water free from some kind of mineral matter which must be removed from the ice cans in order to make cakes of transparent ice. The tendency is for the particles of any kind of solid matter in water used for ice making to accumulate near the vertical axis of the cake of ice, in the part of the cake called the *core*. The water accumulating in the core has, in many cases, a taste somewhat like that of brine. This briny taste is due to the mineral matter. Some minerals have, also, the effect of discoloring the core. In order to rid the core of an ice cake of the briny taste and coloring matter, it is necessary to use some means for removing this objectionable water. It is necessary

---

[1] A further estimate might be stated here to the effect that the high-pressure system of air agitation requires about 6 kilowatt hours per ton of ice, which is approximately one-eighth of the entire power requirement of an ice-making plant. It may be added that the services of one man are required to take care of the freezing-tank room per shift for every 60 tons of ice produced per 24 hours.

to remove the water in the core usually once and sometimes twice from a 300-pound cake of ice. This can be done very efficiently with a core-syphoning apparatus consisting of a small centrifugal pump, directly connected and driven by an electric motor, and a suitable tank, provided with an ejector device for removing the core water by suction.

There are many kinds of natural water, particularly in the eastern states, which can be treated and filtered, without removing the core water, so as to reduce and change the nature of the mineral deposits until the small amount remaining is unobjectionable.

FIG. 165.—Hoist and crane for group of ice cans.

Hoists for Ice-making Plants.—The hoists used in refrigerating plants where ice is made may be operated by hand, by compressed-air motors, or by electric motors. The electrically operated hoist is the one preferred in most plants, particularly if the ice cans are handled in large groups. A typical electric hoist is shown in Fig. 165, where a group of eight ice cans is being handled at a time. In the figure is shown an uncovered portion of the ice tank in which a row of cans has just been placed.

Ice-can Dumps.—Figure 166 shows an excellent design of an automatically operated ice-can dump, which can be used to very good advantage in reasonably large ice-making plants laid out to be operated with the group handling of ice cans. This

Fig. 166.—Automatic can dump.

automatic dump is operated by a hydraulic cylinder H at one side of it. In the upright position of the dump, the ice cans are

Fig. 167.—Ice cans in position for filling.

in the position to be filled with water, as illustrated in Fig. 167, while, in the position shown in Fig. 166, the ice cans are inclined with the top sloping downward, so that the thawing water discharges over the sides of the cans and the cakes of ice when loosened will fall by gravity from them. Figure 168 shows a typical equipment for handling eight ice cans at a time. The crane and hoist for group handling are shown overhead. A can-filling tank, shown behind the crane, discharges purified water into the individual cans, which are supported on an automatic can dump similar to the one shown in Fig. 166. The necessary pipe for

Fig. 168.—Apparatus for handling ice cans in groups.

the thawing water is shown below the pipe discharging the water into the cans.

High-pressure Air Supply for Ice Cans.—A device for discharging high-pressure air into ice cans is represented in Fig. 163. The ice can shown in the figure has a heavy brass pipe extending down the side nearly from top to bottom. This pipe is provided to carry high-pressure air into the bottom of the ice can, the air entering the can about 1 inch above the bottom. There is a groove in the side of the can into which the pipe is set. The pipe is soldered at the lower end and is fastened to the side by slip ferrules, as shown. These slip ferrules permit expansion and contraction of the pipe. At the top of the can, it is fastened by soldering to a heavy brass socket which makes a tight joint with a suitable pipe fitting on the air line supplying the system.

A typical arrangement of piping for a high-pressure air system is shown in Fig. 163. This has the advantages over any of the low-pressure systems in that in the high pressure system it is not necessary to remove the air pipes from the ice cans at all; thus a stopping of agitation is avoided and the consequent formation of a core in the ice cake, and, likewise, labor is saved. Thomas Shipley states that the high-pressure air system produces much better results than a low-pressure system, "even though the low-pressure system is relatively satisfactory with proper care and with some kinds of water for ice making."

It is stated, further, that with a high-pressure air service and automatic can dumps having provision for handling with an electric crane groups of eight or ten cans at a time, the time required to withdraw the cans from the ice tank, carry them with the crane to the automatic dump, remove the ice from them, and then refill them with purified water is only 7 minutes, the service of only one man being needed.

Can-filling Tanks.—For filling the cans in which the ice is made, a very simple device is shown in Fig. 170. This device consists of a row of cans C, each having the same water capacity as the cans in which the ice is to be made. The purified raw water flows into the filling tank through the pipe P, shown in detail in Fig. 171. This filling pipe is provided with a float valve V operated by the float F, in one of the several chambers of the tank. After passing through the float valve, the water discharges into a trough T, which has holes near the bottom for discharging it into the compartments of the tank. A large outlet pipe is connected to the bottom of each of the compartments of the tank and has quick-opening and -closing valves all of which are operated by single lever L at the right-hand side of the tank shown in Fig. 170. It is desirable that the pipes for filling the cans in which the ice is made should have flexible connections to the valves to avoid injuring them in case the carrier of the crane handling the cans should interfere with them.

The holes through which the water discharges from the trough T (Fig. 171) into the compartments of the tank are provided with nozzles, which make an even distribution of water to all the cans. These nozzles are so constructed that changes in the quantity of water delivered to the cans in which the ice is made can be easily made by raising or lowering them. Figure 167

FIG. 170.—Can-filling tanks.

shows a row of cans as they are being filled with water from one of these tanks.

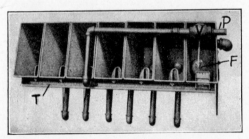

FIG. 171.—Automatic can-filling apparatus.

Location of Direct-expansion Piping.—In some of the large plants which have been laid out for the manipulation of the ice cans by the "basket" method, it has been found necessary to place the direct-expansion piping on the bottom of the tank or to eliminate this piping altogether by the use of the shell-and-tube brine cooler.

A very recent arrangement of direct-expansion piping in an ice plant is shown in Fig. 160.

Operating Costs with "Basket" Arrangement of Ice Cans and Automatic Can Dumps.—The basket system of handling large numbers of ice cans at one time will probably save 30 per cent of the labor charge incurred when they are handled two at a time with the can "dogs." The freezing tank can be made 10 per cent smaller when the basket system is used, and the cost of

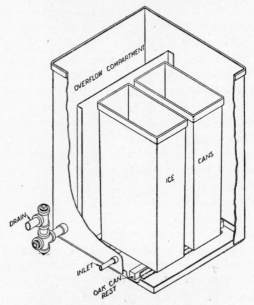

Fig. 172.—Dipping or thawing tank.

repairs is 50 per cent less than when the cans are handled with an old-fashioned two-can hoist. Of importance also, is the fact that there are fewer accidents when the basket system is used. It is stated that one man can lift one basket of ice cans (24 to 30 in a row), place them on the can dump, attend to the thawing, remove the cakes of ice from the cans, and refill them in less than 10 minutes.

Dip Tanks.—The type of automatic can dump shown in Fig. 172 is now being replaced in many plants by a so-called *dip tank.* In order to operate a large heat transfer to the cans in the dip tank, the water may be agitated with compressed air from a high- or medium-pressure system. Such agitation of the water in the dip tank secures, also, a more even distribution of temperatures than would be possible without the agitation and promotes the efficient operation of the dip tank by removing rapidly the cold film of water which tends to accumulate around the cans.[1]

Defects of Ice.—It frequently happens that the ice produced is not perfectly clear, has a white core, or even some taste or flavor.

Milky Ice.—Ice that has a milky appearance is generally the result of small air bubbles in the distilled water, due to insufficient boiling in the reboiler. It can be the result of too rapid condensation in the condenser causing more air to be drawn in than can be removed by the reboiler. This can be prevented by reducing the quantity of condensing water, thereby increasing the pressure of the steam in the boiler. Air frequently leaks into the distilled water pipe or may get into the water during the process of can filling.

White-core Ice.—In plants using distilled water, this is sometimes caused by overworking the boiler. There is an accumulation of mineral matter in the boiler water, often due to the fact that the boiler has not been cleaned so often as it should be. Carrying too much water in the boiler and lack of attention to "blowing off" will also produce this defect. More often, though, the white core is the result of the carbonates of lime or magnesia in the water. As the water in the cans begins to freeze to the walls, these carbonates are rejected to the unfrozen water. Since the center is the last to freeze, this water becomes saturated with these carbonates, thus causing the white core.

Red-core Ice.—If manufactured ice is found to have a red core, it indicates the presence of carbonate of iron from which oxide of iron has been separated. The oxide of iron nearly always comes from the iron pipes and coils in the plant. In order to prevent this defect, the pipes when idle should be kept filled with water which has been distilled and reboiled.

Rotten Ice.—Cakes of ice which are hollow in the center or are incomplete otherwise are said to be "rotten." This condition increases the surface exposed to the air which causes it to melt

---

[1] Tests have shown that the time required for thawing in the dip tank can be reduced about 40 per cent by the introduction of air agitation.

rapidly.   Great care should, therefore, be taken to have no holes in the ice cakes and to insure that they are solidly frozen.

Power for Ice-making Plants.—In practically all the applications of refrigeration, the type of motive power for driving the compressors has changed from steam engines to electric motors and oil engines, the latter being usually of the Diesel type.   When steam engines are used in ice-making plants, it is often convenient to use the condensation from the exhaust steam as the source of water to be frozen, as the water obtained in this way is suitable for use in plants requiring distilled water for ice making.

As the cost of labor and fuel have increased and it has become possible to distribute electric power more and more cheaply, nearly all modern plants near supplies of cheap electric current have come to have their compressors and auxiliary equipment operated by electric motors, because the compressors of an ice-making plant can usually be operated at a constant load. Synchronous electric motors[1] are peculiarly suitable for this service.

With the shift from steam-engine drive to electric motors and oil engines, obviously, the usual source of most of the distilled water for ice making was lost, so that recent ice-making plants have had to be designed for the use of raw water.

Details of Ice-making Plant.—As stated previously, there are several different methods of producing raw-water ice, but the general designing principles are the same.   Engineers arrange the equipment according to the conditions.   A modern form of raw-water ice plant, having a capacity of 40 tons of ice per 24 hours, is shown in Fig. 173.   It should be noticed that the steel freezing tank is divided into eight compartments, each containing a definite number of cans.   These cans are filled by opening one valve, which permits the water from the storage tank at a temperature of about 38 to 40° F. to fill the cans.   The storage tank is placed in the ice-storage room.   Each compartment can

---

[1] The electric power that is transmitted and sold for power purposes is usually alternating rather than direct current.   The two types of alternating-current motors commonly used are either induction or synchronous. A synchronous motor is generally preferred for driving compressors because of its high efficiency, and electric-power companies prefer to furnish electric current for this kind rather than for induction motors, the preference being due to the superior power factor of the former.   Relatively few steam engines are now being installed in new refrigerating plants except in unusual circumstances.

be controlled separately, as each has two valves to control the flow of the brine. A vertical agitator is used to keep the brine in circulation. The more rapid the circulation the greater the transfer of heat.

The freezing tanks should be well insulated. It is common practice to insulate the bottom with 6 inches of cork board, which may consist of three layers of 2 inches each. The sides of the tank may be insulated with either cork board or granulated cork. In general, 12 inches of granulated cork is used, an

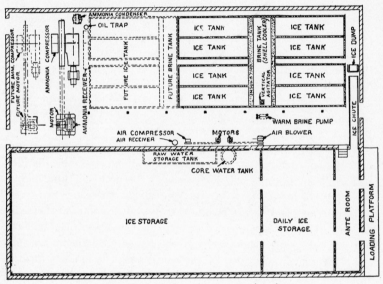

FIG. 173.—General plan of raw-water ice plant.

equivalent insulation of 6 inches of cork board. Figure 174 shows typical construction of a freezing tank.

When a single ice tank is ready to harvest, the brine in this plant is warmed by cooling the storage water for the next filling. This process frees the ice from the cans. The ice is then drawn out and stored in the anteroom or, if for only daily storage, is placed in the "daily" ice-storage room. It often happens that, for certain reasons, the day's output is more than the demand. The surplus is frequently placed in the storage room, where it is kept at a temperature of about 24 to 28° F.

Shell-and-tube Brine Cooler.—The method of cooling the brine may be by direct-expansion coils placed in the tank, as shown in

Fig. 159. Another method is to cool the brine with a shell-and-tube brine cooler. In Fig. 173, this is located in the center of the tank, dividing the freezing tank into two sections. The cooler itself resembles a return fire-tube boiler. It is cylindrical in shape, having a shell through which a large number of tubes pass. The shell brine cooler is nearly filled with liquid ammonia. The liquid ammonia enters at the bottom of the cooler, and the ammonia vapor is removed from the top. The brine is circulated through the tubes and about the shell. In this system, the bulkheads are rigidly fastened to the bottom of the ice tanks, thus forcing the brine to travel in a positive direction and producing an even flow throughout the tank. This arrangement gives a uniform freezing rate.

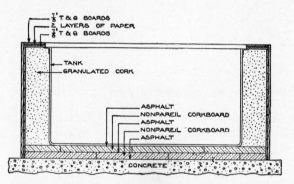

Fig. 174.—Typical construction of ice-freezing tank.

It should be remembered that the length of time allowed for freezing is governed by the temperature of the brine and, also, by the rate of brine circulation. The brine is generally held at about 12 to 15° F. If the rate of freezing is to be increased, the brine temperature must be lowered. In order to lower the temperature, a lower suction pressure is necessary. If the ice is made at a temperature too low, it will crack when the cans are placed in the thawing tanks. This cracking produces unmarketable ice.

With brine at a temperature of 14° F., it will take about 51 hours to freeze a 300-pound cake. If the temperature is decreased to 12° F., a period of about 47 hours is required. By increasing the rate of brine circulation and by keeping the brine at a given temperature, the rate of freezing can be greatly increased.

Refrigeration per Ton of Ice for Varying Water Tempera-tures.—The heat removed to freeze ice is made up of the heat required to cool the water to the freezing point, the latent heat of fusion, the heat removed to bring the ice down to the temperature of the brine, and the heat loss from the freezing tank, cans, and covers.

If the initial temperature of the water is 72° F., the temperature of the brine is 14° F., and the losses are about 20 per cent of the actual refrigeration, the amount of refrigeration required to produce one pound of ice is calculated as follows:

Heat removed to cool water $= 1(72-32)$ $= 40$ B.t.u.
Latent heat of fusion $= 1 \times 144$ $= 144$ B.t.u.
Heat removed to cool ice $= 0.5(32-14) =$ 9 B.t.u.
Total heat without losses $= 193$ B.t.u.
Losses $= 193 \times 0.20 = 38.6$ B.t.u.

Total heat required per pound of ice $= 231.6$ B.t.u.

In order to obtain one ton of ice it will be necessary to produce $\dfrac{231.6 \times 2,000}{288,000} = 1.61$ tons of refrigeration.

If the temperature of the brine is 14° F., the number of tons of refrigeration may be found from the following table:

TONS OF REFRIGERATION PER TON OF ICE

Initial tempera-ture of water ° F.	Tons of ref. per ton of ice	Initial temp. of water ° F.	Tons of ref. per ton of ice
40	1.34	62	1.53
42	1.36	64	1.55
44	1.38	66	1.56
46	1.39	68	1.58
48	1.40	70	1.59
50	1.42	72	1.61
52	1.44	74	1.62
54	1.46	76	1.64
56	1.47	78	1.66
58	1.48		
60	1.50	80	1.68

Time of Freezing of Ice.—The time of freezing ice varies with its thickness, the temperature of the brine, the shape of the can or mould in which the ice is formed, the temperature of the water, and circulation of the brine. The most important factors for a given mould is the mean difference of temperature and the thickness of the ice formed. An empirical formula has been used to determine the freezing time for can ice as follows:

$$\text{Freezing time in hours} = t_f = \frac{7 \times t^2}{32 - t_b}$$

where t = thickness of ice in inches

t_b = temperature of brine, degrees Fahrenheit.

In the case of the plate system the above formula is slightly modified and becomes $t_f = \dfrac{21 \times t^2}{32 - t_s}$ where t_s is the temperature of the freezing surface.

Example: Find the number of hours required to freeze a standard 300-pound cake of ice if the brine temperature is 14° F. The dimensions of a 300-pound ice can are $11\frac{1}{2}$ inches $\times$ $22\frac{1}{2}$ inches $\times$ 46 inches. The average thickness is 11 inches and substituting in formula above, the freezing time in hours is,

$$t_f = \frac{7(11)^2}{32 - 14} = 47 \text{ hours.}$$

Construction and Size of Ice Cans.—Ice cans are made with a taper so that the ice blocks may be easily removed without

Fig. 174a.—Typical construction of an ice-freezing can.

an excessive loss due to thawing. The cans are made of galvanized iron and have a rectangular cross-section as shown in Fig. 174a. The joints are either welded or riveted, and the top is provided with a band to stiffen it.

The standard dimensions for ice cans used in the United States are given in the following table:

Weight of cakes of ice, pounds	Dimensions, inches				Gage of metal U. S. Std.
	Inside at top	Inside at bottom	Inside length	Outside length	
50	8 × 8	7½ × 7½	31	32	16
100	8 × 6	7¼ × 15¼	31	32	16
200	11½ × 22½	10½ × 21½	31	32	16
300	11½ × 22½	10½ × 21½	46	47	16
400	11½ × 22½	10½ × 21½	59	60	14

Number of Cans Required in Freezing Tank.—In order to freeze one 300- pound can of ice with a brine temperature of 14.37° F. a freezing period of 48 hours will be required. From this it is seen that two ice cans must be in the freezing tank for each can that is harvested.

The number of cans per ton of ice varies indirectly with the brine temperature, and for standard 300-pound cans there will be needed 13.3 cans per ton of ice. This relationship can be expressed by the following formula in which N is the number of cans per ton of ice.

$$N = \frac{2,000 \times t_f}{w \times 24}$$

where t_f is the freezing time in hours and w is the weight of an ice cake in pounds.

This formula may be simplified by substituting for w the various weights of the ice cakes formed in standard cans.

$$200\text{-pound can,} \quad N = \frac{t_f}{2.4}$$

$$300\text{-pound can,} \quad N = \frac{t_f}{3.6}$$

$$400\text{-pound can,} \quad N = \frac{t_f}{4.8}$$

In order to operate the ice plant economically, it is important to design the plant for the proper number of cans per ton of ice. If the number of cans per ton of ice is small, a low brine temperature will be needed to freeze the ice in the required time. This low brine temperature will necessitate a low suction pressure. On the other hand, if a large number of cans per ton of ice is used, which means a large number of cans for a given tonnage output, the initial cost will be too great. This will, of course, raise the brine temperature and suction pressure which will produce better operating conditions.

As the brine temperatures commonly used have a range of 10 to 20° F., the number of standard 300-pound cans per ton of ice will vary from about 10 to 20 cans. A general rule is fourteen 300-pound cans per ton of ice for distilled water ice plants, while sixteen 300-pound cans per ton of ice is used for electrically driven raw-water ice plants. These values closely correspond to brine temperatures of 14° to 16° F.

Direct Expansion Piping for Ice Freezing Tanks.—The calculation of the surface needed in an ice tank depends on the type of cooling; that is, whether the cooling is by direct expansion system, flooded direct expansion system or shell-and-tube brine cooler. The shell-and-tube brine cooler may be considered as a flooded system.

The amount of surface needed depends upon the refrigeration required to produce one ton of ice, the heat coefficient of the cooling surface, and the mean difference in temperature of the refrigerant and the brine.

As previously pointed out about 20 per cent is allowed for losses (see p. 319), but it often happens that there is an additional amount of refrigeration needed, as the ice storage house and ante-room are often cooled by brine taken directly from the freezing tank.

In general the heat coefficient for a dry direct-expansion system is about 15 B.t.u. per square foot per hour per degree Fahrenheit difference in temperature, for a flooded system, 20 to 30 B.t.u. per square foot per hour per degree Fahrenheit difference, and for a shell-and-tube brine cooler the heat transfer coefficient is about 90 to 100 B.t.u. per square foot per hour per degree Fahrenheit difference in temperature.

The square feet of surface required per ton of ice may be calculated from the following equation:

$$S = \frac{H}{C \times t_d}$$

where H is the heat removed per ton of ice in B.t.u., C is the heat transfer coefficient and t_d is the mean temperature difference in degrees Fahrenheit between the brine and the refrigerant.

If the temperature of the water is about 70° F. and 1¼-inch direct expansion pipe is to be used, the above formula may be written in the following way:

$$\text{Linear feet of 1¼-inch pipe} = \frac{288{,}000 \times 1.6 \times 2.3^{*}}{C \times 24 \times t_d} = \frac{44{,}160}{C \times t_d}$$

In order to simplify the work of finding the linear feet of 1¼-inch pipe per ton of ice, Fig. 175 may be used. The curves are based on an ice-cooling effect of a 220 B.t.u. per pound and are for the flooded direct-expansion gravity-feed system. A heat-transfer coefficient of 25 B.t.u. per square foot per hour per degree

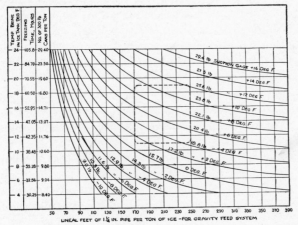

FIG. 175.—Curves based on heat transmission coefficient of 25 B.t.u. per sq. ft. of surface per °F. per hour and 220 B.t.u. per pound of ice cooling effect in freezing tank.

Fahrenheit difference in temperature was used in calculating these curves.

The mean difference in temperature between the brine and the refrigerant is determined by economical considerations. This difference will vary between 6° and 12° F. It should be noted that if a small difference in temperature is used, a larger surface will be needed than with a larger temperature difference. The initial cost of the piping will, therefore, depend on the temperature difference. With a small temperature difference the cost of the power will be less as the suction pressure will be higher.

* 2.3 linear feet of 1¼-inch pipe are equivalent to 1 square foot of external surface.

Surface Required for Shell-and-tube Brine Cooler.—If a shell-and-tube brine cooler is to be installed instead of direct-expansion piping, the area of the brine cooling surface in square feet per ton of ice can be calculated from the following equation:

$$S = \frac{H}{C \times t_d} = \frac{288,000 \times 1.6}{24 \times C \times t_d} = \frac{19,200}{Ct_d}$$

Freezing-tank Design for Can Ice

Size and shape of tank:

    a. Controlled by the size and shape of the building.

    b. Consideration in laying out tank should be given to the harvesting equipment, so as to reduce labor costs to a minimum.

    c. Short tanks are commonly used today.

Number of cans to be installed daily per ton of ice:

    a. Depends upon the efficiency of tanks.

    b. Sometimes chosen so as to give high brine temperature with a given back pressure; sometimes low temperatures are used but must not be so low as to produce cracking.

    c. An economical figure is 7.5 cans of 100 pounds capacity per ton of ice, back pressure of 25 pounds per square inch gage, 14° F. brine, and a temperature head of 2.7° F.; that is, the temperature of the brine would be 2.7° F. above that of the ammonia in the brine-cooling coils. This gives a heat-transfer value for external surface of about 46 B.t.u. per square foot per hour per degree Fahrenheit.

Advantages of flooded system:

    a. Expansion valves eliminated.

    b. Constant level of ammonia in accumulator.

    c. Liquid always available for coils and not controlled by a hand-operated expansion valve.

    d. Fluctuating condenser pressures would not affect the flow of liquid through the coils.

    e. The internal coil surface should be wetted by liquid ammonia to the fullest extent, provided that the coils are of the proper length.

    f. Condensers should be drained automatically, and surplus liquid held in the accumulator and evaporating coils.

Coils:

    a. Split coils should not be installed, as they do not produce an even amount of work, due to the liquid heat's being greater on the bottom coil.

    b. The coils can be designed single, double, triple, or quadruple, depending upon the length of tank.

    c. The length of each individual coil should not exceed 220 feet when 1¼-inch pipe is used.

    Approximately 250 feet of 1¼-inch pipe would be required per ton of ice per day.

Economy:

a. The economy of the ice tanks can be improved by increasing the rate of brine circulation; this will increase the transfer of heat from the can surface to the brine cooling coil surface.

Coefficient of heat transfer for coils (flooded system):

a. Old figure, 15 B.t.u. per square foot per hour per degree Fahrenheit.

b. Government, 20 B.t.u. per square foot per hour per degree Fahrenheit.

c. Late plants, 24 to 28 B.t.u. per square foot per hour per degree Fahrenheit and in certain cases may be as high as 46 B.t.u. per square foot per hour per degree Fahrenheit difference.

Coil Spacing:

a. Present-day design, 14½ inches on centers.

b. Wall coils should be arranged so as to be 3 to 5 inches from the tank wall.

Can Arrangement:

a. Cans should be arranged so as to prevent short circuiting of the brine.

b. Space below cans should be reduced to a minimum; in fact, the floor can be made solid beneath them.

Freezing-tank Design:

a. As a rule, tanks for 400-pound cans are 63 inches deep, but if high agitation is to be used, it will be necessary to make the wall on the "high-brine" side 68 to 70 inches high for some distance away from the propeller.

b. For fair agitation, the tank floor should slope 1 inch for each five cans lengthwise with the tank.

c. Capacity of plant can be increased by having the ice well submerged. For example, a tank designed to freeze ice in 48 hours, with a brine level even with the ice in the cans when the block of ice is completely frozen, would, however, freeze the block in 43 hours provided that the ice were submerged 5 inches.

CHAPTER X

COLD-STORAGE CONSTRUCTION

Insulation.—Refrigeration consists in removing heat from substances and in keeping outside heat away from them. This work is made difficult by the fact that heat flows from places of higher temperature to places of lower temperature and that goods which have been cooled by refrigeration will again absorb heat unless care is taken that no heat shall come into contact with them.

No matter how well a refrigerated compartment is made, some heat is constantly passing into it from the outside. If a way is not found to remove this heat as fast as it comes in, the temperature of the compartment will gradually rise. It is necessary, then, always to carry on the process of refrigeration at such a rate as to offset the inflow of heat. If the temperature of the compartment rises $\frac{1}{2}°$ an hour by inflow, it is necessary to remove $\frac{1}{2}°$ an hour by refrigeration. Clearly, all the work of removing heat is expensive, and it is important that the inflow should be reduced as far as possible, to decrease the cost of refrigeration needed to offset it. For that reason, a good deal of attention is being given to the construction of chambers which will effectively keep out heat.

All that portion of the walls, floor, and ceiling of a refrigerated space, that tends to keep heat from entering is called *insulation*. Of course, no insulation exists that can keep out all the heat, but certain kinds of insulating material can keep out more than others. On the quality of insulation and on the tightness of walls, windows, and doors depend the amount of heat that leaks into a compartment during a given time.

Since the purpose of insulation is to cut down the work of refrigeration, the engineer must consider the relative cost of insulation and refrigeration when he chooses a certain quality of insulating material. It would be poor business to spend more on high-grade insulation to keep the heat out than it would cost to remove that heat by refrigeration. As a rule, however, a

326

poor grade of insulation should never be used, for poor insulation results in uneven temperature in the compartment. Where the temperature is not uniform, goods in the center of the chamber are likely to freeze before those near the walls are cold enough.

Beside keeping out heat effectively, there are five other requirements that good insulating materials must meet:

1. It should be light so that it will not pack and settle, leaving the upper spaces of the wall unprotected.

2. It should not absorb moisture, for damp insulation permits the passage of heat more rapidly than the same material would when dry, and dampness causes decay and fermentation in the insulation itself.

3. It should be proof against disintegration and spontaneous combustion.

4. It should be odorless, so to that will not taint perishable goods, such as butter, stored in the compartment.

5. It should be proof against the tunneling and nesting of rats and other vermin.

Since few insulating materials are waterproof, it is generally necessary to enclose them in materials which are waterproof to prevent their absorbing moisture.

Materials.—We come now to a study of those substances so far classed as *insulating materials*. Among those used in cold-storage compartments and houses, the most common are sawdust, shavings, charcoal, mineral wool, still air, straw or chaff, paper, hair felt, quilting, wood, and cork.

Still Air.—Air is probably the most common insulator of all, because it conducts heat very slowly. It has been in use for a long time in guarding cold-storage compartments against inflow of heat from the outside. The most simple arrangement for insulating with air is a double-chamber wall with an air space between the inner and the outer wall. A room made in this way is surrounded by air spaces on all sides, but the spaces are so large that the air moves easily. Air which has been warmed by contact with the outer wall rises until stopped by the top of the air chamber. Here it is forced, by the rising air under it, over against the cold inner wall; it cools and travels down the inner wall to the bottom. Then the process begins all over again. But when it is said that the air is "cooled by contact with the inner wall," the meaning is that it gives up some of its heat, which then passes through the inner wall and raises the temperature of the compartment. Thus, *moving air*, by absorbing heat from the outer wall and giving it to the inner wall, serves as a heat carrier instead of an insulator.

To keep air from circulating in the manner just described, crosspieces are sometimes nailed between the inner and the outer wall, to form smaller air cells, between 1 and 2 feet square. And, sometimes, instead of only two walls (an inner and an outer), there are three or four walls with air spaces between. Even with these precautions, however, the air circulates and fails to provide effective insulation.

It is possible to keep air motionless by packing the air space with loose materials. Among such materials are sawdust, straw, shavings, and nearly all of the other things that have been mentioned as insulators. Some of them are in themselves slow to conduct heat, but they are also valuable because they divide the air spaces into tiny cells in which there is practically no circulation of air. The filling material is packed firmly so that the cells shall be as small as possible; but it is not compressed, for if the particles of filling are in too close contact with each other, the heat may be conducted from one to the other and so to the inner wall.

Cork.—Of all such insulating material, granulated cork is one of the best. Beside being a non-conductor of heat, it is light, slow to absorb moisture, durable, odorless, and not subject to spontaneous combustion. In fact, it has all but one of the qualities that a good insulating material should have: It is attractive to vermin.

Cork is produced from the bark of the cork tree, belonging to the oak family and grows in Portugal, Spain and also in other Mediterranean countries. The cork tree lives to a ripe old age and is first stripped of its bark at the age of 10 to 15 years. This first stripping is of little value being used only for ornaments. Seven years later the tree is again stripped and these curved strippings are flattened by weights under water and also charred or steamed in large copper boilers to close the pores.

The waste is used for refrigerating purposes and is a by-product. The granulated cork is made from shavings and chips ground up in mills. Care is taken to remove the fibre from the bark which contains grit. The ground cork is then sifted and screened, the coarse and medium sizes are generally used for refrigerating purposes.

Cork is exceedingly light and it packs naturally to about five pounds to the cubic foot. But in order to prevent the smaller pieces from settling, granulated cork is generally packed to a density of about six pounds to the cubic foot.

Cork is porous; that is, it contains many tiny air spaces. If it is granulated, then, and packed between the walls of a refrigerating compartment, there will be particles of air *between* the grains and, still more, little air cells *in* the grains themselves. Thus, the insulating properties of air are added to the insulating properties of the cork itself.

Loose granulated cork can be packed lightly into the space between the inner and outer wall, but this arrangement leaves the grains unprotected against moisture and vermin. To overcome this objection, manufacturers compress granular cork in iron molds and apply heat at about 700° F. In this way, slabs are made, measuring 36 inches in length by 12 inches in width. The slabs have all the good qualities of loose cork but are actually more efficient as heat insulators.

In the formation of these slabs or corkboards as they are often called, the pressure and heat cause the natural resin to act as a binder and holds the particles of cork together.

The thermal conductivity for granulated cork is about 0.31 to 0.33 B.t.u. per square foot per hour per inch of thickness and per degree Fahrenheit. Generally though about twice the thickness of granulated cork is used to that of corkboard. The thermal conductivity for corkboard is about 0.25 to 0.31 B.t.u. per square foot per hour per inch of thickness and per degree Fahrenheit. These values change somewhat with the density which varies from about 6.9 to 10 pounds per cubic foot.

As a guard against moisture and rats, granulated cork is sometimes bound together with pitch or asphalt, but this mixture conducts heat more quickly than either the loose grains or the slabs. A more efficient plan is to use slabs treated to make them vermin proof.

Where the refrigeration compartment is a brick-walled structure, cork slabs are simply laid against the wall after the bricks have been coated with hot pitch. They adhere without the use of further fastening. The inside of the slabs is usually finished with portland cement. In applying cork slabs to a frame wall, waterproof paper is laid on first; then furring strips are nailed on, and the slabs are placed between the furring. For this type of wall, the inside is finished with a layer of waterproof paper next to the cork, and a sheathing of matched and dovetailed boards is placed over that. Some kinds of slab are made up with a nailing strip imbedded in the center so that the slabs may be nailed to the wall or to the sheathing which covers them.

Hair Felt.—Another high-grade insulating material is hair felt. It is made of cattle hair which has been subjected to a careful process of washing and cleaning and compressed into a matlike substance by a felting machine. It is put on the market in sheets or strips varying in width from 2 to 6 feet and in thickness from $\frac{1}{4}$ inch to 2 inches. It may be obtained in 50-foot lengths. It is a good non-conductor of heat and has, also, the advantages of being slow to absorb moisture and easy to keep in place.

Unlike most of the other materials mentioned, hair felt is not a filler but is laid over the surface of the wall. To apply it to a brick-walled surface, a sheathing of matched and grooved boards is nailed over the studding or nailing strips on the wall, and this sheathing is then covered with a layer of waterproof paper. In this way, an air space is made. Furring strips are now run vertically from floor to ceiling, and between them are fitted strips of hair felt from 1 to 2 feet wide. One layer of felt is laid over another, until the insulation is as thick as desired. To finish the wall, another sheathing of waterproof paper and boards is fastened over the felt. Since the nails which held the felt between the furring must be taken out as this finishing layer is put on, they are not driven through the felt but are driven part way through the furring and bent over in such a way as to hold the felt.

The thermal conductivity for hair felt is about 0.246 B.t.u. per square foot per hour per inch of thickness per degree Fahrenheit. The density in pounds per cubic foot is 17.

Wood.—Dry wood is a good non-conductor of heat and is, besides, easy to supply in quantity and to work on. In some refrigeration work, layers of planks have been built up for a thickness of 6 inches or more; but for general use, it is more economical to employ wood in connection with some good filler. Several walls can be constructed, one within the other, and the air space between each two filled with insulation. Boards used in this way must be matched and fitted to form an airtight wall. Rough inside joints can be covered with waterproof paper.

Some woods possess the disadvantage of having a strong odor and of absorbing moisture too readily. Spruce, white pine, hemlock, and basswood are free from these objections and make good insulation, although spruce and basswood are hard to obtain. White pine which has been thoroughly seasoned and freed from rosin makes an insulation second only to spruce in quality. The splintery nature of hemlock makes it more vermin proof than the other woods, but, for the same reason, it is hard to cut and nail.

In general the thermal conductivity for wood is much higher than cork. The thermal conductivity varies from 0.35 B.t.u. per square foot per hour per inch of thickness per degree Fahrenheit for balsa to 1.13 for hard maple.

Shavings.—Where shavings are packed into a large space, they do settle to some extent; but if the space between walls is divided into small compartments by nailing pieces between the studding, trouble of this kind is prevented. Of course, shavings are not absolutely moisture proof, and wherever they are used, care should be taken to protect them against dampness. The same precautions against odor must be taken with shavings as with wooden planks; spruce, hemlock, and white pine are again the best. For convenience, shavings are frequently compressed into bales. In this form, they are much easier to ship and to handle.

Mineral Wool.—A fireproof, vermin-proof insulator with many fine air cells is obtained through the use of mineral wool. It is made by melting furnace slag and limestone and blowing the molten mixture into a fleecy mass by an air blast. The chief objection to this kind of insulator is its brittleness. The fibers break very easily if packed; and because the sharp ends prick the hands of the workmen and fine particles irritate their eyes, it is hard to get men who will do thorough work in using it as a filler. This disadvantage is overcome, to a certain extent, by manufacturing the wool in sheets of various sizes and thicknesses. Such sheets can be handled quite easily. Dampness attacks mineral wool very quickly and injures its insulating qualities. For this reason, mineral-wool filling should always be protected by some waterproof material.

The disagreeable features of mineral wool have been overcome so that today the workman can handle it better than formerly; the fibres are not as brittle having been annealed. The thermal conductivity is about 0.28 B.t.u. per square foot per hour per inch of thickness per degree Fahrenheit. The density is about 13 pounds per cubic foot.

Sawdust.—Sawdust serves as an excellent covering for stored ice, but it is not one of the best insulators for filling the walls of cold-storage compartments. It has a high insulating value only when it is perfectly dry; wet sawdust conducts heat rather quickly. Since sawdust is usually obtained from green wood, it is difficult to get in a dry condition, and even when it is packed dry, it absorbs moisture unless carefully protected.

If sawdust is packed in air spaces while damp, it tends to settle when it dries out, thus leaving an unprotected space at the upper part of the wall. When wet, it rots or ferments and gives off an odor which is likely to taint cold-storage goods. Another objection to sawdust is that it attracts vermin and furnishes a good nesting place for rats and mice.

Straw and Chaff.—Chaff, hay, straw, and grass chopped into fine pieces are sometimes used for insulation, but they do not belong to the better class of insulating materials. Like sawdust, they are excellent non-conductors of heat when dry but are very likely to absorb moisture and to rot.

Charcoal.—Charcoal is used as insulation in some European cold-storage plants, but its use is not favored in this country. While it is an excellent non-conductor of heat, it absorbs moisture, is dirty to handle, and costs more than some better insulators.

Insulating Papers.—All of the insulators which have been taken up have been used for the purpose of preventing the passage of heat. Insulating papers are intended rather to protect other insulating materials from moisture and warm air. They are also fairly useful as non-conductors of heat. The best insulating papers are those that are heavy and that have been coated with asphalt to give them greater durability. Tarred or oiled paper is to be avoided on account of odor, and paper sized with rosin is likely to disintegrate.

In applying the paper, care must be taken not to tear or puncture the sheet, for paper damaged in this way will permit the passage of air. As few nails as possible should be used. It is advisable to use several reinforcing layers on corners and at points likely to be exposed to hard wear.

Quilting.—Quilting is made by placing layers of insulating material, such as mineral wool, flax fiber, hair felt, or seaweed, between two thicknesses of insulating paper and stitching the whole sheet together.

Flax fiber is made from flax straw which has been crushed and treated to deodorize it and remove the nap. It is best used in quilting, for, in that way, it has the protection of waterproof paper against dampness. There are several advantages in the use of eel-grass or seaweed quilting. Such quiltings are good non-conductors of heat and are extremely durable. Seaweed contains a great deal of iodine, and, for this reason, rats and mice avoid it.

Heat Transfer through Insulation.—Nearly all of the insulated walls used in cold-storage construction have been tested for the rate of heat transfer between their surfaces. With this information, it is possible to calculate the amount of heat passing through a heat-insulating wall. Such calculations are not accurate in all cases, because heat-insulating materials vary in condition and are constructed under variable conditions.

The values obtained from such tests are expressed in the number of B.t.u. per hour passing through 1 square foot of wall surface for each Fahrenheit degree difference in temperature between the two sides of the wall. This value is called the *heat-transfer coefficient* for the wall. The amount of heat transferred through the wall can easily be calculated if we know the number of square feet of wall surface, the heat transfer coefficient, and the difference in temperature between the two sides of the wall. The amount of heat passing through the wall in 24 hours can easily be found by multiplying the value found above by 24. This may be expressed in a single formula.

Heat passing through wall per hour $= AC(t_2 - t_1)$, where $A =$ the number of square feet of wall surface; $C =$ heat transfer coefficient; $t_2 =$ temperature of outer wall; $t_1 =$ temperature of inner wall.

As an example, suppose the area of a wall to be 1,500 square feet, the heat transfer coefficient to be 0.11, the outside temperature 80° F., and the inside temperature, 20° F. Then $A = 1,500$ and $C = 0.11$; $(t_2 - t_1) = 80 - 20 = 60°$ F.

The heat transferred per hour $= 1,500 \times 0.11 \times 60 = 9,900$ B.t.u. per hour. For 24 hours, the amount will be $9,900 \times 24 = 237,600$ B.t.u., which will make necessary $237,600/288,000$ or 0.824 ton refrigerating capacity.

This means that additional refrigerating capacity of 0.824 ton is required to remove this heat. In case the wall had a heat-

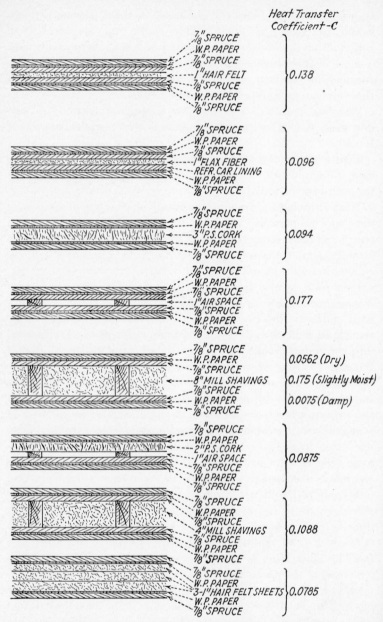

Heat Transfer
Coefficient - C

⅞" SPRUCE
W.P. PAPER
⅞" SPRUCE
1" HAIR FELT
⅞" SPRUCE
W.P. PAPER
⅞" SPRUCE

0.138

⅞" SPRUCE
W.P. PAPER
⅞" SPRUCE
1" FLAX FIBER
REFR. CAR LINING
W.P. PAPER
⅞" SPRUCE

0.096

⅞" SPRUCE
W.P. PAPER
3" P.S. CORK
W.P. PAPER
⅞" SPRUCE

0.094

⅞" SPRUCE
W.P. PAPER
⅞" SPRUCE
1" AIR SPACE
⅞" SPRUCE
W.P. PAPER
⅞" SPRUCE

0.177

⅞" SPRUCE
W.P. PAPER
⅞" SPRUCE
8" MILL SHAVINGS
⅞" SPRUCE
W.P. PAPER
⅞" SPRUCE

0.0562 (Dry)
0.175 (Slightly Moist)
0.0075 (Damp)

⅞" SPRUCE
W.P. PAPER
2" P.S. CORK
1" AIR SPACE
⅞" SPRUCE
W.P. PAPER
⅞" SPRUCE

0.0875

⅞" SPRUCE
W.P. PAPER
⅞" SPRUCE
4" MILL SHAVINGS
⅞" SPRUCE
W.P. PAPER
⅞" SPRUCE

0.1088

⅞" SPRUCE
W.P. PAPER
3-1" HAIR FELT SHEETS
W.P. PAPER
⅞" SPRUCE

0.0785

Fig. 176.—Methods of construction and heat transfer coefficients for types of cold-storage walls.

transfer coefficient twice the one used, the heat passing through would be twice as great. This shows the importance of constructing the walls so as to have a low heat-transfer coefficient.

Some cold-storage compartments have windows which allow considerable heat to pass. The amount of heat transferred in this way can be found by the above method.

The heat-transfer coefficient for a single thickness of window glass is 1.0; for double windows with air space between, it is 0.60.

Figure 176 shows some of the methods used in constructing cold-storage walls. It also gives the heat-transfer coefficient for each type of wall.

Heat Principles.—Heat is the result of the violent motion of molecules or particles which go to make up a substance. The transfer of heat is a matter of first interest in the study of refrigeration. It takes place in three distinct ways: (1) convection, (2) conduction, and (3) radiation.

Convection is the simplest to understand. The word itself comes from a Latin one meaning "to carry." That is exactly what happens: the heat is *carried* from one place to another by some fluid, such as air or water, as when a chip of wood is dropped into a running brook, the chip is carried away by the motion of the water. Now, suppose that some hot water is poured into the stream. At once it enters into circulation with the other water and flows downstream. If a thermometer is placed in the current a few feet downstream, it will register an increase in temperature. In other words, heat is transferred or carried from one place to another by the circulation of a fluid. In a common type of cold-storage room, warm air rises to the top of the room, is cooled by contact with the refrigerating coils, and falls again to the floor. Thus, heat is being transferred *from* the stored goods *to* the refrigerating coils by the circulation of a fluid—air.

Conduction is the transfer of heat *through* a substance. A familiar illustration is the silver spoon in a cup of hot coffee. The bowl of the spoon rests in the coffee; the handle is outside— in the air. In a few moments, the handle of the spoon, though it has not touched the coffee, will be hot. The heat has passed up through the spoon into the handle. To understand thoroughly how this takes place, the theory of heat must be kept in mind. The silver spoon is made up of particles or molecules. The coffee, coming into contact with the bowl of the spoon, sets the molecules violently in motion. These molecules knock against their neighbors. The process goes on until all the molecules in the spoon are agitated. In a game of billiards, a player sets one ball in motion by striking it with a cue; that ball strikes another ball and sets it in motion; and so on. It might be imagined that each ball is a molecule. The transfer of motion, in that instance, corresponds to the transfer of heat by conduction.

The third method of heat transfer is *radiation*. Less is known about radiation than about either conduction or convection, but it is clear that a third form of heat transfer exists, dependent neither upon the circulation of a fluid not upon molecular activity within a substance. For instance, if a stove poker is heated so that it becomes red hot and a hand is then placed a few inches beneath the heated end, there is a sensation of heat. Since heated air rises, obviously, the air heated by the poker goes away from the hand instead of toward it. The heat of the poker is not transferred, therefore, to the hand by convection. Air can conduct heat, but the process is so slow that it takes a considerable time for heat to travel by conduction. The transfer is, then, by the third method, which we call *radiation*. It is the one way by which heat can pass through a vacuum, and, for this reason, it is supposed to depend on vibrations of the ether.

When a cold-storage room is insulated, all of the three kinds of heat transfer are encountered. Some insulating materials are selected because they conduct heat very slowly; still air is much used because it prevents convection; and screens or layers of various materials are employed to guard against the direct radiation of heat. But in constructing walls for a cold-storage plant or a cold-storage compartment, granulated cork, mineral wool, and the other heat-insulating substances are not sufficient: wood, brick, or stone masonry are needed to give support, especially in the outer walls of a building; and, in some cases, partitions are necessary to hold the real insulator in place. Of course, such materials as brick are used principally for strength, rather than for any insulating qualities; but they have, nevertheless, the power to retard heat, to some extent.

In composite walls (insulated lining combined with the outer walls), the coefficient of heat transfer cannot be based on the insulated lining alone but must take into account the passage of heat through the outer walls.

In order to determine the heat-transfer coefficient for a *composite wall*, the surface coefficients, thermal conductivity for the various materials, and the thickness must be known.

In the case of a solid composite wall the heat-transfer coefficient, C, may be calculated from the following equation,

$$C = \cfrac{1}{\cfrac{1}{a_1} + \cfrac{1}{a_2} + \cfrac{1}{a_3} \ etc. + \left(\cfrac{x_1}{c_1} + \cfrac{x_2}{c_2} + \cfrac{x_3}{c_3} \ etc. \right)}$$

where a_1, a_2, a_3, are the surface coefficients for the various materials (table XVII on p. 415) in B.t.u. per square foot per hour per degree Fahrenheit difference, x_1, x_2, x_3, are the thicknesses of the materials in inches, and c_1, c_2, c_3 are the thermal conductivities (table XX, p. 417) for the various materials in B.t.u. per square foot per hour per degree Fahrenheit difference.

When a composite wall contains air spaces, the coefficients for still air and the surface coefficients for the various materials must be used. In case the air spaces are large, little insulating effect is obtained, because the circulating air transfers the heat from one surface to the other by convection.

The heat-transfer coefficient, for example, may be determined as follows for a wall which is made up of 13 inches of brick, ½ inch of cement, 4 inches of corkboard, and ½ inch of cement plaster to finish the surface of the corkboard on the inside wall.

From tables XX and XXI in the appendix the thermal-conductivity coefficients may be obtained and are as follows: brick, $c = 5$; corkboard, $c = 0.3$. The coefficient c for plaster maybe taken the same as for brick, that is, $c = 5$. The surface coefficients for plaster and brick may be taken from table XVII (p. 415) $a_1 = 1.1$ and $a_2 = 1.4 \times 3 = 4.2$ respectively. It should be noted that the effect of moving air on the outside surface of the wall has the effect of increasing this value for still air about three times. The heat-transfer coefficient for this composite wall can then be calculated as below,

$$C = \cfrac{1}{\cfrac{1}{1.10} + \cfrac{1}{4.2} + \cfrac{13}{5} + \cfrac{4}{0.3} + \cfrac{1}{5}}$$

= 0.058 B.t.u. per square foot per hour per degree Fahrenheit difference.

Cold-storage Buildings.—The use of insulating materials with a low heat-transfer coefficient is not sufficient to obtain efficient cold-storage effects. The kind of construction of the building itself is equally important. The first rule is that all the materials used should be of high quality. This does not always mean that they should be the most expensive on the market; but it does mean that the purchase of inferior materials is certain to be poor economy in the end. The two results to be looked for are, of course, good insulating capacity and durability. So far as durability is concerned, the same principles hold good in cold-storage construction as in any other form of building. Materials which will not warp, settle, or decay, and good workmanship in putting them together will avoid the expense of constant repair and the possibility of leakage on account of joints which are not tight. Because of the difficulty of renewing material which has been built into the walls, it is essential, too, that substances be chosen which will not only retard the passage of heat when new but which will also retain their insulating properties. The building should be arranged with a minimum number of doors and windows. No skill of the architect or of the builder can do away with a certain amount of refrigeration loss through and around doors and through the windows. This is due, to some extent, to doors which do not fit snugly. It is desirable to buy special insulated doors which are manufactured especially for cold-storage buildings. These give better satisfaction than ordinary doors.

With windows, the case is different. Windows cannot be constructed without glass, and glass transmits heat more rapidly than any of the other ordinary materials used in a building. The best plan is to do without windows as far as possible. Sufficient light can be easily provided by a well-planned electric system of lighting. Electric lights give off some heat, but the refrigeration loss is much less in proportion to the illumination than it would be by the use of windows. And it must be remembered, at the same time, that the heat from a modern tungsten bulb ceases as soon as the light is turned off, while windows are a constant source of heat leakage.

Heat from Electric Lights, Motors, and Workmen.—In calculations for cold storage rooms allowance must be made for the heat developed by lights, machinery, and workmen. The following table gives the amount of heat in B.t.u. per hour for each electric light during the time that it is lighted. In the table the power required for electric lights is in watts.

Capacity of Electric Lights, Watts	Heat B.t.u. per Hr. per Electric Light
25	85.25
50	170.50
100	341.00
200	682.00
400	1,364.00
600	2,046.00

The table was calculated on the basis of one horse-power being equivalent to 746 watts and also equivalent to 2,545 B.t.u. per hour.[1]

The heat generated by electric motors, fans and other machines is calculated in very much the same way as for electric lights, knowing that one horsepower is equivalent to 2,545 B.t.u. per hour or 42.42 B.t.u. per minute. In the case of electric fans used for air circulation all the electric power used by the motor driving the fan develops heat in the cold storage rooms, so that the total amount of power actually used by the motor is converted into heat. In the case of motors used for operating conveyors and lifts the total horse-power actually used by the motor is converted into heat in the cold storage rooms if no part of the power of the motor is used to operate machinery outside the cold-storage rooms.

The heat given off by men working in cold-storage rooms will vary from 400 to 600 B.t.u. per hour, depending on the kind of work. It is customary to assume that the heat introduced by a man when working is on the average 500 B.t.u. per hour.

The data given in this section will give the necessary information for calculating a large part of the amount of heat, aside from that entering through the walls, for which refrigeration must be provided. It is obvious of course that unnecessary heat should be prevented from entering the cold storage rooms since all this must be removed by the refrigerating system.

Design of Cold-storage Rooms.—All the preceding calculations in heat transfer have been made on the basis of B.t.u. *per square foot of wall surface*, understanding that a rectangular room has six walls—that is, four side walls, a ceiling, and a floor. The floor and ceiling are included, because heat is as likely to pass

---

[1] It is customary to allow one-half to one watt per square foot of floor area in cold storage rooms for the amount of heat which is on the average given off by electric lights.

through them as through the side walls. Since the amount of heat passing into a compartment with any given thickness of wall and efficiency of insulation depends on the number of square feet of wall surface, the best results are obtained with the fewest possible number of square feet of surface. It may seem, at first, that this will depend on the cubic capacity of the compartment and that, in cutting down the wall surface, it is necessary to give up a corresponding amount of storage space, but this is not necessarily the case. For example, a room which has a cubical shape (that is, a room whose height, length, and breadth are the same) has the least wall surface for any given storage capacity. A room 10 feet high, 10 feet long, and 10 feet wide has a volume of 10 × 10 × 10, or 1,000 cubic feet.

Now, to find the total wall surface, the area of the surface of each wall must be calculated, and then the surfaces added together. Each side wall, being 10 feet long and 10 feet high, contains 100 square feet; and four of these walls contain 400 square feet. The floor is 10 feet long and 10 feet wide and contains 100 square feet. The ceiling has the same dimensions and, also, contains 100 square feet. Adding the areas of the floor and ceiling to the area of the side walls, the total wall surface is 600 square feet.

With the same height for the room as before, suppose, now, that the other dimensions are changed so that the room is 25 feet long and 4 feet wide. The volume of the room will be 25 × 4 × 10 or 1,000 cubic feet, exactly the same as in the first example. Two of the side walls—the long ones—are each 25 feet long and 10 feet high, containing 250 square feet each or 500 square feet for the first two sides. The shorter walls are 4 by 10 feet, containing 40 square feet each or 80 square feet for the two sides. The floor is 25 feet long and 4 feet wide, containing 100 square feet. The ceiling has the same dimensions as the floor and, also, contains 100 square feet. Adding all six surfaces together, the total wall surface is 780 square feet, which is 180 square feet more than the room of the same volume which has the cubical shape. The greater wall surface has not gained additional storage space, while it has greatly added to the amount of heat that can pass into the room in a given time.

Air Spaces.—Because air conducts heat very slowly, some engineers have made a practice of leaving air spaces in the construction of walls and floors, especially in the spaces between floor joists. This system would be efficient if the air remained perfectly still, but it does not. Heated air rises, and cold air falls. Thus, when heat from the outer walls comes into contact with the air in a hollow space, that part of the air next to the outer walls tends to rise, and the space it occupied is taken by cooler air, which, in turn, becomes warm and rises. In this way, a circulation of air is set up, and heat is transferred rapidly to the inner walls not by *conduction* but by *convection*. For this reason, all spaces between walls and floors should be filled with some insulating material, such as granulated cork or hair felt, to divide the space up into tiny air cells and prevent free circulation. It is necessary to pack such insulation so tightly that it will not settle.

Where air spaces are left between brick walls and the layers of insulation, moisture is almost certain to enter through the porous bricks, cross the air space, and damage the insulation. In such cases, the inside of the brick wall should be coated with a waterproofing mixture, and the air space filled with an insulator which is fairly moisture proof itself, such as slabs of granulated cork, mixed with asphalt. At best, however, some moisture is sure to pass through outer walls of almost any kind, and it is a good principle always to place the best insulators farthest from the outer walls and to protect them by intervening layers as nearly moisture proof as possible.

Fireproof Construction.—Cold-storage work does not, in general, require fireproof construction. Where a cold-storage plant is located in a thickly built city section, it is necessary, of course, to have a building which conforms to the standards for such localities, but that is for the protection of the city, not of the storage house itself. The principal disadvantage of fireproofing is that the materials used in fireproof construction are usually poor insulators. A second disadvantage is the cost, which more than equals the saving from the lesser fire risk.

Experience has demonstrated that few fires start in the cold-storage compartments themselves. Thus, a reasonable protection is given by the use of brick outer walls with heavy wooden construction within, preferably with a layer of smooth cement plaster inside the insulation, to lend fireproofing properties to the construction.

Wall-construction Design.—The cold-storage wall design shown in Fig. 176a is the cross-section of the wall for a frame building. No air spaces are next to the outside wall, which is filled with shavings. This prevents the free circulation of air. In order to protect the shavings from moisture, the inside surface of the outer wall is coated with a waterproof paper.

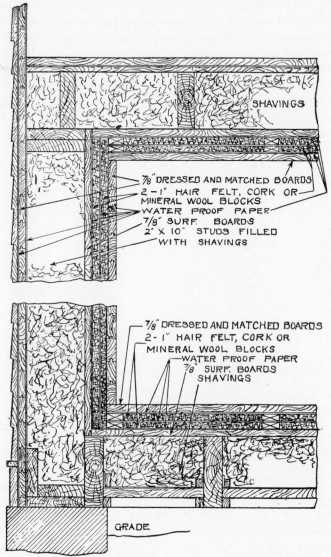

SHAVINGS

⅞" DRESSED AND MATCHED BOARDS
2 – 1" HAIR FELT, CORK OR MINERAL WOOL BLOCKS
WATER PROOF PAPER
⅞" SURF. BOARDS
2" X 10" STUDS FILLED WITH SHAVINGS

⅞" DRESSED AND MATCHED BOARDS
2 – 1" HAIR FELT, CORK OR MINERAL WOOL BLOCKS
WATER PROOF PAPER
⅞" SURF. BOARDS
SHAVINGS

GRADE

Fig. 176a.—Construction of a type of cold-storage wall.

Cold-storage Insulation.—In insulating a cold-storage room, the engineer tries to make it an island in an ocean of heat. Many substances which have been used for insulation have been taken up. Of these substances, cork is most commonly used today. Cork is suitable as a cold-storage insulation because it is: (1) a good non-conductor of heat; (2) moisture proof; (3) durable; (4) odorless and sanitary; (5) slow burning and fire retarding.

A modern cold-storage house is built of fireproof material throughout, being generally a concrete structure. It may be of steel framework with reinforced concrete ceilings and hollow tile walls. It is desirable to make the insulation of the walls continuous. This can be brought about by constructing a

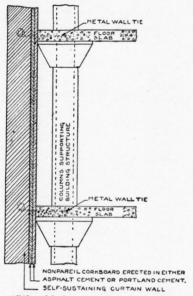

Fig. 176b.—Modern cold storage construction.

self-sustaining curtain wall (Fig. 176b), which is independent of the interior structure except for the small metal ties. The insulation is applied against the inner surface of the curtain wall, which is a continuous sheet without a break from the basement to the roof. *Cork board* is generally used for this purpose. Generally, about 4 inches of cork board are laid in hot asphalt, in such a way that all transverse joints are "broken." This thickness of insulation will pass about 2 B.t.u. per square foot of surface per 24 hours, per degree Fahrenheit difference in temperature. The total heat transmitted through an insulation is expressed in B.t.u. transmitted per square foot, per 24 hours per degree Fahrenheit difference. This value for Nonpareil cork, of 1 inch thickness is 7.9.[1] For waterproof lith board, another common insulator, the value is 8.4. The following table gives the total heat passed per square foot of surface, per day, per degree Fahrenheit difference for various thicknesses of cork board

Thickness of Cork Board, Inches[1]	Transmission, B.t.u. per Square Foot per 24 Hours per Degree Fahrenheit Difference
1	10
2	5
3	$3\frac{1}{2}$
4	3
5	$2\frac{1}{2}$

[1] For granulated cork of the same thickness, these values should be approximately doubled.

Generally speaking, it may be said that the thicknesses of the best cork board which can be economically installed for the several temperatures are as follows:

Temperatures, Degrees Fahrenheit	Thickness of Cork Board, Inches
−20 to −5	8
− 5 to +5	6
5 to 20	5
20 to 35	4
35 to 45	3
45 and above	2

The conductivity of various insulating materials is given in Table XX in the Appendix.

[1] See "Heat Transmission," *Penn. State Coll., Bull.* 30.

CHAPTER XI

AIR CIRCULATION AND VENTILATION IN COLD STORAGE

Air Circulation.—Some air contains more moisture than other air. Moisture in the air is called *humidity*. All air is naturally humid to a certain extent. Natural air does not exist anywhere in a perfectly dry condition. It is only when the percentage of moisture is relatively high, however, that we notice humidity.

Heated air absorbs more moisture than cool air; and air is less able to absorb or to hold moisture as its temperature falls. If moisture is present in sufficient quantity, air will finally absorb so much that it cannot hold more. It is then said to be *saturated*. At lower temperatures, it becomes saturated with less moisture than at higher temperatures. Thus, if air which was saturated at one temperature is cooled, it must give up some of its moisture by precipitation. The moisture given up in this way may remain in the air in the form of finely divided particles of water—as in fog—or it may be precipitated so rapidly that water gathers into large drops which fall as rain. For the same reason, when saturated air meets a cold surface, as the surface of a drinking glass, it gives up part of its moisture, which then gathers on the glass, so that the glass "sweats."

Saturated air when cooling gives up only as much moisture as the reduction in temperature makes necessary, and at the lower temperature it is still saturated; that is, it still holds as much moisture as possible *at that temperature*. Reversing the process, if cool air is heated, its humidity will diminish, for, at a higher temperature, it is capable of holding more moisture than it did originally. Humidity is, therefore, a matter of proportion, and the *relative humidity* of air is calculated by finding what percentage of the moisture which the air *can hold* is actually contained in it. Air when it is saturated at any particular temperature is 100 per cent humid at that temperature. Air which could hold twice as much moisture before reaching the saturation point has a humidity of 50 per cent.

It is necessary in cold-storage rooms to control the humidity of the air, for dampness interferes with the efficiency of the air for preserving goods. When dampness is permitted in cold-storage compartments, a musty odor soon develops that is injurious and objectionable. Dry air preserves perishable substances which damp air will mold. For these reasons, the air in a refrigerated compartment should be kept at a low humidity. Wherever goods—and especially meat—are stored, there is a good deal of moisture absorbed by the air from the goods.

One method of reducing the humidity in cold-storage rooms is to pass the air over some substance which will readily absorb the moisture. Some of the commonly used moisture absorbents are unslacked lime, common salt, and calcium chloride. Of these, the calcium chloride is most commonly used, because it is capable of absorbing a great amount of moisture in proportion to its own bulk and is inexpensive.

A second method depends on the effect of temperature changes on humidity. By this method, moist air is cooled until it becomes saturated, and then it is cooled further by contact with cold surfaces until it gives up some of its moisture. It is then heated so that it may again be able to hold more moisture, but since it has already deposited a certain amount of its moisture, it has less than it can hold, and its relative humidity is, therefore, less than it was before.

In some refrigerating plants, both drying methods are used at the same time. In either case, a circulation of air in the storage rooms is necessary; air cannot be cooled and heated without being put into circulation, nor can it be passed over absorbents without circulation.

Circulation is also needed to keep the air pure. The fungus germs which produce mold are abundant wherever goods are stored. If they are allowed to settle through stagnant air on the goods, they will develop rapidly and counteract the advantage of refrigeration. Circulating air will carry these germs away from the contents of the storage rooms and bring them into contact with the cold refrigerating pipes, where they will be deposited with the moisture. Since these germs cling to moist surfaces, they will be caught on the pipes and prevented from infecting the stored goods.

During the storage of foodstuffs, a gradual process of decomposition is constantly at work. It may be so slow in its action that months will pass before the food is unfit for use. Certain fermentation gases, however, are always being formed, and, unless these are removed, they will lead to an unwholesome atmosphere in the storage rooms, as some of these gases are quickly absorbed by the air; they unite and move with the moisture in the air. Here, then, is another need for circulation. As circulating air deposits its moisture on the cold refrigerating surfaces, it deposits also the fermentation gases which would otherwise foul the storage compartment. Such gases as are not absorbed by the air may be cleared from the storage rooms by ventilation.

A third method of reducing the humidity in cold-storage rooms is by the circulation of air in order to maintain an even temperature in all parts of the storage compartments. If the air did not pass from one part of a storage compartment to another and were allowed to settle and remain stagnant, that part of the compartment next to the cold refrigerating pipes would have a temperature several degrees lower than that part in the middle of the room, so that goods stored near the sides of the room would be frozen before those in the center of the floor were cool enough to keep. Even if there were no danger of freezing goods near the pipes, there would be a tendency to put unnecessary work on the refrigerating machine in order to preserve goods at some distance from the refrigerating pipes. Circulation of air prevents such wastage by equalizing temperature in all parts of a storage room.

Methods of securing circulation are generally classed in two groups: (1) *natural* circulation, in which the air moves because of differences in densities due to changes in temperature; and (2) *forced* circulation, in which a fan generates and directs the air currents.

Refrigeration Effects of Ice-freezing Mixtures.—Though the melting of ice is the commonest method of refrigerating, there are several objections to this form of cooling. The first is the limitation of temperature at which ice can maintain a storage compartment. Ice melts at 32° F.; but this melting cannot keep a room at that temperature, except under the most favorable conditions. With summer heat to contend with, temperatures of 36 to 38° F. are possible. Most goods require storage at temperatures from 2 to 8° lower than this. If ice is mixed with common salt or calcium chloride, a compartment can be effectively cooled. Such a mixture melts at a temperature lower than the melting point of unmixed ice; and because the difference between the temperature of the room and the melting point of the *mixture* is greater than between the temperature of the room and the melting point of *ice*, the mixture melts more rapidly and produces a greater cooling effect. If, for instance, a compartment contains air at a temperature of 33° F., the difference between that temperature and melting ice is 1° F. Now, because the rate at which the ice melts depends on that difference, the melting would be slow. If a sufficient amount of calcium chloride is mixed with the ice to make its melting point 20° F., the temperature difference between the calcium-chloride freezing mixture and the air in the room is then 13° F. Melting will then take place thirteen times as rapidly as when ice alone is used, and the cooling effectiveness of the operation would be greatly increased. A melting process is always taking heat out of the air and, thus, cooling the compartment.

Cooling with ice leaves the air too damp for the best results in cold storage. Air is most easily dried by bringing it into contact with surfaces which are so cold that the moisture it contains is condensed. The colder these surfaces are in relation to the temperature of the air the more moisture will be given up by the air. Now, in the ice-cooling methods of refrigeration, the ice-cooled surfaces are, at the most, but a few degrees colder than the air, so that the moisture which will be condensed is small. Thorough air drying depends on a wide temperature difference between the air and the cooling surface.

Besides temperature, there is one more condition that influences the humidity of air: the amount of moisture present which the air can absorb. Here, again, the ice-cooling method has a disadvantage, for melting ice forms water which the air will absorb as readily as it can. Natural air circulation, too, depends upon the range of temperature. Since the air of a storage room is nearly as cold as the ice, natural air circulation will be poor. In general, it is safe to say that ice-cooled compartments will not be satisfactory except where goods are stored for only a few weeks and where the required temperature is not below 38° F. Even to secure this result, some care must be given to the arrangement of an ice-cooled room. The earliest and simplest method was to place the ice directly in the storage compartment and to keep the goods at the lowest possible temperature. They were often placed in contact with the ice, as the average housewife keeps a head of lettuce fresh. But this method did not keep the goods dry and frequently injured them. In any case, the placing of an ice bunker in the room caused the air to absorb a great deal of moisture and prevented satisfactory circulation. The obvious remedy was to put the ice bunker in a separate compartment, sometimes at the end and sometimes at the sides of the storage room. Because cool air settles and warm air rises, later arrangements were based on an ice bunker elevated above the storage floor and separated from it by a partition. Still more recently, racks were constructed near the ceiling of the room, and the ice was placed on them. The warm air of the compartment thus rose and flowed along the ceiling to the ice bunker, was cooled by

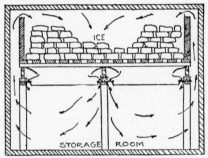

Fig. 177.—Air circulation in storage room refrigerated with ice.

contact with the ice, and fell again through the racks to cool the stored goods.

Pans of a dry absorbent, as, for example, calcium chloride, were so placed that the rising air passed over them and deposited some of its moisture. This method was an improvement, but it failed to provide good circulation of air or to reduce the dampness sufficiently; and the temperature of the storage room was still relatively high.

One of the best methods based on this system is shown in Fig. 177. Here a galvanized-iron dripping pan, placed under the ice racks, catches and drains away the water from the melting ice. Gaps are left around the sides of the pan to permit the passage of cooled air as it descends. The entire ice compartment forms an inner chamber within the storage room, and an air space is left between the walls of the room and the walls of the ice compartment. Through this air space, the warm air rises and flows over the top of the ice.   The cooling and falling of the air make fairly good circulation.

Piping Arrangements for Mechanical Refrigeration.—Most modern cold-storage plants require a refrigerating system of greater efficiency than can be obtained by the use of ice.   For this reason, systems of mechanical refrigeration have come into use.   In some of these, the refrigerant is expanded in the pipes; in others, cold brine is circulated.   Either way involves the use of pipes and coils.

As the arrangement of ice bunkers affected the success of ice-cooled storage, so the placing of these pipes and coils is an important feature of mechanical refrigeration.   The same three arrangements that were explained in connection with the use of ice bunkers hold good in regard to piping: The coils may be placed (1) in the storage room; (2) in a separate chamber divided from the storage room by a partition, or (3) above the storage room.

The problem of low temperature is very simply solved by any of these methods, because, by the application of mechanical refrigeration, any temperature can be obtained as low as $-5°$ F.; and since, by regulating the pressure in the pipes, the engineer can raise or lower the temperature at will, the outside conditions of temperature can be met, and an even temperature can be maintained in winter and summer.

To secure the best circulation, however, the arrangement of pipes must be taken into account.   Clearly, natural circulation is possible when the coils are much lower in temperature than the air of the storage room, because, obviously, the circulation depends on the passage of air between the places of varying temperature.

The same difficulties of circulation and uniform temperature that appeared in the early forms of ice-cooled compartments are encountered when the coils are placed directly in the storage room. Goods in the center of the floor get insufficient cooling, while those near the pipes are in danger of freezing.   But this objection can be overcome by erecting a thin wooden partition to prevent the direct radiation of heat from the goods to the coils.

The low temperature of the coils in systems of mechanical refrigeration is also advantageous in keeping the air dry.   The pipes or cooling surfaces are so much lower in temperature than the circulating air that the air in striking them gives up much of its moisture, which immediately freezes on the cooling surfaces as frost.

Natural Circulation.—The special arrangements by which cooling by coils can be made most effective will now be discussed. Dryness of the air and uniformity of temperature depend very largely on good circulation of the air. In any special arrangements of refrigerating coils, therefore, circulation is of first importance.

The principle of circulation, already outlined, is this: warm air rises, and cold air falls. But it is necessary that a cold-storage room be so arranged that the rising air and the falling air shall not interfere with each other. That is the fault of a piping arrangement in which the pipes are distributed regularly over the ceiling. A body of warm air is always attempting to rise,

Fig. 178.—Cold storage room with brine piping near ceiling.

Fig. 179.—Cold storage room with two groups of brine pipes.

but a body of cold air, occupying the same amount of space, is descending; the circulation, therefore, is complicated and ineffective. If, in such a cold-storage room, goods are piled high, those near the ceiling are liable to freeze. The plan of such a cold-storage room is shown on Fig. 178.

A better method is shown in Fig. 179. Here there are two groups of pipes, one on each side of the room, near the ceiling, and a partition to direct the currents of air under each group. These partitions are made up of shelving and are so arranged that the cold air, on leaving the pipes, will flow downward and outward toward the walls of the room. The warm air rises through the middle of the room between the inside edges of the partitions. Experiments have established certain proportions to be observed in building a storage room on this plan. The sloping partitions are generally inclined 6 inches in 10 feet; that is, on a slope of 1 in 20 or 5 per cent. The width of the air space between inner and outer walls is one-twentieth of the width of the room.

Another important measurement is the distance between the floor and the bottom of the partition. This dimension varies with the width of the room. Where the room is wide, it should be low, so that the heated air will flow along toward the center of the room instead of rising too quickly and leaving a pocket of dead air in the middle of the floor. If the room is narrow, the height may be greater, for the reason that there is so little floor space to provide with circulation in proportion to the volume of the room that there is little danger of the air current's rising too steeply.

A different arrangement based on the same principle is sometimes used for extremely narrow rooms. It allows for a single

Fig. 180.—Cold storage room with damp walls and floors.

Fig. 181.—Cold storage room with vertical rows of brine pipes along walls

group of pipes at one side of the room, instead of the two groups as just explained. As a rule, the single-group system cannot produce such good results. Its value depends on economy in installation costs. As shown in Figs. 179, 180, and 181, the refrigerating pipes in each group are arranged in vertical rows, and under each row is fixed a long, narrow pan to catch the drain off the drippings. Since there is a separate pan for each row, and a space between the pans, the cooled air is allowed to descend freely between the pipes. The use of one broad pan for all the rows would prevent this.

The wastage of floor space on account of the partitions and the difficulty of getting at the coils to make repairs are the two great disadvantages of the method shown in Fig. 179. The circulation secured by this method is, however, good, and because the heated, moisture-laden air gives up its humidity on the cooling surfaces before coming into contact with the floor and walls, these are kept in drier condition than with some other systems.

An example of damp floors and walls is shown in Fig. 180, the air currents absorb moisture from the produce and convey it to the walls. The goods themselves, however, receive cold, dry air. The disadvantages of this system are weaker and less even distribution of circulated air than in some other methods of air circulation.

Still another grouping and arrangement of pipes is shown in Fig. 181. The pipes are placed in vertical rows along the walls, and, unless the room is very narrow, a partition is built to direct the air current. The arrangements for drainage, in this case, are less complicated, and, on account of the simple side-wall construction, repairs to the coils can be made more easily than with the other methods. This arrangement, however, is not favorable to good air circulation, because the cooling surfaces of the refrigerating coils are not placed high enough. Clearly, a strong draft depends on having the coldest part of the room near the ceiling, so that the air, rising by the warmth that it has taken from the goods, will travel the whole height of the room before it becomes cool enough to fall again. In the method illustrated by Fig. 181, the warm air is forced to flow downward by the slope of the upper partitions and by the pressure of more warm air rising under it. When it has passed over the refrigerating pipes and has given up its heat, it flows along the floor until it is forced upward by warm air rising under it. When it has passed over the pipes and has given up its heat, it flows along the floor until forced upward by the rush of cold air behind or until it has slowly gathered warmth from the goods near the floor. Thus, instead of depending on the natural rising of warm air and the natural falling of cold air, this system depends on the forcing of warm air downward (over the sloping partitions) and the forcing of cold air upward (from the floor). Either of the methods shown in Figs. 179 and 180 give unusually good results in regard to air circulation because they are laid out with respect to the natural tendencies of air currents.

The Cooper Combination Method.—Before the study of coil methods of cooling is dropped, the Cooper method deserves mention. It is neither distinctly a coil method nor distinctly an ice-cooling method but makes use of parts of both methods and combines some of the advantages of both. It was designed for use in those sections of the country where the supply of natural ice is plentiful. Crushed ice combined with calcium chloride is placed in a tank which contains a set of brine-filled coils. The brine is cooled by melting the ice, and, on cooling, it flows downward through a pipe to a secondary coil located in the storage room. There it accumulates heat and expands, rising through another pipe to the primary coils again. The circulation of brine is very similar to the gravity circulation of water in an ordinary hot-water heating system. Cool brine flows down by gravity, comes into contact with the heat given off by storage goods, warms, expands, and is forced to rise by the colder brine behind it. Pans of calcium chloride placed along the coils dry the air as it passes over them. By this method, the temperature of a storage room can be kept sufficiently low for any ordinary purpose. It is possible to maintain a room at 14° F. by this system, and rooms thus fitted have been refrigerated as low as 6° F. The value of such a system depends, of course, on a plentiful and cheap supply of ice.

Forced Air Circulation.—In all the cooling methods so far considered, the circulation of air has been produced by gravity. To secure good gravity circulation, that is, circulation caused by the rising of warm air and the falling of cold air, a storage room must have a special arrangement and grouping of refrigerating pipes, and, very often, partitions are needed, which occupy valuable storage space. On the other hand, several of the methods of natural or gravity circulation would be excellent if it were not for the difficulties in obtaining at all times a satisfactory air circulation. For these reasons, most of the most up-to-date storage plants are equipped with fans to set in motion and direct the air currents.

By this mechanical means, a stronger and better circulation is obtained; the air is kept purer, and it is possible to maintain it in a drier condition. Another important advantage of forced circulation is that the temperature of the storage rooms is more even that it could be by the methods of natural or gravity air circulation. The gravity method of circulation depends on a relatively wide range of temperature in the storage room, so that warm air rises vigorously and the cold air falls in the same way. Sometimes, the difference in temperature needed to keep the air in circulation is enough to interfere with proper refrigeration. Air from different parts of a storage room provided only with natural or gravity air circulation will usually vary from 2 to 5° F.

Forced air circulation depends on no such uneven temperature. In fact, the strong currents generated by a fan so mix the air and drive it to every part of a storage room that the temperature is kept very even. The rapidity with which the air moves is an added advantage, for it speeds up all the processes for which circulating air is needed. This swift and well-controlled flow of air is of great assistance in keeping the air at a low humidity. The work of drying air in any system requires circulation over the drying surfaces, and any method providing a swift, positive flow insures a good control of humidity. Air purity is almost entirely dependent on two influences: (1) movement of air and (2) low humidity.

At different seasons of the year, the temperatures of the outside air varies; and this air, passing into the cold-storage rooms in numerous ways, affects the evenness of temperature inside. In the winter, this outside temperature may be lower than that of the cooling surface inside; in the summer, it is many degrees higher. In other words, the quantity of heat that may leak into the cold-storage rooms around the doors or windows or pass in through the walls or be carried in with the produce depends on the season. For this reason, the inside temperature is subject to seasonal differences. Now, the efficiency of natural or gravity air circulation, dependent as it is on the temperature difference between the cooling surfaces and the air, depends, also, on seasonal change, to a large extent. When the temperature of the air is nearly the same as the temperature of the cooling surfaces, there is little or no gravity circulation.

With forced circulation, then, storage conditions, as far as circulation is concerned, are independent of weather and season. This advantage alone is enough to recommend the use of fan circulation wherever a large cold-storage plant is concerned. Although there has been much discussion as to the expense of forced or fan circulation, this system is, in fact, relatively inexpensive. There are but two important items of cost: (1) power for operating the fans and (2) cost of the air ducts. The power item is relatively low, 1 horsepower serving to supply 20,000 cubic feet of storage space. The cost of ducts cannot be figured in this way, but it is small compared to some of the costs of gravity circulation. For instance, the ducts occupy less room than the air passages in a natural or gravity system. In a comparison of costs, the additional space occupied by air passages, and thus taken from the room available for storage purposes, can be counted as the extra costs of the natural or gravity system. Another such cost is the extra refrigerating coil surface required where natural circulation is depended upon. Where the circulation of air is swift and strong, the air passes rapidly over the refrigerating coils and gives up its heat to them quickly. Forced circulation, then, accomplishes the same cooling effect with less refrigerating coil surface. Such items, balanced against the cost of installing a system of fans and air ducts, make clear the advantages of this method over the old, wherever cold storage is carried on on a large scale. And besides the question of economy, there are the advantages of simple operation, especially in the matter of drainage and defrosting.

Just as the problems of the gravity system have to do with the grouping and arrangement of the refrigerating coils, so the problems of a forced circulation system have to do with the placing of air ducts. The refrigerating coils themselves are usually placed in a heat-insulated bunker room at one end of the storage room. The suction side of the fan draws air from the storage room, forces it to pass over the refrigerating coils, and blows it out through the cold-air ducts. These details may be varied, however, to suit the special requirements of any cold-storage plant.

There is a wide variety of arrangements for the cold-air ducts and the return ducts. One of the best methods provides for cold-air ducts along the floor, one at each side of the room. These ducts are long, boxlike passages with small openings along the tops and sides. Through them the air is forced by the fan, and the pressure causes jets of air to spurt out at the openings. In this way, the cold air is thoroughly mixed with the air of the room. Upon absorbing heat, it rises to the return duct which is located in the middle of the ceiling. This duct, too, has openings in the bottom and sides so that it can receive the warm air from all parts of the cold-storage room.

For a narrow room, a cheaper arrangement is sometimes used, providing a cold-air duct along one wall at the floor and a return duct along the opposite wall at the ceiling. In this system, the circulation is diagonally upward; but, except where the room is small, the circulation will not reach to all corners of it. There are a number of other arrangements, each having its advantages.

One method which has given good results differs strongly from those already described. The storage room is fitted with a false floor and a false ceiling, each perforated with a large number of small holes. The cold air is forced through the false floor; and, on account of the small perforations, it enters the room in many fine air jets which mix thoroughly with the air already there. After absorbing heat, it passes from the room through the perforations in the ceiling.

Ventilation.—The same arrangements that will afford good air circulation in a cold-storage room are not sufficient for ventilation. Ventilation is a subject by itself and must be provided for separately, no matter what has been done in the way of securing circulation for maintaining even temperatures and in making it possible to rid the air of moisture. Ventilation must actually change the air, substituting fresh for foul.

Mold and many of the impurities of air found in cold-storage rooms, such as the decomposition gases given off by the produce, are not absorbed by the air but remain suspended in it. To get rid of these gases, the air must be changed by ventilation.

As so much in refrigeration depends on the conditions of the air as to temperature, humidity, and purity, cold-storage rooms cannot be ventilated simply by admitting a quantity of air from the outside, as in ventilating a house. The new air must be at about the same temperature and the same humidity as the air already in the cold-storage rooms, and it must be pure. A final consideration is that the amount of fresh air admitted to a room must be equal to the amount of foul air removed.

It is true that some storage plants are ventilated by the simple method of flooding the compartment with fresh air at intervals by opening the door. This arrangement, however, is slipshod, and the results are certain to be unsatisfactory. During the summer months, the outside air is much warmer than that inside the storage room, and it is likely, furthermore, to be carrying a large percentage of moisture. Such air, on being admitted to a cold-storage room, gives up its heat very quickly, and some of the moisture it carries is condensed on the door and walls. On account of the rapid drop in temperature, the new air becomes saturated and raises the humidity of the compartment. By this method, then, heat is transferred to the goods, and the humidity is raised.

Ventilation is frequently left to take care of itself by leakage of air around doors and windows.   Vent flues are constructed in the walls to conduct the foul air out.   This method, too, is unsatisfactory.   The rate at which air will leak into the room and at which the bad air will pass out depends on the difference in temperature between the air outside and the air inside.   Thus, the efficiency of such a ventilating system depends on conditions of weather and season.   When the outside air is warm, the vent flues will draw downward instead of upward, and to overcome this difficulty, it is necessary to heat the impure air before it will rise and discharge outside through the flues.   Still another objection is that the incoming air is frequently humid.   In leaking through the insulated walls, it loses temperature as it approaches the cold chamber, and in losing temperature, it condenses its water vapor which by producing dampness, is injurious to insulating materials.

The wise cold-storage engineer, instead of making his ventilation depend on leaky walls, builds the cold-storage rooms as nearly airtight as possible.   He then installs at the air intake a few simple pieces of ventilating apparatus—a fan, a cooling coil, a steam coil, and a few pans of calcium chloride.   The cooling coil and the heating coil regulate the temperature of ingoing air, no matter what the weather or what the time of year.

The fresh air is admitted to the intake from a source as high above the ground as possible, and if it contains impurities, it is washed of dust by being passed through a spray.   It is then cooled to a temperature from 8 to 10° F. lower than the temperature of the storage room.   This increases its relative humidity so that it condenses some of its moisture on the cooling coils for the air supply.   Then, on being passed over pans of calcium chloride, it gives up still more moisture.   Now it is ready to be admitted to the circulation of the storage room, where its temperature will be raised, still further lessening its humidity.   This process of ventilation should be gradual but continuous and should go on at such a rate that a week will be required to renew entirely the air of the storage room.

CHAPTER XII

COLD STORAGE OF FOODS

Cold Storage of Dairy Products.—In the storage of dairy products, temperatures ranging from 0 to 38° F. are generally used. In some cases, where butter, for example, is stored for only 2 or 3 months, it may be held at temperatures ranging from 32 to 38° F., provided that it is properly packed. Wholesalers who collect butter from creameries usually store it in iced refrigerators at a temperature of 36 to 38° F. until a large quantity has been collected. The butter thus kept is then shipped to large cities, where it is stored at lower temperatures in rooms cooled by mechanical refrigeration. So stored, it will keep for a long time without spoiling. While it is possible to store butter at 36 to 38° F. for short periods of time, much better results will be obtained by using lower temperatures. When butter is of good quality and properly packed, it can be kept for 5 months without spoiling at temperatures of 12 to 15° F. When it is not well made and properly packed but must be kept without spoiling from one year to the next, best results are obtained at temperatures ranging from 0 to 10° F. or, in extreme cases, even lower.

Butter contains animal matter in the form of fats and may become rancid or moldy. To prevent its becoming rancid, it is necessary to exclude warm air or to keep the temperature low. If low temperatures are used, there is little need for excluding air; yet it is advisable to seal butter in packages as nearly airtight as possible.

Mold which attacks butter is the result of a warm and damp atmosphere. Hence, the remedy is to store butter at a low temperature and exclude air. When the air in the storage room is too dry, the butter loses weight as its water evaporates. It is, then, necessary that the air be more or less damp, and, for this reason, it should come into contact with the butter as little as possible.

Butter is generally stored in wooden tubs, made of either white spruce or ash. The wooden tubs are soaked in lime before being packed with butter. When they are stored in a damp place, considerable moisture is absorbed, thus producing a growth of mold. Water promotes a growth of mold, while brine prevents it from forming. If the tubs have already acquired considerable moisture as a result of being stored in a damp cellar or in improperly constructed cooling rooms, soaking the tubs in brine will be of little value, because of the moisture that they contain.

Packing Butter.—Freshly made butter always contains some buttermilk. When the butter is prepared for storage, the buttermilk should be removed. This is accomplished by working and washing the butter in water. Working it too thoroughly tends to spoil its grain and should, therefore, be avoided. When the buttermilk is fully removed, brine made of pure water and salt should be worked into the butter to take its place. A little extra salt should be added so that it will form brine by mixing with the water which remains in the butter after the washing.

The latest methods used in packing are to pack butter which has been well worked with the brine in small tubs holding 60 pounds. Tubs of this capacity are conical in shape, being a little larger at the top than at the bottom. They are provided with covers made of the same wood. These tubs should be lined with parchment-paper liners cut to the proper size and shape. The butter is then packed solidly in the tubs to eliminate air holes. It has been found best to press it into the tub from the center outward toward the sides. Generally, a pint of brine is placed at the bottom of each tub. This helps to fill the small spaces and drive out the air.

Butter made from cream which was separated from the milk by a centrifugal separator has a better taste when new than that made by the older process in which the cream is raised by setting in cold water. The keeping qualities of butter made by the hand method are, however, better than those of butter made with cream separated by the centrifugal separator. The reason for this is probably due to the fact that the separator leaves in the butter a large amount of casein. This casein ferments and causes the butter to spoil rapidly.

Creamery butter is generally sold in the form of "prints," each weighing 1 pound. In general, when butter is placed in cold storage, there is no certainty how long it will remain; it should not, therefore, be made in prints, for prints do not keep well through long periods of time. The working necessary to make prints breaks down the grain of the butter and injures its keeping quality. For these reasons, butter should be stored in bulk and should be made into prints only for short periods of storage or for immediate sale.

Ventilation of Butter-storage Rooms.—Stored butter and tubs oxidize gradually, causing an accumulation of gases and odors in the storage rooms. To prevent this accumulation, it has been found necessary to ventilate compartments used for butter storage. Rooms containing butter packed in nearly airtight packages need but little ventilation, while rooms containing tub butter need considerably more. In general, however, rooms containing other goods. Generally, there is no special means provided to circulate air in butter-storage rooms. Enough circulation can be obtained by placing the cooling pipes on the walls without covering them with aprons or screens.

Cooling Milk and Cream.—Milk contains bacteria which increase rapidly unless kept at a low temperature. Farmers who supply milk to creameries have usually no facilities for cooling it. Milk received in creameries without having been cooled is generally pasteurized or sterilized.

By *pasteurizing* is meant heating the milk for 30 minutes at a temperature of about 140 F. and then quickly cooling it. This destroys the active bacteria. Milk heated twice, as in pasteurizing, with an interval between the periods of heating, during which it is held at 100° F., is called *sterilized* milk. The bacteria spores not killed in the first heating are allowed to develop during the period the milk is held at 100° F. and are then killed by the second heating. A typical milk cooler is shown in Fig. 181a. In this apparatus cool water may be admitted at C and discharged at D, while cold brine enters at A and leaves at B. In some plants the pipe fittings at B and C are joined and only cold brine is circulated in the pipes. The milk to be cooled is sprayed over the pipes from holes in the bottom of the trough at the top of the figure.

When the centrifugal separator is separating cream from milk, the latter is often heated to a temperature of 100° F. or more. The cream, and sometimes the milk, after separation, is often cooled to 40 or 50° F.

A creamery receives milk which must be cooled in a very short time; this means that large amounts of refrigeration are needed for a few hours each day. The milk must be cooled quickly after being pasteurized and separated. Such operating conditions are not economical for a refrigerating plant which is large enough to produce the desired cooling effect when needed. This is because the equipment is used at its full capacity for only a short period of the day. When the plant is shut down, the brine in a *brine system* takes up heat, and its temperature rises. On the other hand, in the *direct-expansion system*, the suction pressure increases when the plant is shut down and must be reduced by the operation of the compressor when the plant is again started. In the case of the brine system, the above diffi-

Fig. 181*a*.—Typical milk and cream cooler.

culty may be overcome by installing large brine-storage tanks with a small plant. With a large quantity of brine available, the plant can be kept running continuously and can store up refrigeration. A large amount of refrigeration may then be had by circulating the brine from the storage tank through the coils used for refrigerating. This system has all the advantages of a large plant, although it requires only a small investment; furthermore, the smaller plant is obviously economical, even when not operated continuously.

The amount of heat which must be removed from milk is equal to the product of its weight, its specific heat, and the number of degrees through which it is to be cooled. The specific heat of milk is 0.9 B.t.u. per pound per degree Fahrenheit difference in temperature. If, for example, 1,280 gallons of milk are delivered to a creamery every morning and this milk is cooled from 72 to 38° F. in 4 hours, the capacity of the refrigerating plant required to do the cooling is calculated as follows: Each gallon of milk weighs about 8.59 pounds; then 1,280 × 8.59 or 10,995 pounds of milk are to be cooled. The amount of heat to be removed is 10,995 × 0.9 × (72 − 38) or 336,447 B.t.u. in 4 hours.

Since this heat is to be removed in 4 hours, the refrigerating system must be capable of removing per hour 336,447 ÷ 4 or 84,112 B.t.u. The plant must, therefore, have a refrigerating capacity per 24 hours of 84,112 × 24 ÷ 288,000[1] or 7.0 tons.

Now, suppose that a plant of smaller capacity than the above is installed and that refrigeration is "stored" in relatively large brine-storage tanks. The smaller plant must produce the same amount of refrigeration as the larger plant but produces it in 10 hours instead of 4. This smaller plant would then have a capacity of 336,447 ÷ 10 or 33,644 B.t.u. per hour or a rated refrigerating capacity per 24 hours of 33,644 × 24 ÷ 288,000 or 2.8 tons.

Thus, a 3-ton plant with large brine tanks for storage of refrigeration will do the same amount of work as a 7-ton plant. These calculations show the refrigerating capacity needed for the actual cooling and do not allow for losses of the machine. Because of this, the actual required capacity of the machine is somewhat— probably about 25 per cent—larger.

Suppose that the plant is running while the milk is being cooled; the plant then would remove from the milk during this time about 4 × 33,644 or 134,576 B.t.u. This leaves for the brine to remove 336,447 − 134,576 or 201,871 B.t.u.

If a calcium brine having a strength of 80° *salinometer* is used in the brine tanks and the brine may have its temperature raised 18° F. in the removal of heat from the milk, the weight of the brine needed for the storage tanks can then be found when its specific heat and specific gravity are known. In table IX Properties of Calcium Brine (p. 211), the specific heat of brine having a strength of 80° salinometer is 0.844, and the specific gravity is 1.159. Since 201,871 B.t.u. are to be removed by the brine, the weight of the latter is then 201,871 ÷ (18 × 0.844),

[1] See definition of *refrigerating capacity* on p. 277.

which is 13,288 pounds, or, in gallons, it is 13,288 ÷ (8.33 ×
1.159) or 1,376 gallons.

Freezing Ice Cream.—Whenever ice cream is made in bulk,
mechanical refrigeration is used to freeze and harden it. Generally, this method is cheaper and quicker than the old one of
freezing by ice and salt.

An ice cream freezer is shown in Fig. 181*b*. These machines

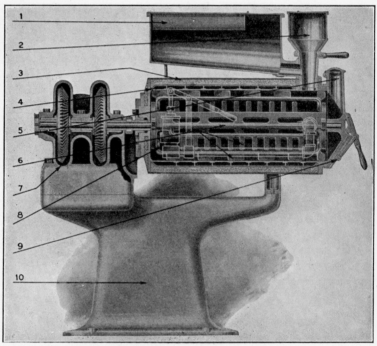

Fig. 181*b*.—Section of brine-cooled ice cream freezer: 1. strainer in mixing
tank; 2. fruit funnel; 3. heat-insulating material; 4. spiral passage for brine
around freezing cylinder; 5. peep hole; 6. blades of dasher; 7. driving gears; 8.
"phantom" view of brine valve. 9. Opening for removing ice cream.

vary in size from 40 to 120 quarts. A freezer consists of a horizontal cylinder around which is a jacket for the refrigerant or
brine. If brine is used for cooling it is generally circulated
through the freezer at about 5° F. If a liquid refrigerant is used
the gage pressure suitable for producing the proper temperature
is about 20 pounds per square inch. The ice cream mixture after
"ripening" is generally supplied to the freezer at about 40 to

50° F. The freezer is constructed with a dasher or paddle for "whipping" the mixture. During the period of freezing which generally takes about 10 to 15 minutes, the ice cream mixture when at 28° F. swells about 80 to 100 per cent in volume. This swelling depends upon the relative temperature, quality of mixture, and the speed of the dasher.

At this temperature, it freezes but flows readily under its own weight. In this condition, it is run into moulds in the form of bricks and is also packed in cans. The ice cream is thus formed, and it is then hardened by lowering its temperature to 0° F. for 36 to 72 hours.

After it is hardened, the moulds or cans are packed in crushed ice and salt. The ice cream is now ready for delivery. Most manufacturers make their own ice for packing. Clear ice is not necessary, and water can be used without filtering.

The exact amount of refrigeration needed to produce ice cream is difficult to determine. This is because the specific heat of an ice-cream mixture before freezing, the latent heat of fusion, and the specific heat of the ice cream after it is frozen will vary with the quality of the ice cream.

The weight of frozen ice cream will depend on the increase in volume and the specific gravity of the mixture. If the swelling is 80 per cent and the specific gravity of the mixture is 1.1, then the weight per gallon of ice cream may be calculated thus:

$$8.33 \times 1.10 \div (1.00 + 0.8) = 5.1 \text{ pounds.}$$

In general, ice cream containing only extract flavors will weigh about 5 pounds per gallon, while ice cream containing fruits and nuts will weigh about 6 pounds per gallon.

If the specific heat of ice cream before freezing is 0.78, the latent heat of fusion is 90, and the specific heat after it is frozen is 0.45, then the refrigeration per gallon can be calculated as follows, for a freezing temperature of 26° F:

Cooling to freezing point = $1 \times 0.78(50–26)$ = 18.72 B.t.u. per lb.
Latent heat of fusion   = 1×90 = 90.00 B.t.u. per lb.
Cooling after freezing   = $1 \times 0.45(26–0)$ = 11.70 B.t.u. per lb.

Total refrigeration per pound   = 120.42 B.t.u. per lb.

The refrigeration *per gallon* of ice cream containing only extract flavors is then equal to $5.1 \times 120.42 = 614.1$ B.t.u. and for ice

cream containing fruits and nuts the refrigeration is equal to 6 ×
120.42 or 722.5 B.t.u. per gallon.

This is not all the refrigeration required as the heat loss through
the insulation and other losses must be added. If these losses are
assumed to be equal to the refrigeration per gallon of ice cream,
then the total refrigeration will be about 1,445 B.t.u. per gallon.

All of the refrigeration required to freeze the ice cream is not
taken out in the freezer, and this amount may be considered
as the heat required to cool the mixture to the freezing point
plus one-half of the heat of fusion. The remaining amount of
heat to be removed to freeze the ice cream is removed in the
hardening room. Having found the amount of heat removed in
the freezing and hardening rooms, the quantity of brine circulated
through the "freeze" can be estimated. Also the amount of
direct expansion piping in the hardening room can be determined.
Of course in making such calculations the insulation and can
losses should be included.

Storage of Cheese.—Newly made cheese is not suitable for the
market, as it must first be cured to make it palatable. When
the market is poor, the cheese must be stored for varying periods
of time. Because of this need of curing and the uncertainties of
demand, the cold storage of cheese has to deal with the curing
as well as with the storing. It has been found that the flavor
of cheese depends on the temperature at which it is cured.

It is the opinion of some cheese makers that cheese should be
cured at a temperature of 60 to 70° F., but extensive tests show
that the flavor is improved by curing at a lower temperature. If
the cheese is of good quality and flavor, it can be kept in storage
for 1 or 2 months at 40° F. After this, the temperature should
be slowly lowered, so that at the end of the third month it reaches
30° F. At this temperature, cheese can be kept in permanent
storage. Curing at high temperatures is accomplished without
the aid of refrigeration. Temperatures in the vicinity of 70° F.
are frequently used. Sometimes, the curing rooms are underground, where a lower temperature is obtainable than in rooms
above.

During the summer months, the cheese maker will usually, by
means of underground passages, admit cool air to the cheese-
storage rooms. Air, in going through these passages, is likely to
become damp, and this dampness and the high temperature are
favorable for the growth of objectionable mold.

One of the difficulties of curing cheese at high temperatures is the shrinkage and loss in weight, as the amount of moisture is greater at high than at low temperatures. It is a good plan, then, to coat the cheese with paraffin and cure it at low temperatures as this will prevent shrinkage. A suitable temperature for curing cheese can be obtained by melting ice, but air cooled by ice has high humidity and causes mold.

There are certain advantages in the storage of cheese at low temperatures (30 to 35° F.) that improve the commercial qualities—namely, giving the product a high market value and less loss in weight. Also, the cheese can be kept for a longer time without destroying its good qualities. In the curing and storage, the best results are obtained by the aid of mechanical refrigeration. With this system, the temperature and also the humidity of the storage rooms can be regulated. As in the storage of butter, the brine system with large brine tanks permits a shutdown overnight. It is often necessary to use drying pans containing calcium chloride to absorb moisture from the air. Calcium chloride dissolves when it absorbs moisture, and when the solution thus formed is allowed to drip over the cooling coils the formation of frost is largely prevented.

Cold Storage of Meat.—Just as dairy products require special conditions of temperature and humidity for successful storage, so the various kinds of meat have special characteristics and special needs.

Meat stored for short periods does not require very low temperatures. A temperature level of 40° F. gives excellent results when the storage period is not above 2 or 3 months. If it is necessary to keep meat longer, it is best to freeze it, gradually bringing its temperature down to 10° F. After this freezing, it can be stored at about 30° F. for periods up to 6 months and sometimes longer.

It is necessary to use considerable care in refrigerating meat, especially where freezing is required. Freezing must be done either slowly or very quickly to a temperature considerably below that of freezing to avoid injury to the quality. Rapid reduction of the temperature of meat to only about the freezing level causes the outer layer of the meat to cool and contract quickly, squeezing and breaking the cells of the inner layers. Meat which has been subjected to such treatment will be found pulpy on the inside. Such freezing is similar to the troubles of baking with a stove which is too hot. When a biscuit or a muffin is baked too rapidly, the outside is hard and crusty, while the center is still raw and uncooked. In like manner, unless the freezing of meat is performed quickly to a very low temperature, as, for example, minus 40° F., only the outer layer of the meat is likely to be frozen, and the inner layers will be insulated against further refrigeration.

"Bone-stink"—decayed marrow—is one of the common results of rapid freezing; but many such cases are actually the result of an unhealthy condition of the animal before slaughtering.

The same rules apply to the thawing out of frozen meat; haste results in poor quality. The thawing-out process when properly done requires 2 or 3 days.

Fresh meat is rich in moisture which must be evaporated for successful storage. It is, therefore, important that the circulation of air be strong enough to pass on all sides of the pieces of meat. Congestion in the storage room is to be avoided; the pieces of meat must be hung far enough apart so that the air can pass readily between them.

In connection with the circulation of air, it is necessary to work out the arrangement of refrigerating coils best suited to the storage rooms. Many such rooms were built originally for some other purpose and have been adapted for use as storage rooms. Where this has taken place, the coils are usually along the walls, with screens or aprons in front of them to give a strong circulation of air. This is not a favorite method, however; it is employed, in most cases, only because it is easy to install them in this way. In new buildings designed from the first for cold-storage purposes, the coils are usually located in a loft above the storage room. This loft is either provided with dripping pans to drain off the water accumulating from the defrosting of the refrigerating coils or fitted with a waterproof floor. Openings between the loft and the storage room are so arranged as to secure a good circulation of air.

To calculate the proper area of cooling surfaces by the amount of heat to be removed, it is necessary to understand all the conditions of temperature, insulation, etc. Siebel has prepared a few practical rules for pipe allowance, which will apply in most cases. The rules are given in the following table.

Type of room	Quantity and size of pipe allowed	Volume of cold-storage rooms, cubic feet of storage space	
		For direct expansion	For brine circulation
For chilling rooms.............	One running foot of 2-inch pipe (or its equivalent)	13 to 14	7 to 8
For storage rooms.............	One running foot of 2-inch pipe	45 to 50	15 to 18
For freezing rooms.............	One running foot of 2-inch pipe	5 to 10	3

Storage of Eggs.—The storage of eggs has come to be extremely important in the marketing of foodstuffs. During the late spring, fresh eggs are abundant and are marketed at a comparately low price. In the middle of winter, they are high priced. Storage assists in keeping a supply always in the market and in regulating the prices throughout the year. If all the fresh eggs produced in April and May were offered for sale at that time, everyone could get all the fresh eggs he needed, and the prices would be very low. But some of these eggs are taken off the market to be placed in storage, and the prices, consequently, do not fall so low. Again, if consumers had to depend in December and January on the eggs produced in those months, only a small part of the buyers could be accomodated, and the prices would be beyond the reach of all but the wealthy. But storage eggs are then put out, and, by increasing the supply, they lower the price.

Egg storage, however, although it is of great service, presents difficult problems in refrigeration. Of all stored products, eggs are most easily affected by temperature, humidity, and the length of the storage period. Those that are not strictly fresh when they are put into storage are even more sensitive to such conditions than fresh eggs would be, and, for that reason, it is practical to store only strictly fresh eggs.

Humidity and Temperature in Egg-storage Rooms.—If the air in a storage room is permitted to become damp and warm, a kind of fungus growth called *mildew* will rapidly develop on the eggs. It will cause them to become musty. Although dampness is largely responsible for this growth, its development can be checked by the maintenance of low temperatures, even though the humidity is fairly high.

The same thing is true, in general, of mold. It will not develop rapidly, even in humid air, if the temperature is kept sufficiently low. A condition of 85 per cent humidity is not likely to injure eggs if the temperature is kept at 30° F. or below and the air is well circulated. If the temperature is increased to 40° F., however, the humidity must be kept not higher than 60 per cent.

Low temperatures, then, are the preventers of mold and mildew. But it is equally important not to go to the other extreme of very dry cold air. The shells of eggs are so porous that they permit the passage of moisture. For that reason, air which is too dry is likely to cause the partial evaporation of the inside of the egg, and this not only removes weight but lowers the quality of the eggs as well. It is also necessary to keep eggs 1 or 2° above the freezing point, which is about 28° F. When an egg freezes, its contents expand and burst the shell. In view of the usual uneven temperature of storage rooms, it is desirable to allow 1 or 2° F. leeway, to avoid accidental freezing.

The permissible range of temperature for the storing of eggs is, then, between 30 and 40° F.; but eggs are satisfactorily stored only when the humidity is controlled as carefully as the temperature and in accordance with it.

What has been said about the too rapid freezing and the too rapid thawing of meat applies equally well to temperature changes of eggs. Cooling or warming should take place gradually. Before being put into a cold-storage room, eggs should first be allowed to remain in a receiving room at a temperature of 50 to 60° F. When the heat has been reduced in this manner, they can be placed in storage. Failure to take these precautions often causes the whites to become watery, especially if the eggs are stored a long time at a low temperature. The low temperature alone is not responsible for this condition, which is probably due to subjecting the eggs to sudden and violent temperatures when they are put in and when they are taken out of storage. A room similar to the receiving room should be provided where the eggs can warm gradually on their removal from storage. The receiving room should not be used for both purposes, for in that way cooled eggs and warm eggs would be placed near each other; the new eggs, having a great deal of moisture, will give it off, and it will then condense upon the shells of the cold eggs. An uneven temperature would also be caused by this arrangement.

Formerly, it was customary to store eggs at temperatures ranging between 38 and 40° F. It was then necessary to turn the cases over from time to time, for the higher temperatures caused the yolks to rise and adhere to the tops of the shell, and this made the eggs decay rapidly. The expense and inconvenience of turning the cases favor the lower temperatures at which the yolks lose their tendency to rise. In modern practice, 40° F. is regarded as a temperature too high for keeping eggs more than a short time; but with good circulation and a control of humidity, the storage period at this temperature may be as much as 2 or 3 months.

Circulation and Ventilation in Egg-storage Rooms.—Proper ventilation and circulation, especially the latter, are very important considerations in the control of humidity. They also serve a variety of other purposes in connection with the storage of eggs. During the period of storage, eggs, however well kept, undergo a gradual decomposition, which results in the giving off of gaseous impurities into the air. Some of these gases are readily absorbed by the moisture in the air. On coming into contact with the cooling surfaces of the refrigerating coils, much of this moisture condenses, purifying the air of germs and decomposition products. Not all of the gases, however, can be disposed of in this way. A relatively small part of them is not absorbed but mixes and circulates with the air. Only by a change of air can the storage room be ridded of this gas. The ventilation required to accomplish the purpose is not very great. Where circulation and the control of humidity are good, new air needs to be admitted only at such rate that a complete change of air will be required once in a week or every week and a half.

The circulation of an egg-storage room should be strong and rapid, for the eggs are not exposed, as meat is, to air currents on all sides; they are packed in individual pockets in crates, and the crates or containers are packed together and piled. Clearly, there is no advantage in simply circulating the air about the piles of crates. It is the little blanket of air surrounding each egg which receives the decomposition gases and carries germs. Effective circulation, then, must reach each individual egg; and to do this, it must be strong and capable of being directed. Rapidity of circulation is desirable, because it makes possible adequate refrigeration with a small area of cooling surface and keeps the air dry at lower temperatures. Satisfactory results for egg storage are difficult to obtain by any method of natural circulation. Forced circulation, with its strong uniform currents and its easy control of humidity, is favored in modern practice.

Packing Eggs for Storage.—On account of the sensitiveness of eggs to various conditions, it is necessary to take special care in packing. A few details of packing may make all the difference between successful and unsuccessful storage.

The greatest trouble to contend with is, of course, breakage. Eggs must be kept whole if they are to be stored successfully. The prevention of breakage is best accomplished by packing the crates at the top and bottom with thoroughly dry excelsior. An air-drying process of 6 months is needed to make excelsior suitable for this purpose.

Second only to the danger from breakage is the danger from mustiness, mold, and rank odors. Mustiness frequently results from packing eggs in cardboard packages which have been allowed to sour or become musty. Mold is favored by warmth and moisture. For this reason, eggs should not be refrigerated during shipping. Place them in a clean refrigerator car *without ice*, for if they are cooled on the road, moisture will gather and condense on their shells when they are unloaded, and mold will start.

Eggs absorb odors very readily from the packing case, from the air of the store room, or from the car in which they are shipped. Wise handlers are careful to prevent their coming into contact with strong odors. The 30-dozen crates in which eggs are usually shipped may taint the eggs unless they are perfectly dry and made from wood with no natural odor. New crates should be used for each shipment, for a crate which is used a second time will give off to the new eggs the odor that it has absorbed from the eggs previously stored in it.

Similar care should be used in selecting the fillers which divide the case into individual compartments, one for each egg. These fillers are usually of straw board and are made in three weights— light, medium, and heavy. Of these, the medium is generally the most serviceable, for the light filler is not strong enough always to prevent breakage, while the heavy grade is so absorbent that it gathers and retains too much moisture. The disadvantages of the heavy filler can be avoided by the use of one of the "odorless" fillers now on the market.

Finally, it is important that the packing cases shall not be airtight. We have already considered how much depends upon a good circulation of air which will reach each separate egg. The crates must, then, be constructed in such a way as to permit the penetration of circulating air.

The following table gives data regarding the storage of foods.

SPACE REQUIRED FOR REFRIGERATED GOODS
Meat rails placed approximately 30 inches on centers

Material	Average weight, pounds	Floor space, sq. ft.	Space occupied, cu. ft.	Clear height of room, feet
1 Barrel apples or potatoes.....	180	4	9	
1 Tub butter................	60	2.5	2.5	
1 Cheese....................	60	2	2	
1 Case eggs (30 dozen)........	70	...	3	
1 Beef.....................	700	9	108	12
1 Sheep....................	75	2	16	8
1 Hog.....................	250			
1 Calf.....................	90			

Cleaning Cold-storage Rooms.—Butter and eggs will be tainted if odors from the previous storage season are allowed to remain. Thus, efficient storage demands that the rooms be thoroughly cleaned and deodorized after each storage season.

A good method of cleaning is to shut off the refrigeration and immediately set about removing frost from the refrigerating pipes. This frost is composed of the germ-laden moisture that has condensed and frozen on the pipes during the storage season. It is a dangerous source of impurity, and, if it is allowed to melt or evaporate in the storage room, it will promote a rapid development of germs. After the frost has been removed, it should be carried out of the storage rooms as soon as possible. If any frost melts and drips on the flour, enough sawdust should be sprinkled over it to absorb it. The sawdust should then be collected and removed.

As soon as the pipes have been quite completely cleared of frost, the room should be given a thorough airing, after which the walls should be heavily coated with whitewash.

CHAPTER XIII

AIR CONDITIONING AND COOLING

Dehumidifying and Cooling Air.—A modern application of mechanical refrigeration is the cooling of air for industrial plants, public auditoriums, and theaters. This is very important in plants which produce photographic films, candies, chewing gum, and some drugs.

In order thoroughly to understand the principles of air cooling, one must have a background of the physical and thermodynamic properties of air, which may be found in articles by W. H. Carrier.[1]

The following is a description of an air dehumidifier made by the Carrier Engineering Corporation and shown in Fig. 182 This dehumidifier is of the self-contained type and consists of nozzles for spraying recirculated water into air which enters through the distributor plates A and leaves at D, after passing through the dust and germ eliminating plates C. These sprays are located in the spray-chamber B, below which is the trough R for distributing the water over the direct expansion coils S, located in the *Baudelot chamber*. The spray nozzles are so arranged that they cause a uniformly dense bank of mist through which the air must pass on its way to the staggered dust and germs eliminating plates. The air is scrubbed by the wet surfaces of the plates and freed from nearly all solid foreign matter, including disease germs.

The air after being washed enters the fan F, which is of the centrifugal type, passes through the fan inlet connection E, and then out of the fan outlet connection H into the duct system. The fan is driven by an electric motor G.

The water is taken from the bottom of the tank through the screen I into the centrifugal pump M, by way of the pipe line J. The centrifugal pump is driven by an electric motor N. The water which is discharged from the pump passes through the pipe line O and the pot-strainer P, which is used to remove any scale and dirt which may be carried by the water supplied to the spray

[1] CARRIER, W. H., *Trans. A. S. M. E.*, 1911.

nozzles. A by-pass Q to the "upper tank" is used for quickly cooling the water when first starting the apparatus. The pipes carrying the refrigerant (entering and leaving) are marked by the letter T in the figure.

An overflow W and a drain to the sewer Y are provided for the "lower tank," and there is also a drain X for the "upper tank." The fresh water connection Z is for supplying the make-up and cleaning water. A small air compressor V driven from the fan shaft supplies air to a thermostat which controls the temperature of the air leaving the apparatus. A three-way valve K in the water-line J, has a pipe line L connected to it which leads to the

Fig. 182.—Air dehumidifier and cooler.

troughs R. This three-way valve, which is also connected into the suction line of the spray pump M, is used for regulating the amount of water taken from the settling tank of the dehumidifier and from the cold water supply.

Psychrometric Chart.—The chart shown in Fig. 183 is used for determining the data needed for designing apparatus for air cooling. It is a modification of the Carrier[1] chart, as arranged by Macintire.[2] In the chart a point A represents the air condition when the *dry-bulb temperature* is 65° F. and the relative humidity is 60 per cent. For this air condition, C is the *tem-*

[1] CARRIER, W. H., *Trans. A. S. M. E.*, 1911.
[2] MACINTIRE, M. J., *Principles of Mechanical Refrigeration.*

perature of the wet-bulb[1] (56.7° F.), and *B* is the dew-point temperature (50.7° F.). The moisture at *A* is then 55 *grains* per pound of dry air. The *total heat* measured from 0° F. is given by the curve so marked in the middle of the chart. The heat removed in cooling air is the difference between the total heats corresponding to the wet-bulb temperatures at the initial and final conditions.

[1] Wet-bulb temperature is obtained when a wetted cloth gauze covers the bulb.

APPENDIX A

PROBLEMS IN REFRIGERATION

1. A creamery must be equipped to cool 1,000 pounds of milk from an initial temperature of 90 to a final temperature of 35° F. How much heat must be removed? Specific heat of milk is 0.95.

2. In problem 1, how many pounds of brine must be supplied to remove this heat if the allowable rise in temperature is 10° F. and the specific heat of the brine is 0.837?

3. How many heat units must be removed from 1 pound of ammonia vapor at atmospheric pressure and 80° F. to liquefy it?

4. A refrigerating room is held at 10° F. by a dense-air machine and operated under the conditions shown by Fig. 184. Determine (a) the

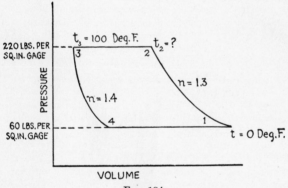

FIG. 184.

temperature at point 4 in the figure; (b) heat removed by 1 pound of air; (c) weight of air per minute per ton of refrigeration; (d) net work per minute per ton of refrigeration, assuming friction loss to be 15 per cent; (e) weight of cooling water per minute per ton of refrigeration, assuming temperature of entering cooling water to be 60° F. and temperature of outlet cooling water to be 70° F.; (f) horsepower required to drive machine per ton of refrigeration; (g) displacement per minute per ton of refrigeration for the compressor, assuming 2 per cent clearance; (h) displacement per minute per ton of refrigeration for expander, assuming 2 per cent clearance; (i) refrigerating effect or coefficient of performance.

5. A cold-storage room is held at 60° F. by an air-refrigerating machine which does not use the air over and over again. The cycle is made up of two adiabatic lines (exponent $n = 1.4$) and two constant-pressure lines. The suction pressure is 15 pounds per square inch absolute, and the dis-

377

charge pressure is 100 pounds per square inch absolute. The temperature of the air entering the air motor or expander is 70° F., and the inlet and outlet temperatures of the cooling water are, respectively, 65 and 90° F. Compressor and expander operate at 200 r.p.m. Find (a) the refrigeration per pound of air; (b) heat removed by the cooling water per pound of air; (c) pounds of cooling water required to cool 1 pound of air; (d) net work per pound of air; (e) displacement of compressor per revolution, assuming 2 per cent clearance; (f) displacement of air motor or expander per revolution, assuming 2 per cent clearance; (g) refrigerating effect or coefficient of performance.

6. How much work is done when 4 pounds of ammonia occupying 8 cubic feet at 141.7 pounds per square inch absolute pressure expands adiabatically to pressure corresponding to saturation temperature of 30° F.? Also, find the value of the exponent n in this case.

7. Find the amount of work done in compressing 1 pound of *dry* ammonia vapor at a pressure of 15.98 pounds per square inch absolute to the condition of 155 pounds per square inch absolute pressure and 200° F. superheat. Also, determine the value of the exponent n.

8. The suction pressure of an ammonia compressor is 30.57 pounds per square inch absolute, and the discharge pressure is 182 pounds per square inch absolute. If the ammonia vapor is compressed adiabatically, find the work done by one pound when the quality of the vapor at the end of compression is 100 per cent. Obtain the value of the exponent n, and check the work done by the use of the expression, $\dfrac{P_2V_2 - P_1V_1}{n-1}$.

9. The temperature of liquid ammonia in the liquid receiver is 75° F., and the pressure in the evaporating coils is 35 pounds per square inch absolute. Find (a) the amount of heat used to cool 1 pound of liquid ammonia; (b) weight of ammonia evaporated to do this cooling; (c) net cooling effect of the pound of original ammonia.

10. The discharge gage pressure of a compressor is 185 pounds per square inch, and liquid ammonia is allowed to enter the expansion valve at 70° F. The evaporating-coil gage pressure is 5 pounds per square inch. Find (a) the amount of heat used to cool 1 pound of liquid ammonia; (b) weight of ammonia evaporated to do this cooling; (c) net cooling effect of the pound of the original ammonia; (d) quality of the ammonia just after it has been cooled to the temperature in the evaporating coil.

11. Find the mean specific heat of 1 pound of liquid ammonia having initial and final temperatures of 70 and 10° F., respectively.

12. The suction pressure of an ammonia compressor is 38 pounds per square inch absolute, and the discharge pressure is 140 pounds per square inch absolute. How many pounds of ammonia per minute must be circulated to produce 1 ton of refrigeration?

13. An ammonia compressor circulates 45 pounds of ammonia per hour at a discharge gage pressure of 175 pounds per square inch. The condensing water enters at 70° F. and leaves at 80° F. The temperature of the liquid ammonia entering the expansion valve is 80° F. How many gallons of water must be supplied to the condenser per hour?

14. If, in problem 13, the liquid ammonia reaches the expansion valve at 75° F. and the temperature in the expansion coils is 15° F., find the number

of heat units required to lower its temperature to the boiling point. How many tons of refrigeration are produced by the cooling coils when this amount of ammonia is circulated?

15. How many pounds of carbon dioxide must be circulated per minute per ton of refrigeration if the pressure in the expansion coils is 284.6 pounds per square inch absolute and the carbon dioxide reaches the expansion valve at a temperature of 77° F.? For the properties of carbon dioxide, see Appendix (p. 407).

16. How many pounds of ammonia are necessary to fill an expansion coil which has 12,000 feet of 2-inch pipe, if the gage pressure is 25 pounds per square inch. Assume the quality of the vapor in the suction line to be 95 per cent.

17. How many pounds of ammonia must be circulated per minute for a 50-ton plant if the suction-gage pressure is 25 pounds per square inch and the temperature of the liquid ammonia at the expansion valve is 80° F.?

18. A compressor of 100-ton rating operates with a discharge gage pressure of 165.3 pounds per square inch and a suction gage pressure of 15.3 pounds per square inch. If the vapor is superheated 25° F. when it enters the compressor, determine the following quantities, assuming the temperature of the liquid ammonia at the expansion valve to be 85° F.: (a) weight of ammonia per minute per ton of refrigeration; (b) horsepower required by compressor per ton of refrigeration; (c) piston displacement per minute per ton of refrigeration; (d) coefficient of performance.

19. A compressor operates with a discharge pressure of 180 pounds per square inch absolute and a suction pressure of 18 pounds per square inch absolute. If the vapor is superheated 40° F. when it enters the compressor, determine the following quantities, assuming the temperature of the liquid ammonia at the expansion valve to be 85° F.: (a) weight of ammonia per minute per ton of refrigeration; (b) horsepower required by compressor per ton of refrigeration; (c) piston displacement per minute per ton of refrigeration; (d) coefficient of performance.

20. Arrange the results of problems 18 and 19 in a table, with the headings showing the effect of the pressures and temperatures upon the performance of the machine.

21. An ammonia compressor operates with dry compression and discharges the vapor at 175 pounds per square inch gage pressure. If the suction-gage pressure is 23 pounds per square inch, what horsepower per ton of refrigeration is required to drive the compressor and engine, the overall efficiency being 80 per cent?

22. What size of double-acting ammonia compressor is necessary to produce 100 tons of refrigeration per 24 hours at a discharge-gage pressure of 120 pounds per square inch and a suction-gage pressure of 15 pounds per square inch? Assume a volumetric efficiency of 75 per cent and dry compression.

23. If ammonia vapor is compressed so that it is dry at the end of compression, determine the number of gallons of cooling water required per minute per ton of refrigeration if the condenser-gage pressure is 150 pounds per square inch and the suction-gage pressure is 25 pounds per square inch. Assume a 10° F. difference in temperature between the liquid ammonia and

the leaving cooling water. The liquid ammonia leaves the condenser at 75° F., and the cooling water enters at 60° F.

24. A compressor discharges ammonia vapor to a condenser at a gage pressure of 190 pounds per square inch. The suction-gage pressure is 19 pounds per square inch, and the ammonia vapor is superheated 20° F. between the evaporating coils and the compressor. Find the temperature of the discharged ammonia vapor and the amount of heat removed (a) to extract the heat of the superheat, (b) to liquefy the ammonia vapor, and (c) to cool the liquid ammonia to 80° F.

25. In problem 24, what percentage of the total heat removed is the heat which is absorbed (a) to remove the superheat, (b) to liquefy the ammonia vapor, and (c) to cool the liquid ammonia? What is the useful refrigeration per pound of ammonia and the heat loss due to superheating the ammonia vapor in the suction line?

26. In problem 24, find the number of pounds of ammonia circulated per minute per ton of refrigeration. If an ice plant requires 1.6 tons of refrigeration to make 1 ton of ice, find the amount of ammonia to be circulated per minute per ton of ice.

27. In problem 24, find the volume of ammonia vapor passing through the compressor per minute per ton of refrigeration and per ton of ice. Assume a volumetric efficiency of 75 per cent. Determine the number of gallons of water per ton of refrigeration and per ton of ice made, assuming a rise in temperature of 10° F. of the cooling water.

28. In problem 24, determine the horsepower required to drive the compressor per ton of refrigeration and ton of ice. Assuming an efficiency of 85 per cent for motor and compressor, what size motor (horsepower) would be required for a 100-ton ice plant?

29. In problem 24, what size double-acting ammonia compressor is required to produce 100 tons of ice per day, and what is the speed at which it is to be driven?

30. A compressor is designed to operate with a temperature of 0° F. in the evaporator and a liquefaction temperature of 96° F., but is operated, instead, at a temperature of 5° F. in the evaporator and at 86° F. liquefaction temperature. Find the increase in capacity over its normal rating. What effects have the increase of evaporator pressure and the decrease of liquefaction temperature upon the capacity of the compressor?

31. The evaporating coils in a refrigerating plant are held at a temperature of 5° F., and the liquid ammonia enters the expansion valve at 80° F. If the liquid ammonia is cooled to 60 instead of 80° F., what is the percentage gain in refrigerating effect by this aftercooling? How many degrees (Fahrenheit) of aftercooling are necessary to gain 1 per cent in refrigerating effect?

32. A compressor operates at a capacity of 100 tons of refrigeration with a discharge-gage pressure of 185 pounds per square inch and a discharge temperature of 263° F. If the suction-gage pressure is 10 pounds per square inch and the vapor is *dry* at the suction valve of the compressor, find the size of discharge and suction pipe if the velocities are 8,000 and 4,000 feet per minute, respectively.

33. In the above problem, if the distance between the compressor and the condenser is 120 feet, find the condenser pressure, assuming that the

pressure drop $(P_1 - P_2)$ is expressed in pounds per square inch by the following equation:

$$P_1 - P_2 = \frac{V^2 L(1 + 3.6 \div d)D}{144 \times 454 \times d}$$

where

V = velocity of the ammonia vapor, feet per second
L = length of pipe, feet
D = density of ammonia vapor at the pressure P_1, pounds per cubic foot
d = diameter of pipe, inches

34. The following data were obtained from a test of a double-acting compressor of 15 tons capacity which was driven by a steam engine.

Size of steam cylinder....................................	9 × 24 in.
Diameter of piston rod...................................	2 in.
Size of compressor cylinder..............................	8 × 16 in.
Diameter of piston rod...................................	2 in.
Duration of test, hours..................................	1.5
Suction pressure, pounds per square inch gage..............	15
Condenser pressure, pounds per square inch gage............	120
Revolutions per minute...................................	72
Temperature of brine, inlet, degrees Fahrenheit.............	36.4
Temperature of brine, outlet, degrees Fahrenheit............	11.1
Difference of inlet and outlet temperatures, degrees Fahrenheit.	
Specific heat of brine....................................	0.757
Weight of brine circulated, pounds........................	8,025
Weight of brine circulated per hour, pounds................	
Refrigeration produced, B.t.u. per hour....................	
Capacity developed, tons per 24 hours.....................	
Temperature of outlet condensing water, degrees Fahrenheit..	68
Temperature of inlet condensing water, degrees Fahrenheit....	55
Difference of temperature of outlet and inlet of condensing water, degrees Fahrenheit..............................	
Weight of cooling water used, pounds......................	19,730
Weight of cooling water used per hour, pounds..............	
B.t.u. absorbed per hour by cooling water..................	
Ammonia temperatures, inlet to condenser, degrees Fahrenheit.	74.7
Ammonia temperatures, outlet to condenser, degrees Fahrenheit..	56.7
Ammonia temperature, difference of outlet and inlet, degrees Fahrenheit..	
Ammonia temperature at cooler, inlet, degrees Fahrenheit.....	64.8
Ammonia temperature at cooler, outlet, degrees Fahrenheit...	0.7
Ammonia temperature difference, cooler inlet and outlet, degrees Fahrenheit....................................	
Weight of ammonia circulated, pounds.....................	427.5
Weight of ammonia circulated, per hour...................	
Weight of dry steam used, pounds.........................	1,049
Weight of dry steam used, per hour.......................	

Mean effective pressure, head end, steam cylinder, pounds per square inch.. 34.9

Mean effective pressure, crank end, steam cylinder, pounds per square inch.. 30.45

Mean effective pressure, head end, ammonia cylinder, pounds per square inch.. 49.7

Mean effective pressure, crank end, ammonia cylinder, pounds per square inch.. 50.8

Indicated horsepower, head end, steam cylinder..............

Indicated horsepower, crank end, steam cylinder.............

Indicated horsepower, total, steam cylinder..................

Indicated horsepower, head end, ammonia cylinder...........

Indicated horsepower, crank end, ammonia cylinder..........

Indicated horsepower, total, ammonia cylinder..............

Mechanical efficiency, per cent............................

Weight of dry steam per indicated horsepower per hour, steam cylinder, pounds...

Weight of dry steam per hour per ton of refrigeration per 24 hours, pounds..

HEAT BALANCE

	Heat gained B.t.u.	Heat lost B.t.u.
Work of compression......................................		
Between compressor and condenser........................		
To condensing water.....................................		
Between condenser and cooler............................		
In cooler...		
Total..		

35. What temperature is required to make a 40 per cent solution of aqua ammonia boil at a pressure of 120 pounds per square inch absolute?

36. A 30 per cent solution of aqua ammonia boils in a generator at 200° F. What is the pressure in the generator?

37. A 36 per cent solution of aqua ammonia enters a generator and boils at 214° F. If the generator gage pressure is 122 pounds per square inch, find the weight of weak aqua ammonia required to absorb 1 pound of ammonia vapor.

38. An absorber operates at a gage pressure of 10 pounds per square inch. If the strong aqua ammonia leaves the absorber at 80° F., what is the strength of the aqua ammonia?

39. How much heat is produced when 5 pounds of ammonia vapor are absorbed in 45 pounds of water? How much heat is required to drive off this same amount of ammonia from the solution which has been made?

40. How much heat will be generated in an absorber and required in a generator per pound of ammonia vapor for the following conditions: strong aqua ammonia, 33 per cent; weak aqua ammonia, 22 per cent?

41. A 35 per cent solution of aqua ammonia leaves an absorber, and a 28 per cent solution of aqua ammonia enters an absorber, how much heat

will be liberated per minute when 40 pounds of ammonia vapor are absorbed per minute?

42. A generator operates at a gage pressure of 122 pounds per square inch. If the ammonia vapor leaving the generator is at a temperature of 208° F., find the partial steam pressure in the generator. What is the ammonia vapor pressure (see p. 233)?

43. How many pounds of strong aqua ammonia must be circulated per pound of ammonia if the concentrations are as follows: strong aqua ammonia, 35 per cent; weak aqua ammonia, 27 per cent?

44. With the conditions in the above problem, and the evaporating coils held at 0° F., how many pounds of strong aqua ammonia must be circulated per minute per ton of refrigeration if the liquid ammonia enters the expansion valve at 80° F.?

45. What is the heat of the liquid of a 20 per cent solution of water and ammonia at 180° F.?

46. Strong aqua ammonia of 35 per cent concentration enters a generator at 150° F., and weak aqua ammonia of 25 per cent concentration leaves the generator at 200° F.; how much heat must be added to the aqua ammonia per pound of ammonia vaporized?

47. A testing box passes 7.9 B.t.u. per hour *through a sample of insulation.* If the inside temperature is 70.6° F. and the outside temperature is 40.7° F., what is the value of the heat-transfer coefficient K if the area of the sample is 3.06 square feet?

48. If the temperatures of the surfaces of the sample in the above problem are 69.1° F. on the inside and 43.5° F. on the outside, what are the surface coefficients and the constant of conduction if the sample is 3 inches thick?

49. One side of a testing box has an outside area of 3.92 square feet and an inside area of 2.2 square feet. If the temperature difference is 25.7° F. and the heat passing through the material is 7.92 B.t.u. per hour, determine the coefficient of conductivity per square foot per 24 hours per degree Fahrenheit per inch of thickness. The test specimen is 3 inches thick.

50. The heat lost per hour through a wall 10 by 10 feet is 800 B.t.u. If the temperatures of the outside air is 90° F. and the inside air is 10° F., find the total loss per square foot per hour per degree Fahrenheit.

51. In a double-pipe condenser, the water velocity is 2.5 feet per second. Determine the number of linear feet of 1¼-inch pipe required for a 40-ton refrigerating plant operating at a compressor discharge pressure of 200 pounds per square inch absolute and a back pressure of 30 pounds per square inch absolute. The compression is dry, and the temperature of the liquid ammonia at the receiver is 85° F. The temperature rise of the cooling water is 10° F.

52. A wall is constructed of 2-inch concrete on the outside, 12 inches of brick, a 1-inch air space, and 1 inch of plaster on the inside. Determine the total heat loss per hour per square foot per degree Fahrenheit.

53. A cold-storage room has an outside wall made of 10 inches of concrete, two courses of 2-inch cork board, and the inner surface covered with ½ inch of cement. Determine the coefficient of transmission for the wall with a 2-inch air space between the concrete and the cork board. Calculate, also, without the air space between the concrete and the cork board.

54. How many tons of refrigeration are required to freeze 5,000 pounds of poultry from an initial temperature of 70° F. to a final temperature of 20° F.?

55. How much heat must be removed to lower the temperature of 1,000 tubs of butter (55 pounds each) from 60 to 10° F.?

56. An ice-storage house has a capacity of 2,000 tons of ice. The house has a floor area of 45 by 50 feet and is 45 feet high. The walls and ceilings are insulated with two layers of 2-inch cork board. The room is held at 22° F. when the outside temperature is 100° F. If the leakage loss for doors, lights, and workmen is taken at 15 per cent of the insulation loss, determine the number of linear feet of 2-inch pipe required. Assume a transmission coefficient of 2 B.t.u. per 24 hours per degree Fahrenheit per square foot for the total thickness.

57. A creamery receives 3,000 gallons of milk a day, cooled from 75 to 38° F. in 3 hours. What is the capacity of a machine which will produce this cooling? Neglect all losses.

58. Suppose a small machine were used in the above creamery, operating 9 hours per day for cooling brine-storage tanks. How many tons capacity in 24 hours should this machine have?

59. How many gallons of calcium brine should be used in the storage tanks in problem 58 if the brine had a strength of 90° F. salinometer? The brine is warmed 20° F. in cooling the milk. Assume that the machine is run for 5 hours while cooling it.

60. A refrigerator is 5 feet high, 4 feet wide, and 3 feet deep. The heat-transfer coefficient is 0.2. How many pounds of ice melt per hour if the temperature of the refrigerator is 48° F. and the temperature of the outside air is 95° F.

61. A cold-storage compartment is 30 feet long, 20 feet wide, and 10 feet high. The heat-transfer coefficient is 0.094. The inside temperature is 28° F. How many tons of refrigerating capacity will be required to maintain this temperature if the temperature of the outside air is 80° F.?

62. A cold-storage compartment is 40 feet long, 30 feet wide, and 10 feet high. Both the end walls and one side wall are exposed to the outside temperature, which is 85° F. The other side wall adjoins another compartment kept at the same temperature. Each end wall contains one double window, and the side wall contains four double windows with air spaces. The temperature of the cold-storage compartments is maintained at 36° F. The construction of the walls of the compartment is such that the heat-transfer coefficient is 0.0785. The rooms above and below this compartment are at a temperature of 36° F. In this compartment are placed 70 tons of beef at a temperature of 90° F. This beef is removed at the end of 48 hours, and a new lot put in. The specific heat of beef is 0.68. How many tons of refrigerating capacity are required to keep this room and its contents cooled?

63. A cold-storage compartment 30 feet long by 25 feet wide by 10 feet high passes 4,000 heat units per hour through the walls. The temperature of this compartment is 36° F. The goods stored here each day require the removal of 400,000 B.t.u. The compartment is cooled by brine coils carrying brine at 25° F. How many running feet of 1½-inch pipe should the cooling coils contain? Assume that each square foot of coil surface will transfer 10 B.t.u. per hour for each degree difference in temperature.

64. Suppose that the amount of heat removed from the above cold-storage compartment is not known. How many running feet of 1½-inch pipe would be required for *direct-expansion* coils?

65. In problem 64, allow a drop in temperature of 6° F. between the ammonia in the expansion coils and the brine. What strength (salinometer degrees) of salt brine would be used?

66. A certain refrigerating system requires 5,000 gallons of calcium brine. It is to be of such strength as to have a freezing point of −1.40° F. If calcium chloride costs $2.15 per 100 pounds, what will be the cost of making the brine?

Note.—Water weighs 8⅓ pounds per gallon. Use specific-gravity values.

67. A refrigerating system circulates 30,000 pounds of calcium brine per hour to maintain the desired temperature. The brine has a strength of 92° on the salinometer. Later, this brine had its strength reduced to 68°, because it was too strong to maintain the desired temperature. If the brine is weakened to 68° salinometer, how much brine would have to be circulated per hour to maintain the same temperature? Assume that the required amount of refrigeration is the same in both cases.

APPENDIX B

TABLES AND CHARTS

TABLE I.—SATURATED AMMONIA: TEMPERATURE TABLE

| Temperature, degrees Fahrenheit | Pressure | | Volume vapor, ft.³/lb. | Density vapor, lbs./ft.³ | Heat content | | Latent heat, B.t.u./lb. | Entropy | | Temperature, degrees Fahrenheit |
| | Absolute, lbs./in.² | Gage, lbs./in.² | | | Liquid, B.t.u./lb. | Vapor, B.t.u./lb. | | Liquid, B.t.u./lb. degrees Fahrenheit | Vapor, B.t.u./lb. degrees Fahrenheit | |
t	p	g. p.	V	1/V	h	H	L	s	S	t
−60	5.55	*18.6	44.73	0.02235	−21.2	589.6	610.8	−0.0517	1.4769	−60
−59	5.74	*18.2	43.37	0.02306	−20.1	590.0	610.1	−0.0490	1.4741	−59
−58	5.93	*17.8	42.05	0.02378	−19.1	590.4	609.5	−0.0464	1.4713	−58
−57	6.13	*17.4	40.79	0.02452	−18.0	590.8	608.8	−0.0438	1.4686	−57
−56	6.33	*17.0	39.56	0.02528	−17.0	591.2	608.2	−0.0412	1.4658	−56
−55	6.54	*16.6	38.38	0.02605	−15.9	591.6	607.5	−0.0386	1.4631	−55
−54	6.75	*16.2	37.24	0.02685	−14.8	592.1	606.9	0.0360	1.4604	−54
−53	6.97	*15.7	36.15	0.02766	−13.8	592.4	606.2	−0.0334	1.4577	−53
−52	7.20	*15.3	35.09	0.02850	−12.7	592.9	605.6	−0.0307	1.4551	−52
−51	7.43	*14.8	34.06	0.02936	−11.7	593.2	604.9	−0.0281	1.4524	−51
−50	7.67	*14.3	33.08	0.03023	−10.6	593.7	604.3	−0.0256	1.4497	−50
−49	7.91	*13.8	32.12	0.03113	−9.6	594.0	603.6	−0.0230	1.4471	−49
−48	8.16	*13.3	31.20	0.03205	−8.5	594.4	602.9	−0.0204	1.4445	−48
−47	8.42	*12.8	30.31	0.03299	−7.4	594.9	602.3	−0.0179	1.4419	−47
−46	8.68	*12.2	29.45	0.03395	−6.4	595.2	601.6	−0.0153	1.4393	−46
−45	8.95	*11.7	28.62	0.03494	−5.3	595.6	600.9	−0.0127	1.4368	−45
−44	9.23	*11.1	27.82	0.03595	−4.3	596.0	600.3	−0.0102	1.4342	−44
−43	9.51	*10.6	27.04	0.03698	−3.2	596.4	599.6	−0.0076	1.4317	−43
−42	9.81	*10.0	26.29	0.03804	−2.1	596.8	598.9	−0.0051	1.4292	−42
−41	10.10	*9.3	25.56	0.03912	−1.1	597.2	598.3	−0.0025	1.4267	−41
−40	10.41	*8.7	24.86	0.04022	0.0	597.6	597.6	0.0000	1.4242	−40
−39	10.72	*8.1	24.18	0.04135	1.1	598.0	596.9	0.0025	1.4217	−39
−38	11.04	*7.4	23.53	0.04251	2.1	598.3	596.2	0.0051	1.4193	−38
−37	11.37	*6.8	22.89	0.04369	3.2	598.7	595.5	0.0076	1.4169	−37
−36	11.71	*6.1	22.27	0.04489	4.3	599.1	594.8	0.0101	1.4144	−36
−35	12.05	*5.4	21.68	0.04613	5.3	599.5	594.2	0.0126	1.4120	−35
−34	12.41	*4.7	21.10	0.04739	6.4	599.9	593.5	0.0151	1.4096	−34
−33	12.77	*3.9	20.54	0.04868	7.4	600.2	592.8	0.0176	1.4072	−33
−32	13.14	*3.2	20.00	0.04999	8.5	600.6	592.1	0.0201	1.4048	−32
−31	13.52	*2.4	19.48	0.05134	9.6	601.0	591.4	0.0226	1.4025	−31
−30	13.90	*1.6	18.97	0.05271	10.7	601.4	590.7	0.0250	1.4001	−30
−29	14.30	*0.8	18.48	0.05411	11.7	601.7	590.0	0.0275	1.3978	−29
−28	14.71	0.0	18.00	0.05555	12.8	602.1	589.3	0.0300	1.3955	−28
−27	15.12	0.4	17.54	0.05701	13.9	602.5	588.6	0.0325	1.3932	−27
−26	15.55	0.8	17.09	0.05850	14.9	602.8	587.9	0.0350	1.3909	−26
−25	15.98	1.3	16.66	0.06003	16.0	603.2	587.2	0.0374	1.3886	−25
−24	16.42	1.7	16.24	0.06158	17.1	603.6	586.5	0.0399	1.3863	−24
−23	16.88	2.2	15.83	0.06317	18.1	603.9	585.8	0.0423	1.3840	−23
−22	17.34	2.6	15.43	0.06479	19.2	604.3	585.1	0.0448	1.3818	−22
−21	17.81	3.1	15.05	0.06644	20.3	604.6	584.3	0.0472	1.3796	−21
−20	18.30	3.6	14.68	0.06813	21.4	605.0	583.6	0.0497	1.3774	−20
−19	18.79	4.1	14.32	0.06985	22.4	605.3	582.9	0.0521	1.3752	−19
−18	19.30	4.6	13.97	0.07161	23.5	605.7	582.2	0.0545	1.3729	−18
−17	19.81	5.1	13.62	0.07340	24.6	606.1	581.5	0.0570	1.3708	−17
−16	20.34	5.6	13.29	0.07522	25.6	606.4	580.8	0.0594	1.3686	−16
−15	20.88	6.2	12.97	0.07709	26.7	606.7	580.0	0.0618	1.3664	−15
−14	21.43	6.7	12.66	0.07898	27.8	607.1	579.3	0.0642	1.3643	−14
−13	21.99	7.3	12.36	0.08092	28.9	607.5	578.6	0.0666	1.3621	−13
−12	22.56	7.9	12.06	0.08289	30.0	607.8	577.8	0.0690	1.3600	−12
−11	23.15	8.5	11.78	0.08490	31.0	608.1	577.1	0.0714	1.3579	−11

* Inches of mercury below 1 standard atmosphere (29.92 in.).

TABLE I.—SATURATED AMMONIA: TEMPERATURE TABLE (*Continued*)

Temperature, degrees Fahrenheit	Pressure		Volume vapor, ft.³/lb.	Density vapor, lbs./ft.³	Heat content		Latent heat, B.t.u./lb.	Entropy		Temperature, degrees Fahrenheit
	Absolute, lbs./in.²	Gage, lbs./in.²			Liquid, B.t.u./lb.	Vapor, B.t.u./lb.		Liquid, B.t.u./lb. degrees Fahrenheit	Vapor, B.t.u./lb. degrees Fahrenheit	
t	p	$g. p.$	V	$1/V$	h	H	L	s	S	t
−10	23.74	9.0	11.50	0.08695	32.1	608.5	576.4	0.0738	1.3558	−10
− 9	24.35	9.7	11.23	0.08904	33.2	608.8	575.6	0.0762	1.3537	− 9
− 8	24.97	10.3	10.97	0.09117	34.3	609.2	574.9	0.0786	1.3516	− 8
− 7	25.61	10.9	10.71	0.09334	35.4	609.5	574.1	0.0809	1.3495	− 7
− 6	26.26	11.6	10.47	0.09555	36.4	609.8	573.4	0.0833	1.3474	− 6
− 5	26.92	12.2	10.23	0.09780	37.5	610.1	572.6	0.0857	1.3454	− 5
− 4	27.59	12.9	9.991	0.1001	38.6	610.5	571.9	0.0880	1.3433	− 4
− 3	28.28	13.6	9.763	0.1024	39.7	610.8	571.1	0.0904	1.3413	− 3
− 2	28.98	14.3	9.541	0.1048	40.7	611.1	570.4	0.0928	1.3393	− 2
− 1	29.69	15.0	9.326	0.1072	41.8	611.4	569.6	0.0951	1.3372	− 1
0	30.42	15.7	9.116	0.1097	42.9	611.8	568.9	0.0975	1.3352	0
1	31.16	16.5	8.912	0.1122	44.0	612.1	568.1	0.0998	1.3332	1
2	31.92	17.2	8.714	0.1148	45.1	612.4	567.3	0.1022	1.3312	2
3	32.69	18.0	8.521	0.1174	46.2	612.7	566.5	0.1045	1.3292	3
4	33.47	18.8	8.333	0.1200	47.2	613.0	565.8	0.1069	1.3273	4
5	34.27	19.6	8.150	0.1227	48.3	613.3	565.0	0.1092	1.3253	5
6	35.09	20.4	7.971	0.1254	49.4	613.6	564.2	0.1115	1.3234	6
7	35.92	21.2	7.798	0.1282	50.5	613.9	563.4	0.1138	1.3214	7
8	36.77	22.1	7.629	0.1311	51.6	614.3	562.7	0.1162	1.3195	8
9	37.63	22.9	7.464	0.1340	52.7	614.6	561.9	0.1185	1.3176	9
10	38.51	23.8	7.304	0.1369	53.8	614.9	561.1	0.1208	1.3157	10
11	39.40	24.7	7.148	0.1399	54.9	615.2	560.3	0.1231	1.3137	11
12	40.31	25.6	6.996	0.1429	56.0	615.5	559.5	0.1254	1.3118	12
13	41.24	26.5	6.847	0.1460	57.1	615.8	558.7	0.1277	1.3099	13
14	42.18	27.5	6.703	0.1492	58.2	616.1	557.9	0.1300	1.3081	14
15	43.14	28.4	6.562	0.1524	59.2	616.3	557.1	0.1323	1.3062	15
16	44.12	29.4	6.425	0.1556	60.3	616.6	556.3	0.1346	1.3043	16
17	45.12	30.4	6.291	0.1590	61.4	616.9	555.5	0.1369	1.3025	17
18	46.13	31.4	6.161	0.1623	62.5	617.2	554.7	0.1392	1.3006	18
19	47.16	32.5	6.034	0.1657	63.6	617.5	553.9	0.1415	1.2988	19
20	48.21	33.5	5.910	0.1692	64.7	617.8	553.1	0.1437	1.2969	20
21	49.28	34.6	5.789	0.1728	65.8	618.0	552.2	0.1460	1.2951	21
22	50.36	35.7	5.671	0.1763	66.9	618.3	551.4	0.1483	1.2933	22
23	51.47	36.8	5.556	0.1800	68.0	618.6	550.6	0.1505	1.2915	23
24	52.59	37.9	5.443	0.1837	69.1	618.9	549.8	0.1528	1.2897	24
25	53.73	39.0	5.334	0.1875	70.2	619.1	548.9	0.1551	1.2879	25
26	54.90	40.2	5.227	0.1913	71.3	619.4	548.1	0.1573	1.2861	26
27	56.08	41.4	5.123	0.1952	72.4	619.7	547.3	0.1596	1.2843	27
28	57.28	42.6	5.021	0.1992	73.5	619.9	546.4	0.1618	1.2825	28
29	58.50	43.8	4.922	0.2032	74.6	620.2	545.6	0.1641	1.2808	29
30	59.74	45.0	4.825	0.2073	75.7	620.5	544.8	0.1663	1.2790	30
31	61.00	46.3	4.730	0.2114	76.8	620.7	543.9	0.1686	1.2773	31
32	62.29	47.6	4.637	0.2156	77.9	621.0	543.1	0.1708	1.2755	32
33	63.59	48.9	4.547	0.2199	79.0	621.2	542.2	0.1730	1.2738	33
34	64.91	50.2	4.459	0.2243	80.1	621.5	541.4	0.1753	1.2721	34
35	66.26	51.6	4.373	0.2287	81.2	621.7	540.5	0.1775	1.2704	35
36	67.63	52.9	4.289	0.2332	82.3	622.0	539.7	0.1797	1.2686	36
37	69.02	54.3	4.207	0.2377	83.4	622.2	538.8	0.1819	1.2669	37
38	70.43	55.7	4.126	0.2423	84.6	622.5	537.9	0.1841	1.2652	38
39	71.87	57.2	4.048	0.2470	85.7	622.7	537.0	0.1863	1.2635	39
40	73.32	58.6	3.971	0.2518	86.8	623.0	536.2	0.1885	1.2618	40
41	74.80	60.1	3.897	0.2566	87.9	623.2	535.3	0.1908	1.2602	41
42	76.31	61.6	3.823	0.2616	89.0	623.4	534.4	0.1930	1.2585	42
43	77.83	63.1	3.752	0.2665	90.1	623.7	533.6	0.1952	1.2568	43
44	79.38	64.7	3.682	0.2716	91.2	623.9	532.7	0.1974	1.2552	44

TABLE I.—SATURATED AMMONIA: TEMPERATURE TABLE (*Continued*)

Temperature, degrees Fahrenheit	Pressure		Volume vapor, ft.³/lb.	Density vapor, lbs./ft.³	Heat content		Latent heat, B.t.u./lb.	Entropy		Temperature, degrees Fahrenheit
	Absolute, lbs./in.²	Gage, lbs./in.²			Liquid, B.t.u./lb.	Vapor, B.t.u./lb.		Liquid, B.t.u./lb. degrees Fahrenheit	Vapor, B.t.u./lb. degrees Fahrenheit	
t	p	g. p.	V	1/V	h	H	L	s	S	t
45	80.96	66.3	3.614	0.2767	92.3	624.1	531.8	0.1996	1.2535	**45**
46	82.55	67.9	3.547	0.2819	93.5	624.4	530.9	0.2018	1.2519	46
47	84.18	69.5	3.481	0.2872	94.6	624.6	530.0	0.2040	1.2502	47
48	85.82	71.1	3.418	0.2926	95.7	624.8	529.1	0.2062	1.2486	48
49	87.49	72.8	3.355	0.2981	96.8	625.0	528.2	0.2083	1.2469	49
50	89.19	74.5	3.294	0.3036	97.9	625.2	527.3	0.2105	1.2453	**50**
51	90.91	76.2	3.234	0.3092	99.1	625.5	526.4	0.2127	1.2437	51
52	92.66	78.0	3.176	0.3149	100.2	625.7	525.5	0.2149	1.2421	52
53	94.43	79.7	3.119	0.3207	101.3	625.9	524.6	0.2171	1.2405	53
54	96.23	81.5	3.063	0.3265	102.4	626.1	523.7	0.2192	1.2389	54
55	98.06	83.4	3.008	0.3325	103.5	626.3	522.8	0.2214	1.2373	**5**
56	99.91	85.2	2.954	0.3385	104.7	626.5	521.8	0.2236	1.2357	56
57	101.8	87.1	2.902	0.3446	105.8	626.7	520.9	0.2257	1.2341	57
58	103.7	89.0	2.851	0.3508	106.9	626.9	520.0	0.2279	1.2325	58
59	105.6	90.9	2.800	0.3571	108.1	627.1	519.0	0.2301	1.2310	59
60	107.6	92.9	2.751	0.3635	109.2	627.3	518.1	0.2322	1.2294	**60**
61	109.6	94.9	2.703	0.3700	110.3	627.5	517.2	0.2344	1.2278	61
62	111.6	96.9	2.656	0.3765	111.5	627.7	516.2	0.2365	1.2262	62
63	113.6	98.9	2.610	0.3832	112.6	627.9	515.3	0.2387	1.2247	63
64	115.7	101.0	2.565	0.3899	113.7	628.0	514.3	0.2408	1.2231	64
65	117.8	103.1	2.520	0.3968	114.8	628.2	513.4	0.2430	1.2216	**65**
66	120.0	105.3	2.477	0.4037	116.0	628.4	512.4	0.2451	1.2201	66
67	122.1	107.4	2.435	0.4108	117.1	628.6	511.5	0.2473	1.2186	67
68	124.3	109.6	2.393	0.4179	118.3	628.8	510.5	0.2494	1.2170	68
69	126.5	111.8	2.352	0.4251	119.4	628.9	509.5	0.2515	1.2155	69
70	128.8	114.1	2.312	0.4325	120.5	629.1	508.6	0.2537	1.2140	**70**
71	131.1	116.4	2.273	0.4399	121.7	629.3	507.6	0.2558	1.2125	71
72	133.4	118.7	2.235	0.4474	122.8	629.4	506.6	0.2579	1.2110	72
73	135.7	121.0	2.197	0.4551	124.0	629.6	505.6	0.2601	1.2095	73
74	138.1	123.4	2.161	0.4628	125.1	629.8	504.7	0.2622	1.2080	74
75	140.5	125.8	2.125	0.4707	126.2	629.9	503.7	0.2643	1.2065	**75**
76	143.0	128.3	2.089	0.4786	127.4	630.1	502.7	0.2664	1.2050	76
77	145.4	130.7	2.055	0.4867	128.5	630.2	501.7	0.2685	1.2035	77
78	147.9	133.2	2.021	0.4949	129.7	630.4	500.7	0.2706	1.2020	78
79	150.5	135.8	1.988	0.5031	130.8	630.5	499.7	0.2728	1.2006	79
80	153.0	138.3	1.955	0.5115	132.0	630.7	498.7	0.2749	1.1991	**80**
81	155.6	140.9	1.923	0.5200	133.1	630.8	497.7	0.2769	1.1976	81
82	158.3	143.6	1.892	0.5287	134.3	631.0	496.7	0.2791	1.1962	82
83	161.0	146.3	1.861	0.5374	135.4	631.1	495.7	0.2812	1.1947	83
84	163.7	149.0	1.831	0.5462	136.6	631.3	494.7	0.2833	1.1933	84
85	166.4	151.7	1.801	0.5552	137.8	631.4	493.6	0.2854	1.1918	**85**
86	169.2	154.5	1.772	0.5643	138.9	631.5	492.6	0.2875	1.1904	86
87	172.0	157.3	1.744	0.5735	140.1	631.7	491.6	0.2895	1.1889	87
88	174.8	160.1	1.716	0.5828	141.2	631.8	490.6	0.2917	1.1875	88
89	177.7	163.0	1.688	0.5923	142.4	631.9	489.5	0.2937	1.1860	89
90	180.6	165.9	1.661	0.6019	143.5	632.0	488.5	0.2958	1.1846	**90**
91	183.6	168.9	1.635	0.6116	144.7	632.1	487.4	0.2979	1.1832	91
92	186.6	171.9	1.609	0.6214	145.8	632.2	486.4	0.3000	1.1818	92
93	189.6	174.9	1.584	0.6314	147.0	632.3	485.3	0.3021	1.1804	93
94	192.7	178.0	1.559	0.6415	148.2	632.5	484.3	0.3041	1.1789	94
95	195.8	181.1	1.534	0.6517	149.4	632.6	483.2	0.3062	1.1775	**95**
96	198.9	184.2	1.510	0.6620	150.5	632.6	482.1	0.3083	1.1761	96
97	202.1	187.4	1.487	0.6725	151.7	632.8	481.1	0.3104	1.1747	97
98	205.3	190.6	1.464	0.6832	152.9	632.9	480.0	0.3125	1.1733	98
99	208.6	193.9	1.441	0.6939	154.0	632.9	478.9	0.3145	1.1719	99

TABLE I.—SATURATED AMMONIA: TEMPERATURE TABLE (*Continued*)

Temperature, degrees Fahrenheit	Pressure		Volume vapor, ft.³/lb.	Density vapor, lbs./ft.³	Heat content		Latent heat, B.t.u./lb.	Entropy		Temperature, degrees Fahrenheit
	Absolute, lbs./in.²	Gage, lbs./in.²			Liquid, B.t.u./lb.	Vapor, B.t.u./lb.		Liquid, B.t.u./lb. degrees Fahrenheit	Vapor, B.t.u./lb. degrees Fahrenheit	
t	p	g. p.	V	1/V	h	H	L	s	S	t
100	211.9	197.2	1.419	0.7048	155.2	633.0	477.8	0.3166	1.1705	**100**
101	215.2	200.5	1.397	0.7159	156.4	633.1	476.7	0.3187	1.1691	101
102	218.6	203.9	1.375	0.7270	157.6	633.2	475.6	0.3207	1.1677	102
103	222.0	207.3	1.354	0.7384	158.7	633.3	474.6	0.3228	1.1663	103
104	225.4	210.7	1.334	0.7498	159.9	633.4	473.5	0.3248	1.1649	104
105	228.9	214.2	1.313	0.7615	161.1	633.4	472.3	0.3269	1.1635	**105**
106	232.5	217.8	1.293	0.7732	162.3	633.5	471.2	0.3289	1.1621	106
107	236.0	221.3	1.274	0.7852	163.5	633.6	470.1	0.3310	1.1607	107
108	239.7	225.0	1.254	0.7972	164.6	633.6	469.0	0.3330	1.1593	108
109	243.3	228.6	1.235	0.8095	165.8	633.7	467.9	0.3351	1.1580	109
110	247.0	232.3	1.217	0.8219	167.0	633.7	466.7	0.3372	1.1566	**110**
111	250.8	236.1	1.198	0.8344	168.2	633.8	465.6	0.3392	1.1552	111
112	254.5	239.8	1.180	0.8471	169.4	633.8	464.4	0.3413	1.1538	112
113	258.4	243.7	1.163	0.8600	170.6	633.9	463.3	0.3433	1.1524	113
114	262.2	247.5	1.145	0.8730	171.8	633.9	462.1	0.3453	1.1510	114
115	266.2	251.5	1.128	0.8862	173.0	633.9	460.9	0.3474	1.1497	**115**
116	270.1	255.4	1.112	0.8996	174.2	634.0	459.8	0.3495	1.1483	116
117	274.1	259.4	1.095	0.9132	175.4	634.0	458.6	0.3515	1.1469	117
118	278.2	263.5	1.079	0.9269	176.6	634.0	457.4	0.3535	1.1455	118
119	282.3	267.6	1.063	0.9408	177.8	634.0	456.2	0.3556	1.1441	119
120	286.4	271.7	1.047	0.9549	179.0	634.0	455.0	0.3576	1.1427	**120**
121	290.6	275.9	1.032	0.9692	180.2	634.0	453.8	0.3597	1.1414	121
122	294.8	280.1	1.017	0.9837	181.4	634.0	452.6	0.3618	1.1400	122
123	299.1	284.4	1.002	0.9983	182.6	634.0	451.4	0.3638	1.1386	123
124	303.4	288.7	0.987	1.0132	183.9	634.0	450.1	0.3659	1.1372	124
125	307.8	293.1	0.973	1.028	185.1	634.0	448.9	0.3679	1.1358	**125**

Table II.—Saturated Ammonia: Absolute-pressure Table

Pressure (abs.), lbs./in.²	Temperature, degrees Fahrenheit	Volume vapor, ft.³/lb.	Density vapor, lbs./ft.³	Heat content Liquid, B.t.u./lb.	Heat content Vapor, B.t.u./lb.	Latent heat, B.t.u./lb.	Entropy Liquid, B.t.u./lb. degrees Fahrenheit	Entropy Evaporation, B.t.u./lb. degrees Fahrenheit	Entropy Vapor, B.t.u./lb. degrees Fahrenheit	Pressure (abs.), lbs./in.²
p	t	V	$1/V$	h	H	L	s	L/T	S	p
5.0	−63.11	49.31	0.02029	−24.5	588.3	612.8	−0.0599	1.5456	1.4857	5.0
5.5	−60.27	45.11	0.02217	−21.5	589.5	611.0	−0.0524	1.5301	1.4777	5.5
6.0	−57.64	41.59	0.02405	−18.7	590.6	609.3	−0.0455	1.5158	1.4703	6.0
6.5	−55.18	38.59	0.02591	−16.1	591.6	607.7	−0.0390	1.5026	1.4636	6.5
7.0	−52.88	36.01	0.02777	−13.7	592.5	606.2	−0.0330	1.4904	1.4574	7.0
7.5	−50.70	33.77	0.02962	−11.3	593.4	604.7	−0.0274	1.4790	1.4516	7.5
8.0	−48.64	31.79	0.03146	− 9.2	594.2	603.4	−0.0221	1.4683	1.4462	8.0
8.5	−46.69	30.04	0.03329	− 7.1	595.0	602.1	−0.0171	1.4582	1.4411	8.5
9.0	−44.83	28.48	0.03511	− 5.1	595.7	600.8	−0.0123	1.4486	1.4363	9.0
9.5	−43.05	27.08	0.03693	− 3.2	596.4	599.6	−0.0077	1.4396	1.4319	9.5
10.0	−41.34	25.81	0.03874	− 1.4	597.1	598.5	−0.0034	1.4310	1.4276	10.0
10.5	−39.71	24.66	0.04055	+ 0.3	597.7	597.4	+0.0007	1.4228	1.4235	10.5
11.0	−38.14	23.61	0.04235	2.0	598.3	596.3	0.0047	1.4149	1.4196	11.0
11.5	−36.62	22.65	0.04414	3.6	598.9	595.3	0.0085	1.4074	1.4159	11.5
12.0	−35.16	21.77	0.04593	5.1	599.4	594.3	0.0122	1.4002	1.4124	12.0
12.5	−33.74	20.96	0.04772	6.7	600.0	593.3	0.0157	1.3933	1.4090	12.5
13.0	−32.37	20.20	0.04950	8.1	600.5	592.4	0.0191	1.3866	1.4057	13.0
13.5	−31.05	19.50	0.05128	9.6	601.0	591.4	0.0225	1.3801	1.4026	13.5
14.0	−29.76	18.85	0.05305	10.9	601.4	590.5	0.0257	1.3739	1.3996	14.0
14.5	−28.51	18.24	0.05482	12.2	601.9	589.7	0.0288	1.3679	1.3967	14.5
15.0	−27.29	17.67	0.05658	13.6	602.4	588.8	0.0318	1.3620	1.3938	15.0
15.5	−26.11	17.14	0.05834	14.8	602.8	588.0	0.0347	1.3564	1.3911	15.5
16.0	−24.95	16.64	0.06010	16.0	603.2	587.2	0.0375	1.3510	1.3885	16.0
16.5	−23.83	16.17	0.06186	17.2	603.6	586.4	0.0403	1.3456	1.3859	16.5
17.0	−22.73	15.72	0.06361	18.4	604.0	585.6	0.0430	1.3405	1.3835	17.0
17.5	−21.66	15.30	0.06535	19.6	604.4	584.8	0.0456	1.3354	1.3810	17.5
18.0	−20.61	14.90	0.06710	20.7	604.8	584.1	0.0482	1.3305	1.3787	18.0
18.5	−19.59	14.53	0.06884	21.8	605.1	583.3	0.0507	1.3258	1.3765	18.5
19.0	−18.58	14.17	0.07058	22.9	605.5	582.6	0.0531	1.3211	1.3742	19.0
19.5	−17.60	13.83	0.07232	23.9	605.8	581.9	0.0555	1.3166	1.3721	19.5
20.0	−16.64	13.50	0.07405	25.0	606.2	581.2	0.0578	1.3122	1.3700	20.0
20.5	−15.70	13.20	0.07578	26.0	606.5	580.5	0.0601	1.3078	1.3679	20.5
21.0	−14.78	12.90	0.07751	27.0	606.8	579.8	0.0623	1.3036	1.3659	21.0
21.5	−13.87	12.62	0.07924	27.9	607.1	579.2	0.0645	1.2995	1.3640	21.5
22.0	−12.98	12.35	0.08096	28.9	607.4	578.5	0.0666	1.2955	1.3621	22.0
22.5	−12.11	12.09	0.08268	29.8	607.7	577.9	0.0687	1.2915	1.3602	22.5
23.0	−11.25	11.85	0.08440	30.8	608.1	577.3	0.0708	1.2876	1.3584	23.0
23.5	−10.41	11.61	0.08612	31.7	608.3	576.6	0.0728	1.2838	1.3566	23.5
24.0	− 9.58	11.39	0.08783	32.6	608.6	576.0	0.0748	1.2801	1.3549	24.0
24.5	− 8.76	11.17	0.08955	33.5	608.9	575.4	0.0768	1.2764	1.3532	24.5
25.0	− 7.96	10.96	0.09126	34.3	609.1	574.8	0.0787	1.2728	1.3515	25.0
25.5	− 7.17	10.76	0.09297	35.2	609.4	574.2	0.0805	1.2693	1.3498	25.5
26.0	− 6.39	10.56	0.09468	36.0	609.7	573.7	0.0824	1.2658	1.3482	26.0
26.5	− 5.63	10.38	0.09638	36.8	609.9	573.1	0.0842	1.2625	1.3467	26.5
27.0	− 4.87	10.20	0.09809	37.7	610.2	572.5	0.0860	1.2591	1.3451	27.0
27.5	− 4.13	10.02	0.09979	38.4	610.4	572.0	0.0878	1.2558	1.3436	27.5
28.0	− 3.40	9.853	0.1015	39.3	610.7	571.4	0.0895	1.2526	1.3421	28.0
28.5	− 2.68	9.691	0.1032	40.0	610.9	570.9	0.0912	1.2494	1.3406	28.5
29.0	− 1.97	9.534	0.1049	40.8	611.1	570.3	0.0929	1.2463	1.3392	29.0
29.5	− 1.27	9.383	0.1066	41.6	611.4	569.8	0.0945	1.2433	1.3378	29.5
30	− 0.57	9.236	0.1083	42.3	611.6	569.3	0.0962	1.2402	1.3364	30
31	+ 0.79	8.955	0.1117	43.8	612.0	568.2	0.0993	1.2343	1.3336	31
32	2.11	8.693	0.1150	45.2	612.4	567.2	0.1024	1.2286	1.3310	32
33	3.40	8.445	0.1184	46.6	612.8	566.2	0.1055	1.2230	1.3285	33
34	4.66	8.211	0.1218	48.0	613.2	565.2	0.1084	1.2176	1.3260	34

TABLE II.—SATURATED AMMONIA: ABSOLUTE-PRESSURE TABLE (*Continued*)

Pressure (abs.), lbs./in.²	Temperature, degrees Fahrenheit	Volume vapor, ft.³/lb.	Density vapor, lbs./ft.³	Heat content		Latent heat, B.t.u./lb.	Entropy			Pressure (abs.), lbs./in.²
				Liquid, B.t.u./lb.	Vapor, B.t.u./lb.		Liquid, B.t.u./lb. degrees Fahrenheit	Evaporation, B.t.u./lb. degrees Fahrenheit	Vapor, B.t.u./lb. degrees Fahrenheit	
p	t	V	$1/V$	h	H	L	s	L/T	S	p
35	5.89	7.991	0.1251	49.3	613.6	564.3	0.1113	1.2123	1.3236	**35**
36	7.09	7.782	0.1285	50.6	614.0	563.4	0.1141	1.2072	1.3213	36
37	8.27	7.584	0.1319	51.9	614.3	562.4	0.1168	1.2022	1.3190	37
38	9.42	7.396	0.1352	53.2	614.7	561.5	0.1195	1.1973	1.3168	38
39	10.55	7.217	0.1386	54.4	615.0	560.6	0.1221	1.1925	1.3146	39
40	11.66	7.047	0.1419	55.6	615.4	559.8	0.1246	1.1879	1.3125	**40**
41	12.74	6.885	0.1452	56.8	615.7	558.9	0.1271	1.1833	1.3104	41
42	13.81	6.731	0.1486	57.9	616.0	558.1	0.1296	1.1788	1.3084	42
43	14.85	6.583	0.1519	59.1	616.3	557.2	0.1320	1.1745	1.3065	43
44	15.88	6.442	0.1552	60.2	616.6	556.4	0.1343	1.1703	1.3046	44
45	16.88	6.307	0.1586	61.3	616.9	555.6	0.1366	1.1661	1.3027	**45**
46	17.87	6.177	0.1619	62.4	617.2	554.8	0.1389	1.1620	1.3009	46
47	18.84	6.053	0.1652	63.4	617.4	554.0	0.1411	1.1580	1.2991	47
48	19.80	5.934	0.1685	64.5	617.7	553.2	0.1433	1.1540	1.2973	48
49	20.74	5.820	0.1718	65.5	618.0	552.5	0.1454	1.1502	1.2956	49
50	21.67	5.710	0.1751	66.5	618.2	551.7	0.1475	1.1464	1.2939	**50**
51	22.58	5.604	0.1785	67.5	618.5	551.0	0.1496	1.1427	1.2923	51
52	23.48	5.502	0.1818	68.5	618.7	550.2	0.1516	1.1390	1.2906	52
53	24.36	5.404	0.1851	69.5	619.0	549.5	0.1536	1.1354	1.2890	53
54	25.23	5.309	0.1884	70.4	619.2	548.8	0.1556	1.1319	1.2875	54
55	26.09	5.218	0.1917	71.4	619.4	548.0	0.1575	1.1284	1.2859	**55**
56	26.94	5.129	0.1950	72.3	619.7	547.4	0.1594	1.1250	1.2844	56
57	27.77	5.044	0.1983	73.3	619.9	546.6	0.1613	1.1217	1.2830	57
58	28.59	4.962	0.2015	74.2	620.1	545.9	0.1631	1.1184	1.2815	58
59	29.41	4.882	0.2048	75.0	620.3	545.3	0.1650	1.1151	1.2801	59
60	30.21	4.805	0.2081	75.9	620.5	544.6	0.1668	1.1119	1.2787	**60**
61	31.00	4.730	0.2114	76.8	620.7	543.9	0.1685	1.1088	1.2773	61
62	31.78	4.658	0.2147	77.7	620.9	543.2	0.1703	1.1056	1.2759	62
63	32.55	4.588	0.2180	78.5	621.1	542.6	0.1720	1.1026	1.2746	63
64	33.31	4.519	0.2213	79.4	621.3	541.9	0.1737	1.0996	1.2733	64
65	34.06	4.453	0.2245	80.2	621.5	541.3	0.1754	1.0966	1.2720	**65**
66	34.81	4.389	0.2278	81.0	621.7	540.7	0.1770	1.0937	1.2707	66
67	35.54	4.327	0.2311	81.8	621.9	540.1	0.1787	1.0907	1.2694	67
68	36.27	4.267	0.2344	82.6	622.0	539.4	0.1803	1.0879	1.2682	68
69	36.99	4.208	0.2377	83.4	622.2	538.8	0.1819	1.0851	1.2670	69
70	37.70	4.151	0.2409	84.2	622.4	538.2	0.1835	1.0823	1.2658	**70**
71	38.40	4.095	0.2442	85.0	622.6	537.6	0.1850	1.0795	1.2645	71
72	39.09	4.041	0.2475	85.8	622.8	537.0	0.1866	1.0768	1.2634	72
73	39.78	3.988	0.2507	86.5	622.9	536.4	0.1881	1.0741	1.2622	73
74	40.46	3.937	0.2540	87.3	623.1	535.8	0.1896	1.0715	1.2611	74
75	41.13	3.887	0.2573	88.0	623.2	535.2	0.1910	1.0689	1.2599	**75**
76	41.80	3.838	0.2606	88.8	623.4	534.6	0.1925	1.0663	1.2588	76
77	42.46	3.790	0.2638	89.5	623.5	534.0	0.1940	1.0637	1.2577	77
78	43.11	3.744	0.2671	90.2	623.7	533.5	0.1954	1.0612	1.2566	78
79	43.76	3.699	0.2704	90.9	623.8	532.9	0.1968	1.0587	1.2555	79
80	44.40	3.655	0.2736	91.7	624.0	532.3	0.1982	1.0563	1.2545	**80**
81	45.03	3.612	0.2769	92.4	624.1	531.7	0.1996	1.0538	1.2534	81
82	45.66	3.570	0.2801	93.1	624.3	531.2	0.2010	1.0514	1.2524	82
83	46.28	3.528	0.2834	93.8	624.4	530.6	0.2024	1.0490	1.2514	83
84	46.89	3.488	0.2867	94.5	624.6	530.1	0.2037	1.0467	1.2504	84
85	47.50	3.449	0.2899	95.1	624.7	529.6	0.2051	1.0443	1.2494	**85**
86	48.11	3.411	0.2932	95.8	624.8	529.0	0.2064	1.0420	1.2484	86
87	48.71	3.373	0.2964	96.5	625.0	528.5	0.2077	1.0397	1.2474	87
88	49.30	3.337	0.2997	97.2	625.1	527.9	0.2090	1.0375	1.2465	88
89	49.89	3.301	0.3030	97.8	625.2	527.4	0.2103	1.0352	1.2455	89

Table II.—Saturated Ammonia: Absolute-pressure Table (*Continued*)

Pressure (abs.), lbs./in.²	Temperature, degrees Fahrenheit	Volume vapor, ft.³/lb.	Density vapor, lbs./ft.³	Heat content Liquid, B.t.u./lb.	Heat content Vapor, B.t.u./lb.	Latent heat, B.t.u./lb.	Entropy Liquid, B.t.u./lb. degrees Fahrenheit	Entropy Evaporation, B.t.u./lb. degrees Fahrenheit	Entropy Vapor, B.t.u./lb. degrees Fahrenheit	Pressure (abs.), lbs./in.²
p	t	V	$1/V$	h	H	L	s	L/T	S	p
90	50.47	3.266	0.3062	98.4	625.3	526.9	0.2115	1.0330	1.2445	90
91	51.05	3.231	0.3095	99.1	625.5	526.4	0.2128	1.0308	1.2436	91
92	51.62	3.198	0.3127	99.8	625.6	525.8	0.2141	1.0286	1.2427	92
93	52.19	3.165	0.3160	100.4	625.7	525.3	0.2153	1.0265	1.2418	93
94	52.76	3.132	0.3192	101.0	625.8	524.8	0.2165	1.0243	1.2408	94
95	53.32	3.101	0.3225	101.6	625.9	524.3	0.2177	1.0222	1.2399	95
96	53.87	3.070	0.3258	102.3	626.1	523.8	0.2190	1.0201	1.2391	96
97	54.42	3.039	0.3290	102.9	626.2	523.3	0.2201	1.0181	1.2382	97
98	54.97	3.010	0.3323	103.5	626.3	522.8	0.2213	1.0160	1.2373	98
99	55.51	2.980	0.3355	104.1	626.4	522.3	0.2225	1.0140	1.2365	99
100	56.05	2.952	0.3388	104.7	626.5	521.8	0.2237	1.0119	1.2356	100
102	57.11	2.896	0.3453	105.9	626.7	520.8	0.2260	1.0079	1.2339	102
104	58.16	2.843	0.3518	107.1	626.9	519.8	0.2282	1.0041	1.2323	104
106	59.19	2.791	0.3583	108.3	627.1	518.8	0.2305	1.0002	1.2307	106
108	60.21	2.741	0.3648	109.4	627.3	517.9	0.2327	0.9964	1.2291	108
110	61.21	2.693	0.3713	110.5	627.5	517.0	0.2348	0.9927	1.2275	110
112	62.20	2.647	0.3778	111.7	627.7	516.0	0.2369	0.9890	1.2259	112
114	63.17	2.602	0.3843	112.8	627.9	515.1	0.2390	0.9854	1.2244	114
116	64.13	2.559	0.3909	113.9	628.1	514.2	0.2411	0.9819	1.2230	116
118	65.08	2.517	0.3974	114.9	628.2	513.2	0.2431	0.9784	1.2215	118
120	66.02	2.476	0.4039	116.0	628.4	512.4	0.2452	0.9749	1.2201	120
122	66.94	2.437	0.4104	117.1	628.6	511.5	0.2471	0.9715	1.2186	122
124	67.86	2.399	0.4169	118.1	628.7	510.6	0.2491	0.9682	1.2173	124
126	68.76	2.362	0.4234	119.1	628.9	509.8	0.2510	0.9649	1.2159	126
128	69.65	2.326	0.4299	120.1	629.0	508.9	0.2529	0.9616	1.2145	128
130	70.53	2.291	0.4364	121.1	629.2	508.1	0.2548	0.9584	1.2132	130
132	71.40	2.258	0.4429	122.1	629.3	507.2	0.2567	0.9552	1.2119	132
134	72.26	2.225	0.4494	123.1	629.5	506.4	0.2585	0.9521	1.2106	134
136	73.11	2.193	0.4559	124.1	629.6	505.5	0.2603	0.9490	1.2093	136
138	73.95	2.162	0.4624	125.1	629.8	504.7	0.2621	0.9460	1.2081	138
140	74.79	2.132	0.4690	126.0	629.9	503.9	0.2638	0.9430	1.2068	140
142	75.61	2.103	0.4755	126.9	630.0	503.1	0.2656	0.9400	1.2056	142
144	76.42	2.075	0.4820	127.9	630.2	502.3	0.2673	0.9371	1.2044	144
146	77.23	2.047	0.4885	128.8	630.3	501.5	0.2690	0.9342	1.2032	146
148	78.03	2.020	0.4951	129.7	630.4	500.7	0.2707	0.9313	1.2020	148
150	78.81	1.994	0.5016	130.6	630.5	499.9	0.2724	0.9285	1.2009	150
152	79.60	1.968	0.5081	131.5	630.6	499.1	0.2740	0.9257	1.1997	152
154	80.37	1.943	0.5147	132.4	630.7	498.3	0.2756	0.9229	1.1985	154
156	81.13	1.919	0.5212	133.3	630.9	497.6	0.2772	0.9202	1.1974	156
158	81.89	1.895	0.5277	134.2	631.0	496.8	0.2788	0.9175	1.1963	158
160	82.64	1.872	0.5343	135.0	631.1	496.1	0.2804	0.9148	1.1952	160
162	83.39	1.849	0.5408	135.9	631.2	495.3	0.2820	0.9122	1.1942	162
164	84.12	1.827	0.5473	136.8	631.3	494.5	0.2835	0.9096	1.1931	164
166	84.85	1.805	0.5539	137.6	631.4	493.8	0.2850	0.9070	1.1920	166
168	85.57	1.784	0.5604	138.4	631.5	493.1	0.2866	0.9044	1.1910	168
170	86.29	1.764	0.5670	139.3	631.6	492.3	0.2881	0.9019	1.1900	170
172	87.00	1.744	0.5735	140.1	631.7	491.6	0.2895	0.8994	1.1889	172
174	87.71	1.724	0.5801	140.9	631.7	490.8	0.2910	0.8969	1.1879	174
176	88.40	1.705	0.5866	141.7	631.8	490.1	0.2925	0.8944	1.1869	176
178	89.10	1.686	0.5932	142.5	631.9	489.4	0.2939	0.8920	1.1859	178
180	89.78	1.667	0.5998	143.3	623.0	488.7	0.2954	0.8896	1.1850	180
182	90.46	1.649	0.6063	144.1	632.1	488.0	0.2968	0.8872	1.1840	182
184	91.14	1.632	0.6129	144.8	632.1	487.3	0.2982	0.8848	1.1830	184
186	91.80	1.614	0.6195	145.6	632.2	486.6	0.2996	0.8825	1.1821	186
188	92.47	1.597	0.6261	146.4	623.3	485.9	0.3010	0.8801	1.1811	188

TABLE II.—SATURATED AMMONIA: ABSOLUTE-PRESSURE TABLE (*Continued*)

Pressure (abs.), lbs./in.²	Temperature, degrees Fahrenheit	Volume vapor, ft.³/lb.	Density vapor, lbs./ft.³	Heat content		Latent heat, B.t.u./lb.	Entropy			Pressure (abs.), lbs./in.²
				Liquid, B.t.u./lb.	Vapor, B.t.u./lb.		Liquid, B.t.u./lb. degrees Fahrenheit	Evaporation, B.t.u./lb. degrees Fahrenheit	Vapor, B.t.u./lb. degrees Fahrenheit	
p	t	V	$1/V$	h	H	L	s	L/T	S	p
190	93.13	1.581	0.6326	147.2	632.4	485.2	0.3024	0.8778	1.1802	**190**
192	93.78	1.564	0.6392	147.9	632.4	484.5	0.3037	0.8755	1.1792	192
194	94.43	1.548	0.6458	148.7	632.5	483.8	0.3050	0.8733	1.1783	194
196	95.07	1.533	0.6524	149.5	632.6	483.1	0.3064	0.8710	1.1774	196
198	95.71	1.517	0.6590	150.2	632.6	482.4	0.3077	0.8688	1.1765	198
200	96.34	1.502	0.6656	150.9	632.7	481.8	0.3090	0.8666	1.1756	**200**
205	97.90	1.466	0.6821	152.7	632.8	480.1	0.3122	0.8612	1.1734	205
210	99.43	1.431	0.6986	154.6	633.0	478.4	0.3154	0.8559	1.1713	210
215	100.94	1.398	0.7152	156.3	633.1	476.8	0.3185	0.8507	1.1692	215
220	102.42	1.367	0.7318	158.0	633.2	475.2	0.3216	0.8455	1.1671	220
225	103.87	1.336	0.7484	159.7	633.3	473.6	0.3246	0.8405	1.1651	**225**
230	105.30	1.307	0.7650	161.4	633.4	472.0	0.3275	0.8356	1.1631	230
235	106.71	1.279	0.7817	163.1	633.5	470.4	0.3304	0.8307	1.1611	235
240	108.09	1.253	0.7984	164.7	633.6	468.9	0.3332	0.8260	1.1592	240
245	109.46	1.227	0.8151	166.4	633.7	467.3	0.3360	0.8213	1.1573	245
250	110.80	1.202	0.8319	168.0	633.8	465.8	0.3388	0.8167	1.1555	**250**
255	112.12	1.178	0.8487	169.5	633.8	464.3	0.3415	0.8121	1.1536	255
260	113.42	1.155	0.8655	171.1	633.9	462.8	0.3441	0.8077	1.1518	260
265	114.71	1.133	0.8824	172.6	633.9	461.3	0.3468	0.8033	1.1501	265
270	115.97	1.112	0.8993	174.1	633.9	459.8	0.3494	0.7989	1.1483	270
275	117.22	1.091	0.9162	175.6	634.0	458.4	0.3519	0.7947	1.1466	**275**
280	118.45	1.072	0.9332	177.1	634.0	456.9	0.3545	0.7904	1.1449	280
285	119.66	1.052	0.9502	178.6	634.0	455.4	0.3569	0.7863	1.1432	285
290	120.86	1.034	0.9672	180.0	634.0	454.0	0.3594	0.7821	1.1415	290
295	122.05	1.016	0.9843	181.5	634.0	452.5	0.3618	0.7781	1.1399	295
300	123.21	0.999	1.0015	182.9	634.0	451.1	0.3642	0.7741	1.1383	**300**

TABLE III.—SATURATED AMMONIA: GAGE-PRESSURE TABLE

Pressure (gage), lbs./in.²	Temperature degrees Fahrenheit	Volume vapor, ft.³/lb.	Density vapor, lbs./ft.³	Heat content		Latent heat, B.t.u./lb.	Entropy			Pressure (gage), lbs./in.²
				Liquid, B.t.u./lb.	Vapor, B.t.u./lb.		Liquid, B.t.u./lb. degrees Fahrenheit	Evaporation, B.t.u./lb. degrees Fahrenheit	Vapor, B.t.u./lb. degrees Fahrenheit	
g. p.	t	V	1/V	h	H	L	s	L/T	S	g. p.
20*	−63.9	50.5	0.0198	−25.3	588.0	613.3	−0.062	1.550	1.488	20*
19*	−61.0	46.2	0.0217	−22.3	589.2	611.5	−0.055	1.535	1.480	19*
18*	−58.4	42.6	0.0235	−19.5	590.3	609.8	−0.048	1.521	1.473	18*
17*	−55.9	39.5	0.0253	−16.9	591.3	608.2	−0.041	1.507	1.466	17*
16*	−53.6	36.8	0.0272	−14.5	592.2	606.7	−0.035	1.495	1.460	16*
15*	−51.4	34.5	0.0290	−12.2	593.1	605.3	−0.029	1.483	1.454	15*
14*	−49.4	32.5	0.0308	−10.0	593.9	603.9	−0.023	1.472	1.449	14*
13*	−47.4	30.7	0.0326	− 7.9	594.7	602.6	−0.019	1.462	1.443	13*
12*	−45.6	29.1	0.0344	− 5.9	595.4	601.3	−0.014	1.452	1.438	12*
11*	−43.8	27.6	0.0362	− 4.0	596.1	600.1	−0.010	1.443	1.433	11*
10*	−42.1	26.3	0.0380	− 2.2	596.8	599.0	−0.005	1.434	1.429	10*
9*	−40.4	25.2	0.0397	− 0.5	597.4	597.9	−0.001	1.426	1.425	9*
8*	−38.9	24.1	0.0415	+ 1.2	598.0	596.8	+0.003	1.418	1.421	8*
7*	−37.3	23.1	0.0433	2.8	598.6	595.8	0.007	1.411	1.418	7*
6*	−35.9	22.2	0.0450	4.4	599.1	594.7	0.010	1.405	1.415	6*
5*	−34.5	21.4	0.0468	5.9	599.6	593.7	0.014	1.397	1.411	5*
4*	−33.1	20.6	0.0485	7.4	600.2	592.8	0.017	1.390	1.407	4*
3*	−31.8	19.9	0.0503	8.8	600.7	591.9	0.020	1.384	1.404	3*
2*	−30.5	19.2	0.0520	10.2	601.2	591.0	0.024	1.377	1.401	2*
1*	−29.2	18.6	0.0538	11.5	601.6	590.1	0.027	1.371	1.398	1*
0	−28.0	18.0	0.0555	12.8	602.1	589.3	0.030	1.366	1.396	0
1	−25.6	16.9	0.0590	15.4	603.0	587.6	0.036	1.354	1.390	1
2	−23.4	16.0	0.0626	17.8	603.8	586.0	0.041	1.344	1.385	2
3	−21.2	15.1	0.0661	20.1	604.6	584.5	0.047	1.333	1.380	3
4	−19.2	14.4	0.0695	22.3	605.3	583.0	0.052	1.324	1.376	4
5	−17.2	13.7	0.0730	24.4	606.0	581.6	0.056	1.315	1.371	5
6	−15.3	13.1	0.0765	26.4	606.6	580.2	0.061	1.306	1.367	6
7	−13.5	12.5	0.0799	28.4	607.3	578.9	0.065	1.298	1.363	7
8	−11.8	12.0	0.0834	30.3	607.9	577.6	0.070	1.290	1.360	8
9	−10.1	11.5	0.0868	32.1	608.4	576.3	0.074	1.282	1.356	9
10	− 8.4	11.1	0.0902	33.8	609.0	575.2	0.078	1.275	1.353	10
11	− 6.9	10.7	0.0937	35.5	609.5	574.0	0.081	1.268	1.349	11
12	− 5.3	10.3	0.0971	37.1	610.0	572.9	0.085	1.261	1.346	12
13	− 3.8	9.96	0.100	38.8	610.5	571.7	0.088	1.255	1.343	13
14	− 2.4	9.63	0.104	40.4	611.0	570.6	0.092	1.248	1.340	14
15	− 1.0	9.32	0.107	41.9	611.4	569.5	0.095	1.242	1.337	15
16	+ 0.4	9.04	0.111	43.4	611.9	568.5	0.098	1.236	1.334	16
17	1.7	8.78	0.114	44.8	612.3	567.5	0.101	1.230	1.331	17
18	3.0	8.53	0.117	46.2	612.7	566.5	0.104	1.225	1.329	18
19	4.3	8.28	0.121	47.6	613.1	565.5	0.107	1.219	1.326	19
20	5.5	8.06	0.124	48.9	613.5	564.6	0.110	1.214	1.324	20
21	6.7	7.85	0.127	50.2	613.9	563.7	0.113	1.209	1.322	21
22	7.9	7.65	0.131	51.5	614.2	562.7	0.116	1.204	1.320	22
23	9.1	7.46	0.134	52.8	614.6	561.8	0.119	1.199	1.318	23
24	10.2	7.28	0.138	54.0	614.9	560.9	0.121	1.194	1.315	24
25	11.3	7.11	0.141	55.3	615.3	560.0	0.124	1.189	1.313	25
26	12.4	6.94	0.144	56.5	615.6	559.1	0.126	1.185	1.311	26
27	13.5	6.78	0.148	57.6	615.9	558.3	0.129	1.180	1.309	27
28	14.5	6.63	0.151	58.8	616.2	557.4	0.131	1.176	1.307	28
29	15.6	6.49	0.154	59.9	616.5	556.6	0.134	1.171	1.305	29
30	16.6	6.35	0.158	61.0	616.8	555.8	0.136	1.167	1.303	30
31	17.6	6.22	0.161	62.1	617.1	555.0	0.138	1.163	1.301	31
32	18.6	6.09	0.164	63.2	617.4	554.2	0.140	1.159	1.299	32
33	19.5	5.97	0.168	64.2	617.6	553.4	0.143	1.155	1.298	33
34	20.5	5.85	0.171	65.3	617.9	552.6	0.145	1.151	1.296	34

* Inches of mercury below 1 standard atmosphere (29.92 inches).

TABLE III.—SATURATED AMMONIA: GAGE-PRESSURE TABLE (*Continued*)

Pressure (gage), lbs./in.²	Temperature, degrees Fahrenheit	Volume vapor, ft.³/lb.	Density vapor, lbs./ft.³	Heat content Liquid, B.t.u./lb.	Heat content Vapor, B.t.u./lb.	Latent heat, B.t.u./lb.	Entropy Liquid, B.t.u./lb. degrees Fahrenheit	Entropy Evaporation, B.t.u./lb. degrees Fahrenheit	Entropy Vapor, B.t.u./lb. degrees Fahrenheit	Pressure (gage), lbs./in.²
g. p.	t	V	1/V	h	H	L	s	L/T	S	g. p.
35	21.4	5.74	0.174	66.3	618.2	551.9	0.147	1.148	1.295	**35**
36	22.3	5.64	0.177	67.3	618.4	551.1	0.149	1.144	1.293	36
37	23.2	5.54	0.181	68.3	618.7	550.4	0.151	1.140	1.291	37
38	24.1	5.44	0.184	69.2	618.9	549.7	0.153	1.137	1.290	38
39	25.0	5.34	0.187	70.2	619.1	548.9	0.155	1.133	1.288	39
40	25.8	5.25	0.191	71.2	619.4	548.2	0.157	1.130	1.287	**40**
41	26.7	5.16	0.194	72.1	619.6	547.5	0.159	1.126	1.285	41
42	27.5	5.07	0.197	73.0	619.8	546.8	0.161	1.123	1.284	24
43	28.3	4.99	0.201	73.9	620.0	546.1	0.163	1.119	1.282	43
44	29.2	4.91	0.204	74.8	620.3	545.5	0.164	1.116	1.280	44
45	30.0	4.83	0.207	75.7	620.5	544.8	0.166	1.113	1.279	**45**
46	30.8	4.76	0.210	76.6	620.7	544.1	0.168	1.110	1.278	46
47	31.5	4.68	0.214	77.4	620.9	543.5	0.170	1.107	1.277	47
48	32.3	4.61	0.217	78.3	621.1	542.8	0.171	1.104	1.275	48
49	33.1	4.54	0.220	79.1	621.3	542.2	0.173	1.101	1.274	49
50	33.8	4.48	0.224	80.0	621.5	541.5	0.175	1.098	1.273	**50**
51	34.6	4.41	0.227	80.8	621.7	540.9	0.177	1.095	1.272	51
52	35.3	4.35	0.230	81.6	621.8	540.2	0.178	1.092	1.270	52
53	36.1	4.29	0.233	82.4	622.0	539.6	0.180	1.089	1.269	53
54	36.8	4.23	0.237	83.2	622.2	539.0	0.181	1.086	1.267	54
55	37.5	4.17	0.240	84.0	622.4	538.4	0.183	1.083	1.266	**55**
56	38.2	4.12	0.243	84.8	622.5	537.7	0.185	1.080	1.265	56
57	38.9	4.06	0.246	85.6	622.7	537.1	0.186	1.078	1.264	57
58	39.6	4.01	0.250	86.3	622.9	536.6	0.188	1.075	1.263	58
59	40.3	3.96	0.253	87.0	623.0	536.0	0.189	1.072	1.261	59
60	40.9	3.91	0.256	87.8	623.2	535.4	0.191	1.069	1.260	**60**
61	41.6	3.86	0.260	88.6	623.4	534.8	0.192	1.067	1.259	61
62	42.3	3.81	0.263	89.3	623.5	534.2	0.194	1.064	1.258	62
63	42.9	3.77	0.266	90.0	623.7	533.7	0.195	1.062	1.257	63
64	43.6	3.72	0.269	90.7	623.8	533.1	0.196	1.060	1.256	64
65	44.2	3.67	0.273	91.5	624.0	532.5	0.198	1.057	1.255	**65**
66	44.8	3.63	0.276	92.2	624.1	531.9	0.199	1.055	1.254	66
67	45.5	3.59	0.279	92.9	624.2	531.3	0.201	1.052	1.253	67
68	46.1	3.55	0.282	93.6	624.4	530.8	0.202	1.050	1.252	68
69	46.7	3.51	0.286	94.3	624.5	530.2	0.203	1.048	1.251	69
70	47.3	3.47	0.289	94.9	624.6	529.7	0.205	1.045	1.250	**70**
71	47.9	3.43	0.292	95.6	624.8	529.2	0.206	1.043	1.249	71
72	48.5	3.39	0.295	96.3	624.9	528.6	0.207	1.041	1.248	72
73	49.1	3.35	0.299	97.0	625.1	528.1	0.209	1.038	1.247	73
74	49.7	3.32	0.302	97.6	625.2	527.6	0.210	1.036	1.246	74
75	50.3	3.28	0.305	98.3	625.3	527.0	0.211	1.034	1.245	**75**
76	50.9	3.24	0.308	98.9	625.4	526.5	0.212	1.032	1.244	76
77	51.5	3.21	0.312	99.5	625.5	526.0	0.214	1.029	1.243	77
78	52.0	3.17	0.315	100.2	625.7	525.5	0.215	1.027	1.242	78
79	52.6	3.14	0.318	100.8	625.8	525.0	0.216	1.025	1.241	79
80	53.1	3.11	0.322	101.5	625.9	524.4	0.217	1.023	1.240	**80**
81	53.7	3.08	0.325	102.1	626.0	523.9	0.219	1.020	1.239	81
82	54.3	3.05	0.328	102.7	626.1	523.4	0.220	1.018	1.238	82
83	54.8	3.02	0.331	103.3	626.3	522.9	0.221	1.016	1.237	83
84	55.3	2.99	0.335	103.9	626.4	522.5	0.222	1.015	1.237	84
85	55.9	2.96	0.338	104.5	626.5	522.0	0.223	1.013	1.236	**85**
86	56.4	2.94	0.341	105.1	626.6	521.5	0.224	1.011	1.235	86
87	57.0	2.91	0.344	105.7	626.7	521.0	0.226	1.008	1.234	87
88	57.5	2.88	0.348	106.3	626.8	520.5	0.227	1.006	1.233	88
89	58.0	2.85	0.351	106.9	626.9	520.0	0.228	1.005	1.233	89

TABLE III.—SATURATED AMMONIA: GAGE-PRESSURE TABLE (*Continued*)

Pressure (gage), lbs./in.²	Temperature, degrees Fahrenheit	Volume vapor, ft.³/lb.	Density vapor, lbs./ft.³	Heat content		Latent heat, B.t.u./lb.	Entropy			Pressure (gage), lbs./in.²
				Liquid, B.t.u./lb.	Vapor, B.t.u./lb.		Liquid, B.t.u./lb. degrees Fahrenheit	Evaporation, B.t.u./lb. degrees Fahrenheit	Vapor, B.t.u./lb. degrees Fahrenheit	
g. p.	*t*	*V*	*1/V*	*h*	*H*	*L*	*s*	*L/T*	*S*	*g. p.*
90	58.5	2.82	0.354	107.5	627.0	519.5	0.229	1.003	1.232	**90**
91	59.0	2.80	0.357	108.1	627.1	519.0	0.230	1.001	1.231	91
92	59.6	2.77	0.361	108.7	627.2	518.5	0.231	0.999	1.230	92
93	60.1	2.75	0.364	109.3	627.3	518.0	0.232	0.997	1.229	93
94	60.6	2.72	0.367	109.8	627.4	517.6	0.233	0.995	1.228	94
95	61.1	2.70	0.370	110.4	627.5	517.1	0.235	0.993	1.228	**95**
96	61.6	2.68	0.374	111.0	627.6	516.6	0.236	0.991	1.227	96
97	62.0	2.65	0.377	111.6	627.7	516.1	0.237	0.989	1.226	97
98	62.5	2.63	0.380	112.1	627.8	515.7	0.238	0.988	1.226	98
99	63.0	2.61	0.383	112.6	627.9	515.3	0.239	0.986	1.225	99
100	63.5	2.59	0.287	113.2	628.0	514.8	0.240	0.984	1.224	**100**
102	64.5	2.54	0.393	114.2	628.1	513.9	0.242	0.981	1.223	102
104	65.4	2.50	0.400	115.3	628.3	513.0	0.244	0.977	1.221	104
106	66.4	2.46	0.406	116.4	628.5	512.1	0.246	0.974	1.220	106
108	67.3	2.42	0.413	117.4	628.6	511.2	0.248	0.970	1.218	108
110	68.2	2.39	0.419	118.5	628.8	510.3	0.250	0.967	1.217	**110**
112	69.1	2.35	0.426	119.5	628.9	509.4	0.252	0.964	1.216	112
114	70.0	2.31	0.432	120.5	629.1	508.6	0.254	0.960	1.214	114
116	70.8	2.28	0.439	121.5	629.3	507.8	0.256	0.957	1.213	116
118	71.7	2.25	0.445	122.5	629.4	506.9	0.257	0.954	1.211	118
120	72.6	2.21	0.452	123.5	629.5	506.0	0.259	0.951	1.210	**120**
122	73.4	2.18	0.458	124.5	629.7	505.2	0.261	0.948	1.209	122
124	74.2	2.15	0.465	125.4	629.8	504.4	0.263	0.945	1.208	124
126	75.1	2.12	0.471	126.3	629.9	503.6	0.364	0.942	1.206	126
128	75.9	2.09	0.478	127.3	630.1	502.8	0.266	0.939	1.205	128
130	76.7	2.06	0.484	128.2	630.2	502.0	0.268	0.936	1.204	**130**
132	77.5	2.04	0.491	129.1	630.3	501.2	0.270	0.933	1.203	132
134	78.3	2.01	0.497	130.0	630.4	500.4	0.271	0.930	1.201	134
136	79.1	1.98	0.504	130.9	630.5	499.6	0.273	0.927	1.200	136
138	79.9	1.96	0.510	131.8	630.7	498.9	0.274	0.925	1.199	138
140	80.6	1.93	0.517	132.7	630.8	498.1	0.276	0.922	1.198	**140**
142	81.4	1.91	0.523	133.6	630.9	497.3	0.278	0.919	1.197	142
144	82.2	1.89	0.530	134.5	631.0	496.5	0.279	0.917	1.196	144
146	82.9	1.86	0.536	135.3	631.1	495.8	0.281	0.914	1.195	146
148	83.6	1.84	0.543	136.2	631.2	495.0	0.283	0.911	1.194	148
150	84.4	1.82	0.550	137.0	631.3	494.3	0.284	0.909	1.193	**150**
152	85.1	1.80	0.556	137.9	631.4	493.5	0.286	0.906	1.192	152
154	85.8	1.78	0.563	138.7	631.5	492.8	0.287	0.904	1.191	154
156	86.5	1.76	0.569	139.5	631.6	492.1	0.289	0.901	1.190	156
158	87.2	1.74	0.576	140.3	631.7	491.4	0.290	0.899	1.189	158
160	88.0	1.72	0.582	141.1	631.8	490.7	0.292	0.896	1.188	**160**
162	88.6	1.70	0.589	141.9	631.9	490.0	0.293	0.894	1.187	162
164	89.3	1.68	0.595	142.7	631.9	489.2	0.294	0.891	1.185	164
166	90.0	1.66	0.602	143.5	632.0	488.5	0.296	0.889	1.185	166
168	90.7	1.64	0.609	144.3	632.1	487.8	0.297	0.886	1.183	168
170	91.4	1.62	0.615	145.1	632.1	487.0	0.299	0.884	1.183	**170**
172	92.0	1.61	0.622	145.8	632.2	486.4	0.300	0.882	1.182	172
174	92.7	1.59	0.628	146.6	632.3	485.7	0.302	0.879	1.181	174
176	93.4	1.57	0.635	147.4	632.4	485.0	0.303	0.877	1.180	176
178	94.0	1.56	0.641	148.2	632.5	484.3	0.304	0.875	1.179	178
180	94.7	1.54	0.648	148.9	632.5	483.6	0.305	0.873	1.178	**180**
182	95.3	1.53	0.655	149.7	632.6	482.9	0.307	0.870	1.177	182
184	95.9	1.51	0.661	150.5	632.7	482.2	0.308	0.868	1.176	184
186	96.6	1.50	0.668	151.2	632.7	481.5	0.309	0.866	1.175	186
188	97.2	1.48	0.674	151.9	632.8	480.9	0.311	0.863	1.174	188

TABLE III.—SATURATED AMMONIA: GAGE-PRESSURE TABLE (*Continued*)

Pressure (gage), lbs./in.²	Temperature, degrees Fahrenheit	Volume vapor, ft.³/lb.	Density vapor, lbs./ft.³	Heat content			Entropy			Pressure (gage), lbs./in.²
				Liquid, B.t.u./lb.	Vapor, B.t.u./lb.	Latent heat, B.t.u./lb.	Liquid, B.t.u./lb. degrees Fahrenheit	Evaporation, B.t.u./lb. degrees Fahrenheit	Vapor, B.t.u./lb. degrees Fahrenheit	
g. p.	t	V	1/V	h	H	L	s	L/T	S	g. p.
190	97.8	1.47	0.681	152.6	632.8	480.2	0.312	0.861	1.173	**190**
192	98.4	1.45	0.688	153.4	632.9	479.5	0.314	0.859	1.173	192
194	99.0	1.44	0.694	154.0	632.9	478.9	0.315	0.857	1.172	194
196	99.7	1.43	0.701	154.8	633.0	478.2	0.316	0.855	1.171	196
198	100.3	1.41	0.708	155.5	633.0	477.5	0.317	0.853	1.170	198
200	100.9	1.40	0.714	156.2	633.1	476.9	0.318	0.851	1.169	**200**
205	102.3	1.37	0.731	158.0	633.2	475.2	0.321	0.846	1.167	205
210	103.8	1.34	0.747	159.6	633.3	473.7	0.324	0.841	1.165	210
215	105.2	1.31	0.764	161.3	633.4	472.1	0.327	0.836	1.163	215
220	106.6	1.28	0.781	163.0	633.5	470.5	0.330	0.831	1.161	220
225	108.0	1.25	0.797	164.6	633.6	469.0	0.333	0.826	1.159	**225**
230	109.4	1.23	0.814	166.3	633.7	467.4	0.336	0.822	1.158	230
235	110.7	1.20	0.831	167.9	633.8	465.9	0.339	0.817	1.156	235
240	112.0	1.18	0.848	169.4	633.8	464.4	0.341	0.813	1.154	240
245	113.3	1.16	0.864	171.0	633.9	462.9	0.344	0.808	1.152	245
250	114.6	1.13	0.881	172.6	633.9	461.3	0.346	0.804	1.150	**250**
255	115.9	1.11	0.898	174.1	634.0	459.9	0.349	0.799	1.148	255
260	117.1	1.09	0.915	175.6	634.0	458.4	0.352	0.795	1.147	260
265	118.4	1.07	0.932	177.0	634.0	457.0	0.354	0.791	1.145	265
270	119.6	1.05	0.949	178.5	634.0	455.5	0.357	0.786	1.143	270
275	120.8	1.03	0.966	179.9	634.0	454.1	0.359	0.783	1.142	**275**
280	122.0	1.02	0.983	181.4	634.0	452.6	0.362	0.778	1.140	280
285	123.1	1.00	1.000	182.8	634.0	451.2	0.364	0.774	1.138	285
290	124.3	0.98	1.018	184.2	634.0	449.8	0.367	0.770	1.137	290
295	125.4	0.97	1.035	185.6	634.0	448.4	0.369	0.766	1.135	295
300	126.5	0.95	1.052	187.0	633.9	446.9	0.371	0.762	1.133	**300**

TABLE IV.—PROPERTIES OF LIQUID AMMONIA

Temperature, degrees Fahrenheit, t	Pressure (abs.), lbs./in.², p	Volume, ft.³/lb., v	Density, lbs./ft.³, $\frac{1}{v}$	Specific heat, B.t.u./lb., degrees Fahrenheit, c	Heat content, B.t.u./lb., h	Latent heat, B.t.u./lb., L	Latent heat of pressure variation, B.t.u./lb., lb./in.², l	Variation of p with h (t constant), B.t.u./lb., lb./in.², $\left(\frac{\partial h}{\partial p}\right)_t$	Compressibility, per lb./in.² × 10⁶, $-\frac{1}{v}\left(\frac{\partial v}{\partial p}\right)_t$	Temperature, degrees Fahrenheit, t
Triple point*	0.88	0.01961*	51.00							−107.86
		0.02182	45.83							
−100	1.24	0.02197	45.52	(1.040)	(−63.0)	(633)				−100
−95	1.52	0.02207	45.32	(1.042)	(−57.8)	(631)				−95
−90	1.86	0.02216	45.12	(1.043)	(−52.6)	(628)				−90
−85	2.27	0.02226	44.92	(1.045)	(−47.4)	(625)				−85
−80	2.74	0.02236	44.72	(1.046)	(−42.2)	(622)				−80
−75	3.29	0.02246	44.52	(1.048)	(−36.9)	(619)				−75
−70	3.94	0.02256	44.32	(1.050)	(−31.7)	(616)				−70
−65	4.69	0.02267	44.11	(1.052)	(−26.4)	(613)				−65
−60	5.55	0.02278	43.91	1.054	−21.18	610.8	−0.0016	0.0026	4.4	−60
−55	6.54	0.02288	43.70	1.056	−15.90	607.5	−0.0016	0.0026	4.5	−55
−50	7.67	0.02299	43.49	1.058	−10.61	604.3	−0.0017	0.0026	4.6	−50
−45	8.95	0.02310	43.28	1.060	−5.31	600.9	−0.0017	0.0026	4.7	−45
−40	10.41	0.02322	43.08	1.062	0.00	597.6	−0.0018	0.0025	4.8	−40
−35	12.05	0.02333	42.86	1.064	+5.32	594.2	−0.0018	0.0025	5.0	−35
−30	13.90	0.02345	42.65	1.066	10.66	590.7	−0.0019	0.0025	5.1	−30
−25	15.98	0.02357	42.44	1.068	16.00	587.2	−0.0019	0.0024	5.2	−25
−20	18.30	0.02369	42.22	1.070	21.36	583.6	−0.0020	0.0024	5.4	−20
−15	20.88	0.02381	42.00	1.073	26.73	580.0	−0.0020	0.0024	5.5	−15
−10	23.74	0.02393	41.78	1.075	32.11	576.4	−0.0021	0.0023	5.7	−10
−5	26.92	0.02406	41.56	1.078	37.51	572.6	−0.0022	0.0023	5.8	−5
0	30.42	0.02419	41.34	1.080	42.92	568.9	−0.0022	0.0022	6.0	0
5	34.27	0.02432	41.11	1.083	48.35	565.0	−0.0023	0.0022	6.2	5
10	38.51	0.02446	40.89	1.085	53.79	561.1	−0.0024	0.0021	6.4	10
15	43.14	0.02460	40.66	1.088	59.24	557.1	−0.0025	0.0021	6.6	15
20	48.21	0.02474	40.43	1.091	64.71	553.1	−0.0025	0.0020	6.8	20
25	53.73	0.02488	40.20	1.094	70.20	548.9	−0.0026	0.0020	7.0	25
30	59.74	0.02503	39.96	1.097	75.71	544.8	−0.0027	0.0019	7.3	30
35	66.26	0.02518	39.72	1.100	81.23	540.5	−0.0028	0.0019	7.5	35
40	73.32	0.02533	39.49	1.104	86.77	536.2	−0.0029	0.0018	7.8	40
45	80.96	0.02548	39.24	1.108	92.34	531.8	−0.0030	0.0017	8.1	45

50	8.4	0.0017	−0.0031	527.3	97.93	1.112	39.00	0.02564	89.19	50
55	8.8	0.0016	−0.0032	522.8	103.54	1.116	38.75	0.02581	98.06	55
60	9.1	0.0015	−0.0033	518.1	109.18	1.120	38.50	0.02597	107.6	60
65	9.5	0.0014	−0.0034	513.4	114.85	1.125	38.25	0.02614	117.8	65
70	10.0	0.0013	−0.0035	508.6	120.54	1.129	38.00	0.02632	128.8	70
75	10.4	0.0012	−0.0037	503.7	126.25	1.133	37.74	0.02650	140.5	75
80	10.9	0.0011	−0.0038	498.7	131.99	1.138	37.48	0.02668	153.0	80
85	11.4	0.0010	−0.0040	493.6	137.75	1.142	37.21	0.02687	166.4	85
90	12.0	0.0009	−0.0041	488.5	143.54	1.147	36.95	0.02707	180.6	90
95	12.6	0.0008	−0.0043	483.2	149.36	1.151	36.67	0.02727	195.8	95
100	13.3	0.0006	−0.0045	477.8	155.21	1.156	36.40	0.02747	211.9	100
105	14.1	0.0005	−0.0047	472.3	161.09	1.162	36.12	0.02769	228.9	105
110	14.9	0.0003	−0.0049	466.7	167.01	1.168	35.84	0.02790	247.0	110
115	15.8	0.0001	−0.0051	460.9	172.97	1.176	35.55	0.02813	266.2	115
120	16.7	0.0000	−0.0053	455.0	178.98	1.183	35.26	0.02836	286.4	120
125	...	...	...	(449)	(185)	(1.189)	34.96	0.02860	307.8	125
130	...	...	...	(443)	(191)	(1.197)	34.66	0.02885	330.3	130
135	...	...	...	(436)	(197)	(1.205)	34.35	0.02911	354.1	135
140	...	...	...	(430)	(203)	(1.213)	34.04	0.02938	379.1	140
145	...	...	...	(423)	(210)	(1.222)	33.72	0.02966	405.5	145
150	...	...	...	(416)	(216)	(1.23)	33.39	0.02995	433.2	150
155	...	...	...	(409)	(222)	(1.24)	33.06	0.03025	462.3	155
160	...	...	...	(401)	(229)	(1.25)	32.72	0.03056	492.8	160
165	...	...	...	(394)	(235)	(1.26)	32.37	0.03089	524.8	165
170	...	...	...	(386)	(241)	(1.27)	32.01	0.03124	558.4	170
175	...	...	...	(377)	(248)	(1.29)	31.65	0.03160	593.5	175
180	...	...	...	(369)	(255)	(1.30)	31.27	0.03198	630.3	180
185	...	...	...	(360)	(262)	(1.32)	30.88	0.03238	668.7	185
190	...	...	...	(351)	(269)	(1.34)	30.48	0.03281	708.9	190
195	...	...	...	(342)	(276)	(1.36)	30.06	0.03326	750.9	195
200	...	...	...	(332)	(283)	(1.38)	29.63	0.03375	794.7	200
210	...	...	...	(310)	(297)	(1.43)	28.72	0.03482	888.1	210
220	...	...	...	(287)	(313)	(1.49)	27.7	0.0361	989.5	220
230	...	...	...	(260)	(329)	(1.57)	26.6	0.0376	1,099.5	230
240	...	...	...	(229)	(346)	(1.70)	25.3	0.0395	1,218.5	240
250	...	...	...	(192)	(365)	(1.90)	23.7	0.0422	1,347	250
260	...	...	...	(142)	(387)	(2.33)	21.6	0.0463	1,486	260
270	...	...	...	(52)	(419)	(5.30)	17.3	0.0577	1,635	270
271.4	∞	—	—	0	(433)	∞	14.6	0.0686	1,657	Critical

* Properties of solid ammonia at the triple point (−107.86° F).

NOTE.—The figures in parentheses were calculated from empirical equations given in *Bur. Standards Sci. Papers* 313 and 315 and represent values obtained by extrapolation beyond the range covered in the experimental work.

Table V.—Properties of Superheated Ammonia Vapor

V = volume in cubic feet per pound; H = heat content in B.t.u. per pound;
S = entropy in B.t.u. per pound, degrees Fahrenheit

Temperature, degrees Fahrenheit	Absolute pressure in pounds per square inch (saturation temperature in italics)											
	15 *−27.29°*			16 *−24.95°*			17 *−22.73°*			18 *−20.61°*		
	V	H	S	V	H	S	V	H	S	V	H	S
Saturation	*17.67*	*602.4*	*1.3938*	*16.64*	*603.2*	*1.3885*	*15.72*	*604.0*	*1.3835*	*14.90*	*604.8*	*1.3787*
−20	18.01	606.4	1.4031	16.86	606.0	1.3948	15.83	605.6	1.3870	14.93	605.1	1.3795
−10	18.47	611.9	1.4154	17.29	611.5	1.4072	16.24	611.1	1.3994	15.32	610.7	1.3921
0	18.92	617.2	1.4272	17.72	616.9	1.4191	16.65	616.6	1.4114	15.70	616.2	1.4042
10	19.37	622.5	1.4386	18.14	622.2	1.4306	17.05	621.9	1.4230	16.08	621.6	1.4158
20	19.82	627.8	1.4497	18.56	627.5	1.4417	17.45	627.2	1.4342	16.46	626.9	1.4270
30	20.26	633.0	1.4604	18.97	632.7	1.4525	17.84	632.5	1.4450	16.83	632.2	1.4380
40	20.70	638.2	1.4709	19.39	638.0	1.4630	18.23	637.7	1.4556	17.20	637.5	1.4486
50	21.14	643.4	1.4812	19.80	643.2	1.4733	18.62	642.9	1.4659	17.57	642.7	1.4590
60	21.58	648.5	1.4912	20.21	648.3	1.4834	19.01	648.1	1.4761	17.94	647.9	1.4691
70	22.01	653.7	1.5011	20.62	653.5	1.4933	19.39	653.3	1.4860	18.30	653.1	1.4790
80	22.44	658.9	1.5108	21.03	658.7	1.5030	19.78	658.5	1.4957	18.67	658.4	1.4887
90	22.88	664.0	1.5203	21.43	663.9	1.5125	20.16	663.7	1.5052	19.03	663.6	1.4983
100	23.31	669.2	1.5296	21.84	669.1	1.5218	20.54	668.9	1.5146	19.39	668.8	1.5077
110	23.74	674.4	1.5388	22.24	674.3	1.5310	20.92	674.1	1.5238	19.75	674.0	1.5169
120	24.17	679.6	1.5478	22.65	679.5	1.5401	21.30	679.3	1.5328	20.11	679.2	1.5260
130	24.60	684.8	1.5567	23.05	684.7	1.5490	21.68	684.5	1.5418	20.47	684.4	1.5349
140	25.03	690.0	1.5655	23.45	689.9	1.5578	22.06	689.8	1.5506	20.83	689.7	1.5438
150	25.46	695.3	1.5742	23.86	695.1	1.5665	22.44	695.0	1.5593	21.19	694.9	1.5525
160	25.88	700.5	1.5827	24.26	700.4	1.5750	22.82	700.3	1.5678	21.54	700.2	1.5610
170	26.31	705.8	1.5911	24.66	705.7	1.5835	23.20	705.6	1.5763	21.90	705.5	1.5695
180	26.74	711.1	1.5995	25.06	711.0	1.5918	23.58	710.9	1.5846	22.26	710.8	1.5778
190	27.16	716.4	1.6077	25.46	716.3	1.6001	23.95	716.2	1.5929	22.61	716.1	1.5861
200	27.59	721.7	1.6158	25.86	721.6	1.6082	24.33	721.5	1.6010	22.97	721.4	1.5943
220	28.44	732.4	1.6318	26.66	732.3	1.6242	25.08	732.2	1.6170	23.68	732.2	1.6103

Temperature	19 *−18.58°*			20 *−16.64°*			21 *−14.78°*			22 *−12.98°*		
Saturation	*14.17*	*605.5*	*1.3742*	*13.50*	*606.2*	*1.3700*	*12.90*	*606.8*	*1.3659*	*12.35*	*607.4*	*1.3621*
−10	14.49	610.3	1.3851	13.74	610.0	1.3784	13.06	609.6	1.3720	12.45	609.2	1.3659
0	14.85	615.9	1.3973	14.09	615.5	1.3907	13.40	615.2	1.3844	12.77	614.8	1.3784
10	15.21	621.3	1.4090	14.44	621.0	1.4025	13.73	620.7	1.3962	13.09	620.4	1.3903
20	15.57	626.7	1.4203	14.78	626.4	1.4138	14.06	626.1	1.4077	13.40	625.8	1.4018
30	15.93	632.0	1.4312	15.11	631.7	1.4248	14.38	631.5	1.4187	13.71	631.2	1.4129
40	16.28	637.3	1.4419	15.45	637.0	1.4356	14.70	636.8	1.4295	14.02	636.6	1.4237
50	16.63	642.5	1.4523	15.78	642.3	1.4460	15.02	642.1	1.4400	14.32	641.9	1.4342
60	16.98	647.7	1.4625	16.12	647.5	1.4562	15.34	647.3	1.4502	14.63	647.1	1.4445
70	17.33	653.0	1.4724	16.45	652.8	1.4662	15.65	652.6	1.4602	14.93	652.4	1.4545
80	17.67	658.2	1.4822	16.78	658.0	1.4760	15.97	657.8	1.4700	15.23	657.7	1.4643
90	18.02	663.4	1.4918	17.10	663.2	1.4856	16.28	663.1	1.4796	15.53	662.9	1.4740
100	18.36	668.6	1.5012	17.43	668.5	1.4950	16.59	668.3	1.4891	15.83	668.1	1.4834
110	18.70	673.8	1.5104	17.76	673.7	1.5042	16.90	673.5	1.4983	16.12	673.4	1.4927
120	19.04	679.1	1.5195	18.08	678.9	1.5133	17.21	678.8	1.5075	16.42	678.6	1.5019
130	19.38	684.3	1.5285	18.41	684.2	1.5223	17.52	684.0	1.5165	16.72	683.9	1.5109
140	19.72	689.5	1.5373	18.73	689.4	1.5312	17.83	689.3	1.5253	17.01	689.2	1.5197
150	20.06	694.8	1.5460	19.05	694.7	1.5399	18.14	694.6	1.5340	17.31	694.4	1.5285
160	20.40	700.1	1.5546	19.37	700.0	1.5485	18.44	699.8	1.5426	17.60	699.7	1.5371
170	20.74	705.4	1.5631	19.70	705.3	1.5569	18.75	705.1	1.5510	17.89	705.0	1.5456
180	21.08	710.7	1.5714	20.02	710.6	1.5653	19.06	710.5	1.5595	18.19	710.4	1.5539
190	21.42	716.0	1.5797	20.34	715.9	1.5736	19.36	715.8	1.5678	18.48	715.7	1.5622
200	21.75	721.3	1.5878	20.66	721.2	1.5817	19.67	721.1	1.5759	18.77	721.1	1.5704
220	22.43	732.1	1.6039	21.30	732.0	1.5978	20.28	731.9	1.5920	19.35	731.8	1.5865

TABLE V.—PROPERTIES OF SUPERHEATED AMMONIA VAPOR (*Continued*)

Temperature, degrees Fahrenheit	Absolute pressure in pounds per square inch (saturation temperature in italics)										
	23 −11.25°			24 −9.58°			25 −7.96°			26 −6.39°		
	V	H	S	V	H	S	V	H	S	V	H	S
Saturation	*11.85*	*608.1*	*1.3584*	*11.39*	*608.6*	*1.3549*	*10.96*	*609.1*	*1.3515*	*10.56*	*609.7*	*1.3482*
−10	11.89	608.8	1.3600									
0	12.20	614.5	1.3726	11.67	614.1	1.3670	11.19	613.8	1.3616	10.74	613.4	1.3564
10	12.50	620.0	1.3846	11.96	619.7	1.3791	11.47	619.4	1.3738	11.01	619.1	1.3686
20	12.80	625.5	1.3961	12.25	625.2	1.3907	11.75	625.0	1.3855	11.28	624.7	1.3804
30	13.10	630.9	1.4073	12.54	630.7	1.4019	12.03	630.4	1.3967	11.55	630.2	1.3917
40	13.40	636.3	1.4181	12.82	636.1	1.4128	12.30	635.8	1.4077	11.81	635.6	1.4027
50	13.69	641.6	1.4287	13.11	641.4	1.4234	12.57	641.2	1.4183	12.08	641.0	1.4134
60	13.98	646.9	1.4390	13.39	646.7	1.4337	12.84	646.5	1.4287	12.34	646.3	1.4238
70	14.27	652.2	1.4491	13.66	652.0	1.4438	13.11	651.8	1.4388	12.59	651.6	1.4339
80	14.56	657.5	1.4589	13.94	657.3	1.4537	13.37	657.1	1.4487	12.85	656.9	1.4439
90	14.84	662.7	1.4686	14.22	662.6	1.4634	13.64	662.4	1.4584	13.11	662.2	1.4536
100	15.13	668.0	1.4780	14.49	667.8	1.4729	13.90	667.7	1.4679	13.36	667.5	1.4631
110	15.41	673.2	1.4873	14.76	673.1	1.4822	14.17	673.0	1.4772	13.61	672.8	1.4725
120	15.70	678.5	1.4965	15.04	678.4	1.4914	14.43	678.2	1.4864	13.87	678.1	1.4817
130	15.98	638.8	1.5055	15.31	683.6	1.5004	14.69	683.5	1.4954	14.12	683.4	1.4907
140	16.26	689.0	1.5144	15.58	688.9	1.5093	14.95	688.8	1.5043	14.37	688.7	1.4996
150	16.55	694.3	1.5231	15.85	694.2	1.5180	15.21	694.1	1.5131	14.62	694.0	1.5084
160	16.83	699.6	1.5317	16.12	699.5	1.5266	15.47	699.4	1.5217	14.87	699.3	1.5170
170	17.11	704.9	1.5402	16.39	704.8	1.5352	15.73	704.7	1.5303	15.12	704.6	1.5256
180	17.39	710.3	1.5486	16.66	710.2	1.5436	15.99	710.1	1.5387	15.37	710.0	1.5340
190	17.67	715.6	1.5569	16.93	715.5	1.5518	16.25	715.4	1.5470	15.62	715.3	1.5423
200	17.95	721.0	1.5651	17.20	720.9	1.5600	16.50	720.8	1.5552	15.86	720.7	1.5505
220	18.51	731.7	1.5812	17.73	731.7	1.5761	17.02	731.6	1.5713	16.36	731.5	1.5666
240	19.07	742.6	1.5969	18.27	742.6	1.5919	17.53	742.5	1.5870	16.85	742.4	1.5824

	27 −4.87°			28 −3.40°			30 −0.57°			32 +2.11°		
Saturation	*10.20*	*610.2*	*1.3451*	*9.853*	*610.7*	*1.3421*	*9.236*	*611.6*	*1.3364*	*8.693*	*612.4*	*1.3310*
0	10.33	613.0	1.3513	9.942	612.7	1.3465	9.250	611.9	1.3371			
10	10.59	618.8	1.3637	10.20	618.4	1.3589	9.492	617.8	1.3497	8.874	617.1	1.3411
20	10.85	624.4	1.3755	10.45	624.1	1.3708	9.731	623.5	1.3618	9.099	622.9	1.3532
30	11.11	629.9	1.3869	10.70	629.6	1.3822	9.966	629.1	1.3733	9.321	628.5	1.3649
40	11.37	635.4	1.3979	10.95	635.1	1.3933	10.20	634.6	1.3845	9.540	634.1	1.3762
50	11.62	640.8	1.4087	11.19	640.5	1.4041	10.43	640.1	1.3953	9.757	639.6	1.3871
60	11.87	646.1	1.4191	11.44	645.9	1.4145	10.65	645.5	1.4059	9.972	645.1	1.3977
70	12.12	651.5	1.4292	11.68	651.2	1.4247	10.88	650.9	1.4161	10.18	650.5	1.4080
80	12.37	656.8	1.4392	11.92	656.6	1.4347	11.10	656.2	1.4261	10.40	655.9	1.4181
90	12.61	662.1	1.4489	12.15	661.9	1.4445	11.33	661.6	1.4359	10.61	661.2	1.4280
100	12.86	667.4	1.4585	12.39	667.2	1.4540	11.55	666.9	1.4456	10.81	666.6	1.4376
110	13.10	672.7	1.4679	12.63	672.5	1.4634	11.77	672.2	1.4550	11.02	671.9	1.4470
120	13.34	678.0	1.4771	12.86	677.8	1.4726	11.99	677.5	1.4642	11.23	677.3	1.4563
130	13.59	683.3	1.4861	13.10	683.1	1.4817	12.21	682.9	1.4733	11.44	682.6	1.4655
140	13.83	688.6	1.4950	13.33	688.4	1.4906	12.43	688.2	1.4823	11.64	687.9	1.4744
150	14 07	693.9	1.5038	13.56	693.7	1.4994	12.65	693.5	1.4911	11.85	693.3	1.4833
160	14.31	699.2	1.5125	13.80	699.1	1.5081	12.87	698.8	1.4998	12.05	698.6	1.4920
170	14.55	704.5	1.5210	14.03	704.4	1.5167	13.08	704.2	1.5083	12.26	704.0	1.5006
180	14.79	709.9	1.5295	14.26	709.8	1.5251	13.30	709.6	1.5168	12.46	709.4	1.5090
190	15.03	715.2	1.5378	14.49	715.1	1.5334	13.52	714.9	1.5251	12.66	714.7	1.5174
200	15.27	720.6	1.5460	14.72	720.5	1.5416	13.73	720.3	1.5334	12.86	720.1	1.5256
220	15.75	731.4	1.5621	15.18	731.3	1.5578	14.16	731.1	1.5495	13.27	731.0	1.5418
240	16.23	742.3	1.5779	15.64	742.2	1.5736	14.59	742.0	1.5653	13.67	741.9	1.5576
260	16.70	753.2	1.5933	16.10	753.2	1.5890	15.02	753.0	1.5808	14.08	752.9	1.5731

Table V.—Properties of Superheated Ammonia Vapor (Continued)

Temperature, degrees Fahrenheit	Absolute pressure in pounds per square inch (saturation temperature in italics)										
	34 4.66°			36 7.09°			38 9.42°			40 11.66°		
	V	H	S	V	H	S	V	H	S	V	H	S
Saturation	8.211	613.2	1.3260	7.782	614.0	1.3213	7.396	614.7	1.3168	7.047	615.4	1.3125
10	8.328	616.4	1.3328	7.842	615.7	1.3250	7.407	615.0	1.3175			
20	8.542	622.3	1.3452	8.046	621.7	1.3375	7.603	621.0	1.3301	7.203	620.4	1.3231
30	8.753	628.0	1.3570	8.247	627.4	1.3494	7.795	626.9	1.3422	7.387	626.3	1.3353
40	8.960	633.6	1.3684	8.445	633.1	1.3609	7.983	632.6	1.3538	7.568	632.1	1.3470
50	9.166	639.2	1.3793	8.640	638.7	1.3720	8.170	638.3	1.3650	7.746	637.8	1.3583
60	9.369	644.7	1.3900	8.833	644.2	1.3827	8.353	643.8	1.3758	7.922	643.4	1.3692
70	9.570	650.1	1.4004	9.024	649.7	1.3932	8.535	649.3	1.3863	8.096	648.9	1.3797
80	9.770	655.5	1.4105	9.214	655.2	1.4033	8.716	654.8	1.3965	8.268	654.4	1.3900
90	9.969	660.9	1.4204	9.402	660.6	1.4133	8.895	660.2	1.4065	8.439	659.9	1.4000
100	10.17	666.3	1.4301	9.589	666.0	1.4230	9.073	665.6	1.4163	8.609	665.3	1.4098
110	10.36	671.6	1.4396	9.775	671.3	1.4325	9.250	671.0	1.4258	8.777	670.7	1.4194
120	10.56	677.0	1.4489	9.961	676.7	1.4419	9.426	676.4	1.4352	8.945	676.1	1.4288
130	10.75	682.3	1.4581	10.15	682.1	1.4510	9.602	681.8	1.4444	9.112	681.5	1.4381
140	10.95	687.7	1.4671	10.33	687.4	1.4601	9.776	687.2	1.4534	9.278	686.9	1.4471
150	11.14	693.0	1.4759	10.51	692.8	1.4689	9.950	692.6	1.4623	9.444	692.3	1.4561
160	11.33	698.4	1.4846	10.69	698.2	1.4777	10.12	698.0	1.4711	9.609	697.7	1.4648
170	11.53	703.8	1.4932	10.88	703.6	1.4863	10.30	703.3	1.4797	9.774	703.1	1.4735
180	11.72	709.2	1.5017	11.06	709.0	1.4948	10.47	708.7	1.4883	9.938	708.5	1.4820
190	11.91	714.5	1.5101	11.24	714.4	1.5032	10.64	714.2	1.4966	10.10	714.0	1.4904
200	12.10	720.0	1.5183	11.42	719.8	1.5115	10.81	719.6	1.5049	10.27	719.4	1.4987
220	12.48	730.8	1.5346	11.78	730.6	1.5277	11.16	730.5	1.5212	10.59	730.3	1.5150
240	12.86	741.7	1.5504	12.14	741.6	1.5436	11.50	741.4	1.5371	10.92	741.3	1.5309
260	13.24	752.7	1.5659	12.50	752.6	1.5591	11.84	752.4	1.5526	11.24	752.3	1.5465
280	13.62	763.8	1.5811	12.86	763.7	1.5743	12.18	763.5	1.5678	11.56	763.4	1.5617

	42 13.81°			44 15.88°			46 17.87°			48 19.80°		
Saturation	6.731	616.0	1.3084	6.442	616.6	1.3046	6.177	617.2	1.3009	5.934	617.7	1.2973
20	6.842	619.8	1.3164	6.513	619.1	1.3099	6.213	618.5	1.3036	5.937	617.8	1.2976
30	7.019	625.8	1.3287	6.683	625.2	1.3224	6.377	624.6	1.3162	6.096	624.0	1.3103
40	7.192	631.6	1.3405	6.850	631.1	1.3343	6.538	630.5	1.3283	6.251	630.0	1.3225
50	7.363	637.3	1.3519	7.014	636.8	1.3457	6.696	636.4	1.3398	6.404	635.9	1.3341
60	7.531	643.0	1.3628	7.176	642.5	1.3567	6.851	642.1	1.3509	6.554	641.6	1.3453
70	7.697	648.5	1.3734	7.336	648.1	1.3674	7.005	647.7	1.3617	6.702	647.3	1.3561
80	7.862	654.1	1.3838	7.494	653.7	1.3778	7.157	653.3	1.3721	6.848	652.9	1.3666
90	8.026	659.5	1.3939	7.650	659.2	1.3880	7.308	658.9	1.3823	6.993	658.5	1.3768
100	8.188	665.0	1.4037	7.806	664.7	1.3978	7.457	664.4	1.3922	7.137	664.0	1.3868
110	8.349	670.4	1.4133	7.960	670.1	1.4075	7.605	669.8	1.4019	7.280	669.5	1.3965
120	8.510	675.9	1.4228	8.114	675.6	1.4169	7.753	675.3	1.4114	7.421	675.0	1.4061
130	8.669	681.3	1.4320	8.267	681.0	1.4263	7.899	680.7	1.4207	7.562	680.5	1.4154
140	8.828	686.7	1.4411	8.419	686.4	1.4354	8.045	686.2	1.4299	7.702	685.9	1.4246
150	8.986	692.1	1.4501	8.570	691.9	1.4444	8.190	691.6	1.4389	7.842	691.4	1.4336
160	9.144	697.5	1.4589	8.721	697.3	1.4532	8.335	697.1	1.4477	7.981	696.8	1.4425
170	9.301	702.9	1.4676	8.871	702.7	1.4619	8.479	702.5	1.4564	8.119	702.3	1.4512
180	9.458	708.3	1.4761	9.021	708.1	1.4704	8.623	707.9	1.4650	8.257	707.7	1.4598
190	9.614	713.8	1.4845	9.171	713.6	1.4789	8.766	713.4	1.4735	8.395	713.2	1.4683
200	9.770	719.2	1.4928	9.320	719.0	1.4872	8.909	718.8	1.4818	8.532	718.7	1.4766
210	9.925	724.7	1.5009	9.474	724.5	1.4954	9.052	724.3	1.4900	8.669	724.2	1.4848
220	10.08	730.1	1.5091	9.617	730.0	1.5035	9.194	729.8	1.4981	8.805	729.6	1.4930
240	10.39	741.1	1.5251	9.913	741.0	1.5195	9.477	740.8	1.5141	9.077	740.6	1.5090
260	10.70	752.2	1.5406	10.21	752.0	1.5350	9.760	751.9	1.5297	9.348	751.7	1.5246
280	11.01	763.3	1.5559	10.50	763.1	1.5503	10.04	763.0	1.5450	9.619	762.9	1.5399

Tᴀʙʟᴇ V.—Pʀᴏᴘᴇʀᴛɪᴇs ᴏғ Sᴜᴘᴇʀʜᴇᴀᴛᴇᴅ Aᴍᴍᴏɴɪᴀ Vᴀᴘᴏʀ (*Continued*)

Temperature, degrees Fahrenheit	Absolute pressure in pounds per square inch (saturation temperature in italics)										
	50 *21.67°*			55 *26.09°*			60 *30.21°*			65 *34.06°*		
	V	*H*	*S*	*V*	*H*	*S*	*V*	*H*	*S*	*V*	*H*	*S*
Saturation	*5.710*	*618.2*	*1.2939*	*5.219*	*619.5*	*1.2860*	*4.805*	*620.5*	*1.2787*	*4.454*	*621.5*	*1.2720*
30	5.838	623.4	1.3046	5.275	621.9	1.2911						
40	5.988	629.5	1.3169	5.415	628.1	1.3037	4.933	626.8	1.2913	4.527	625.4	1.2798
50	6.135	635.4	1.3286	5.551	634.1	1.3156	5.060	632.9	1.3035	4.647	631.7	1.2922
60	6.280	641.2	1.3399	5.685	640.1	1.3271	5.184	639.0	1.3152	4.764	637.8	1.3041
70	6.423	646.9	1.3508	5.816	645.9	1.3381	5.307	644.9	1.3265	4.879	643.8	1.3156
80	6.564	652.6	1.3613	5.947	651.6	1.3489	5.428	650.7	1.3373	4.991	649.7	1.3266
90	6.704	658.2	1.3716	6.075	657.3	1.3593	5.547	656.4	1.3479	5.103	655.5	1.3373
100	6.843	663.7	1.3816	6.202	662.7	1.3694	5.665	662.1	1.3581	5.213	661.3	1.3476
110	6.980	669.2	1.3914	6.329	668.5	1.3793	5.781	667.7	1.3681	5.321	667.0	1.3577
120	7.117	674.7	1.4009	6.454	674.1	1.3889	5.897	673.3	1.3778	5.429	672.6	1.3675
130	7.252	680.2	1.4103	6.528	679.6	1.3984	6.012	678.9	1.3873	5.536	678.2	1.3771
140	7.387	685.7	1.4195	6.702	685.1	1.4076	6.126	684.4	1.3966	5.642	683.8	1.3866
150	7.521	691.1	1.4286	6.825	690.6	1.4167	6.239	689.9	1.4058	5.747	689.4	1.3958
160	7.655	696.6	1.4374	6.947	696.0	1.4257	6.352	695.5	1.4148	5.852	694.9	1.4048
170	7.788	702.1	1.4462	7.069	701.5	1.4345	6.464	701.0	1.4236	5.956	700.4	1.4137
180	7.921	707.5	1.4548	7.190	707.0	1.4431	6.576	706.5	1.4323	6.060	706.0	1.4224
190	8.053	713.0	1.4633	7.311	712.5	1.4517	6.687	712.0	1.4409	6.163	711.5	1.4310
200	8.185	718.5	1.4716	7.432	718.0	1.4600	6.798	717.5	1.4493	6.266	717.1	1.4394
210	8.317	724.0	1.4799	7.552	723.5	1.4683	6.909	723.1	1.4576	6.368	722.6	1.4478
220	8.448	729.4	1.4880	7.671	729.0	1.4765	7.019	728.6	1.4658	6.471	728.2	1.4560
240	8.710	740.5	1.5040	7.910	741.1	1.4925	7.238	739.7	1.4819	6.674	739.3	1.4722
260	8.970	751.6	1.5197	8.148	751.2	1.5082	7.457	750.9	1.4976	6.877	750.5	1.4880
280	9.230	762.7	1.5350	8.385	762.4	1.5235	7.675	762.1	1.5130	7.078	761.8	1.5034
300	9.489	774.0	1.5500	8.621	773.6	1.5386	7.892	773.3	1.5281	7.279	773.1	1.5185

Temperature	70 *37.70°*			75 *41.13°*			80 *44.40°*			85 *47.50°*		
Saturation	*4.151*	*622.4*	*1.2658*	*3.887*	*623.2*	*1.2599*	*3.655*	*624.0*	*1.2545*	*3.449*	*624.7*	*1.2494*
40	4.177	623.9	1.2688									
50	4.290	630.4	1.2816	3.982	629.1	1.2715	3.712	627.7	1.2619	3.473	626.4	1.2527
60	4.401	636.6	1.2937	4.087	635.5	1.2839	3.812	634.3	1.2745	3.569	633.0	1.2656
70	4.509	642.7	1.3054	4.189	641.7	1.2957	3.909	640.6	1.2866	3.662	639.5	1.2779
80	4.615	648.7	1.3166	4.289	647.7	1.3071	4.005	646.7	1.2981	3.753	645.7	1.2896
90	4.719	654.6	1.3274	4.388	653.7	1.3180	4.098	652.8	1.3092	3.842	651.8	1.3008
100	4.822	660.4	1.3378	4.485	659.6	1.3286	4.190	658.7	1.3199	3.930	657.8	1.3117
110	4.924	666.1	1.3480	4.581	665.4	1.3389	4.281	664.6	1.3303	4.016	663.8	1.3221
120	5.025	671.8	1.3579	4.676	671.1	1.3489	4.371	670.4	1.3404	4.101	669.6	1.3323
130	5.125	677.5	1.3676	4.770	676.8	1.3586	4.460	676.1	1.3502	4.186	675.4	1.3422
140	5.224	683.1	1.3770	4.863	682.5	1.3682	4.548	681.8	1.3598	4.269	681.2	1.3519
150	5.323	688.7	1.3863	4.956	688.1	1.3775	4.635	687.5	1.3692	4.352	686.9	1.3614
160	5.420	694.3	1.3954	5.048	693.7	1.3866	4.722	693.2	1.3784	4.434	692.6	1.3706
170	5.518	699.9	1.4043	5.139	699.3	1.3956	4.808	698.8	1.3874	4.515	698.2	1.3797
180	5.615	705.5	1.4131	5.230	704.9	1.4044	4.893	704.4	1.3963	4.596	703.9	1.3886
190	5.711	711.0	1.4217	5.320	710.5	1.4131	4.978	710.0	1.4050	4.677	709.5	1.3974
200	5.807	716.6	1.4302	5.410	716.1	1.4217	5.063	715.6	1.4136	4.757	715.2	1.4060
210	5.902	722.2	1.4386	5.500	721.7	1.4301	5.147	721.3	1.4220	4.836	720.8	1.4145
220	5.998	727.7	1.4469	5.589	727.3	1.4384	5.231	726.9	1.4304	4.916	726.4	1.4228
230	6.093	733.3	1.4550	5.678	732.9	1.4466	5.315	732.5	1.4386	4.995	732.1	1.4311
240	6.187	738.9	1.4631	5.767	738.5	1.4546	5.398	738.1	1.4467	5.074	737.7	1.4392
260	6.376	750.1	1.4789	5.943	749.8	1.4705	5.565	749.4	1.4626	5.230	749.0	1.4551
280	6.563	761.4	1.4943	6.119	761.1	1.4860	5.730	760.7	1.4781	5.386	760.4	1.4707
300	6.750	772.7	1.5095	6.294	772.4	1.5011	5.894	772.1	1.4933	5.541	771.8	1.4859

TABLE V.—PROPERTIES OF SUPERHEATED AMMONIA VAPOR (*Continued*)

Temperature, degrees Fahrenheit	Absolute pressure in pounds per square inch (saturation temperature in italics)											
	90 *50.47°*			95 *53.32°*			100 *56.05°*			105 *58.67°*		
	V	H	S	V	H	S	V	H	S	V	H	S
Saturation	*3.266*	*625.3*	*1.2445*	*3.101*	*625.9*	*1.2399*	*2.952*	*626.5*	*1.2356*	*2.817*	*627.0*	*1.2314*
60	3.353	631.8	1.2571	3.160	630.5	1.2489	2.985	629.3	1.2409			
70	3.442	638.3	1.2695	3.245	637.2	1.2616	3.068	636.0	1.2539	2.907	634.9	1.2464
80	3.529	644.7	1.2814	3.329	643.6	1.2736	3.149	642.6	1.2661	2.985	641.5	1.2589
90	3.614	650.9	1.2928	3.411	649.9	1.2852	3.227	649.0	1.2778	3.061	648.0	1.2708
100	3.698	657.0	1.3038	3.491	656.1	1.2963	3.304	655.2	1.2891	3.135	654.3	1.2822
110	3.780	663.0	1.3144	3.570	662.1	1.3070	3.380	661.3	1.2999	3.208	660.5	1.2931
120	3.862	668.9	1.3247	3.647	668.1	1.3174	3.454	667.3	1.3104	3.279	666.6	1.3037
130	3.942	674.7	1.3347	3.724	674.0	1.3275	3.527	673.3	1.3206	3.350	672.6	1.3139
140	4.021	680.5	1.3444	3.799	679.8	1.3373	3.600	679.2	1.3305	3.419	678.5	1.3239
150	4.100	686.3	1.3539	3.874	685.6	1.3469	3.672	685.0	1.3401	3.488	684.4	1.3336
160	4.178	692.0	1.3633	3.949	691.4	1.3562	3.743	690.8	1.3495	3.556	690.2	1.3431
170	4.255	697.7	1.3724	4.022	697.1	1.3654	3.813	696.6	1.3588	3.623	696.0	1.3524
180	4.332	703.4	1.3813	4.096	702.8	1.3744	3.883	702.3	1.3678	3.690	701.8	1.3615
190	4.408	709.0	1.3901	4.168	708.5	1.3833	3.952	708.0	1.3767	3.757	707.5	1.3704
200	4.484	714.7	1.3988	4.241	714.2	1.3919	4.021	713.7	1.3854	3.823	713.3	1.3792
210	4.560	720.4	1.4073	4.313	719.9	1.4005	4.090	719.4	1.3940	3.888	719.0	1.3878
220	4.635	726.0	1.4157	4.384	725.6	1.4089	4.158	725.1	1.4024	3.954	724.7	1.3963
230	4.710	731.7	1.4239	4.455	731.3	1.4172	4.226	730.8	1.4108	4.019	730.4	1.4046
240	4.785	737.3	1.4321	4.526	736.9	1.4254	4.294	736.5	1.4190	4.083	736.1	1.4129
250	4.859	743.0	1.4401	4.597	742.6	1.4334	4.361	742.2	1.4271	4.148	741.9	1.4210
260	4.933	748.7	1.4481	4.668	748.3	1.4414	4.428	747.9	1.4350	4.212	747.6	1.4290
280	5.081	760.0	1.4637	4.808	759.7	1.4570	4.562	759.4	1.4507	4.340	759.0	1.4447
290	5.155	765.8	1.4713	4.878	765.5	1.4647	4.629	765.1	1.4584	4.403	764.8	1.4524
300	5.228	771.5	1.4789	4.947	771.2	1.4723	4.695	770.8	1.4660	4.466	770.5	1.4600

Temperature, degrees Fahrenheit	110 *61.21°*			115 *63.65°*			120 *66.02°*			125 *68.31°*		
Saturation	*2.693*	*627.5*	*1.2275*	*2.580*	*628.0*	*1.2237*	*2.476*	*628.4*	*1.2201*	*2.380*	*628.8*	*1.2166*
70	2.761	633.7	1.2392	2.628	632.5	1.2323	2.505	631.3	1.2255	2.392	630.0	1.2189
80	2.837	640.5	1.2519	2.701	639.4	1.2451	2.576	638.3	1.2386	2.461	637.2	1.2322
90	2.910	647.0	1.2640	2.772	646.0	1.2574	2.645	645.0	1.2510	2.528	644.0	1.2448
100	2.981	653.4	1.2755	2.841	652.5	1.2690	2.712	651.6	1.2628	2.593	650.7	1.2568
110	3.051	659.7	1.2866	2.909	658.8	1.2802	2.778	658.0	1.2741	2.657	657.1	1.2682
120	3.120	665.8	1.2972	2.975	665.0	1.2910	2.842	664.2	1.2850	2.719	663.5	1.2792
130	3.188	671.9	1.3076	3.040	671.1	1.3015	2.905	670.4	1.2956	2.780	669.7	1.2899
140	3.255	677.8	1.3176	3.105	677.2	1.3116	2.967	676.5	1.3058	2.840	675.8	1.3002
150	3.321	683.7	1.3274	3.168	683.1	1.3215	3.029	682.5	1.3157	2.900	681.8	1.3102
160	3.386	689.6	1.3370	3.231	689.0	1.3311	3.089	688.4	1.3254	2.958	687.8	1.3199
170	3.451	695.4	1.3463	3.294	694.9	1.3405	3.149	694.3	1.3348	3.016	693.7	1.3294
180	3.515	701.2	1.3555	3.355	700.7	1.3497	3.209	700.2	1.3441	3.074	699.6	1.3387
190	3.579	707.0	1.3644	3.417	706.5	1.3587	3.268	706.0	1.3531	3.131	705.5	1.3478
200	3.642	712.8	1.3732	3.477	712.3	1.3675	3.326	711.8	1.3620	3.187	711.3	1.3567
210	3.705	718.5	1.3819	3.538	718.1	1.3762	3.385	717.6	1.3707	3.243	717.2	1.3654
220	3.768	724.3	1.3904	3.598	723.8	1.3847	3.442	723.4	1.3793	3.299	723.0	1.3740
230	3.830	730.0	1.3988	3.658	729.6	1.3931	3.500	729.2	1.3877	3.354	728.8	1.3825
240	3.892	735.7	1.4070	3.717	735.3	1.4014	3.557	734.9	1.3960	3.409	734.5	1.3908
250	3.954	741.5	1.4151	3.776	741.1	1.4096	3.614	740.7	1.4042	3.464	740.3	1.3990
260	4.015	747.2	1.4232	3.835	746.8	1.4176	3.671	746.5	1.4123	3.519	746.1	1.4071
270	4.076	752.9	1.4311	3.894	752.6	1.4256	3.727	752.2	1.4202	3.573	751.9	1.4151
280	4.137	758.7	1.4389	3.952	758.4	1.4334	3.783	758.0	1.4281	3.627	757.7	1.4230
290	4.198	764.5	1.4466	4.011	764.1	1.4411	3.839	763.8	1.4359	3.681	763.5	1.4308
300	4.259	770.2	1.4543	4.069	769.9	1.4488	3.895	769.6	1.4435	3.735	769.3	1.4385

TABLE V.—PROPERTIES OF SUPERHEATED AMMONIA VAPOR (*Continued*)

Temperature, degrees Fahrenheit	130 70.53°			135 72.69°			140 74.79°			145 76.83°		
	V	H	S	V	H	S	V	H	S	V	H	S
Saturation	*2.291*	*629.2*	*1.2132*	*2.209*	*629.6*	*1.2100*	*2.132*	*629.9*	*1.2068*	*2.061*	*630.2*	*1.2038*
80	2.355	636.0	1.2260	2.257	634.9	1.2199	2.166	633.8	1.2140	2.080	632.6	1.2082
90	2.421	643.0	1.2388	2.321	642.0	1.2329	2.228	640.9	1.2272	2.141	639.9	1.2216
100	2.484	649.7	1.2509	2.382	648.8	1.2452	2.288	647.8	1.2396	2.200	646.9	1.2342
110	2.546	656.3	1.2625	2.442	655.4	1.2569	2.347	654.5	1.2515	2.257	653.6	1.2462
120	2.606	662.7	1.2736	2.501	661.9	1.2681	2.404	661.1	1.2628	2.313	660.2	1.2577
130	2.665	668.9	1.2843	2.559	668.2	1.2790	2.460	667.4	1.2738	2.368	666.7	1.2687
140	2.724	675.1	1.2947	2.615	674.4	1.2894	2.515	673.7	1.2843	2.421	673.0	1.2793
150	2.781	681.2	1.3048	2.671	680.5	1.2996	2.569	679.9	1.2945	2.474	679.2	1.2896
160	2.838	687.2	1.3146	2.726	686.6	1.3094	2.622	686.0	1.3045	2.526	685.4	1.2996
170	2.894	693.2	1.3241	2.780	692.6	1.3191	2.675	692.0	1.3141	2.577	691.4	1.3093
180	2.949	699.1	1.3335	2.834	698.6	1.3284	2.727	698.0	1.3236	2.627	697.5	1.3188
190	3.004	705.0	1.3426	2.887	704.5	1.3376	2.779	704.0	1.3328	2.677	703.4	1.3281
200	3.059	710.9	1.3516	2.940	710.4	1.3466	2.830	709.9	1.3418	2.727	709.4	1.3372
210	3.113	716.7	1.3604	2.992	716.2	1.3554	2.880	715.8	1.3507	2.776	715.3	1.3461
220	3.167	722.5	1.3690	3.044	722.1	1.3641	2.931	721.6	1.3594	2.825	721.2	1.3548
230	3.220	728.3	1.3775	3.096	727.9	1.3726	2.981	727.5	1.3679	2.873	727.1	1.3634
240	3.273	734.1	1.3858	3.147	733.7	1.3810	3.030	733.3	1.3763	2.921	732.9	1.3718
250	3.326	739.9	1.3941	3.198	739.6	1.3893	3.080	739.2	1.3846	2.969	738.8	1.3801
260	3.379	745.7	1.4022	3.249	745.4	1.3974	3.129	745.0	1.3928	3.017	744.6	1.3883
270	3.431	751.5	1.4102	3.300	751.2	1.4054	3.179	750.8	1.4008	3.064	750.5	1.3964
280	3.483	757.3	1.4181	3.350	757.0	1.4133	3.227	756.7	1.4088	3.111	756.3	1.4043
290	3.535	763.1	1.4259	3.400	762.8	1.4212	3.275	762.5	1.4166	3.158	762.2	1.4122
300	3.587	769.0	1.4336	3.450	768.6	1.4289	3.323	768.3	1.4243	3.205	768.0	1.4199
320	3.690	780.6	1.4487	3.550	780.3	1.4441	3.420	780.0	1.4395	3.298	779.7	1.4352

Temperature, degrees Fahrenheit	150 78.81°			155 80.75°			160 82.64°			165 84.49°		
Saturation	*1.994*	*630.5*	*1.2009*				*1.872*	*631.1*	*1.1952*			
90	2.061	638.8	1.2161				1.914	636.6	1.2055			
100	2.118	645.9	1.2289				1.969	643.9	1.2186			
110	2.174	652.8	1.2410				2.023	651.0	1.2311			
120	2.228	659.4	1.2526				2.075	657.8	1.2429			
130	2.281	665.9	1.2638				2.125	664.4	1.2542			
140	2.334	672.3	1.2745				2.175	670.9	1.2652			
150	2.385	678.6	1.2849				2.224	677.2	1.2757			
160	2.435	684.8	1.2949				2.272	683.5	1.2859			
170	2.485	690.9	1.3047				2.319	689.7	1.2958			
180	2.534	696.9	1.3142				2.365	695.8	1.3054			
190	2.583	702.9	1.3236	(Data not available)			2.411	701.9	1.3148	(Data not available)		
200	2.631	708.9	1.3327				2.457	707.9	1.3240			
210	2.679	714.8	1.3416				2.502	713.9	1.3331			
220	2.726	720.7	1.3504				2.547	719.9	1.3419			
230	2.773	726.6	1.3590				2.591	725.8	1.3506			
240	2.820	732.5	1.3675				2.635	731.7	1.3591			
250	2.866	738.4	1.3758				2.679	737.6	1.3675			
260	2.912	744.3	1.3840				2.723	743.5	1.3757			
270	2.958	750.1	1.3921				2.766	749.4	1.3838			
280	3.004	756.0	1.4001				2.809	755.3	1.3919			
290	3.049	761.8	1.4079				2.852	761.2	1.3998			
300	3.095	767.7	1.4157				2.895	767.1	1.4076			
320	3.185	779.4	1.4310				2.980	778.9	1.4229			
340	3.274	791.2	1.4459				3.064	790.7	1.4379			

Table V.—Properties of Superheated Ammonia Vapor (*Continued*)

Temperature, degrees Fahrenheit	170 86.29°			180 89.78°			190 93.13°			200 96.34°		
	V	H	S	V	H	S	V	H	S	V	H	S
Saturation	1.764	631.6	1.1900	1.667	632.0	1.1850	1.581	632.4	1.1802	1.502	632.7	1.1756
90	1.784	634.4	1.1952	1.668	632.2	1.1853						
100	1.837	641.9	1.2087	1.720	639.9	1.1992	1.615	637.8	1.1899	1.520	635.6	1.1809
110	1.889	649.1	1.2215	1.770	647.3	1.2123	1.663	645.4	1.2034	1.567	643.4	1.1947
120	1.939	656.1	1.2336	1.818	654.4	1.2247	1.710	652.6	1.2160	1.612	650.9	1.2077
130	1.988	662.8	1.2452	1.865	661.3	1.2364	1.755	659.7	1.2281	1.656	658.1	1.2200
140	2.035	669.4	1.2563	1.910	668.0	1.2477	1.799	666.5	1.2396	1.698	665.0	1.2317
150	2.081	675.9	1.2669	1.955	674.5	1.2586	1.842	673.2	1.2506	1.740	671.8	1.2429
160	2.127	682.3	1.2773	1.999	681.0	1.2691	1.884	679.7	1.2612	1.780	678.4	1.2537
170	2.172	688.5	1.2873	2.042	687.3	1.2792	1.925	686.1	1.2715	1.820	684.9	1.2641
180	2.216	694.7	1.2971	2.084	693.6	1.2891	1.966	692.5	1.2815	1.859	691.3	1.2742
190	2.260	700.8	1.3066	2.126	699.8	1.2987	2.005	698.7	1.2912	1.897	697.7	1.2840
200	2.303	706.9	1.3159	2.167	705.9	1.3081	2.045	704.9	1.3007	1.935	703.9	1.2935
210	2.346	713.0	1.3249	2.208	712.0	1.3172	2.084	711.1	1.3099	1.972	710.1	1.3029
220	2.389	719.0	1.3338	2.248	718.1	1.3262	2.123	717.2	1.3189	2.009	716.3	1.3120
230	2.431	724.9	1.3426	2.288	724.1	1.3350	2.161	723.2	1.3278	2.046	722.4	1.3209
240	2.473	730.9	1.3512	2.328	730.1	1.3436	2.199	729.3	1.3365	2.082	728.4	1.3296
250	2.514	736.8	1.3596	2.367	736.1	1.3521	2.236	735.3	1.3450	2.118	734.5	1.3382
260	2.555	742.8	1.3679	2.407	742.0	1.3605	2.274	741.3	1.3534	2.154	740.5	1.3467
270	2.596	748.7	1.3761	2.446	748.0	1.3687	2.311	747.3	1.3617	2.189	746.5	1.3550
280	2.637	754.6	1.3841	2.484	753.9	1.3768	2.348	753.2	1.3698	2.225	752.5	1.3631
290	2.678	760.5	1.3921	2.523	759.9	1.3847	2.384	759.2	1.3778	2.260	758.5	1.3712
300	2.718	766.4	1.3999	2.561	765.8	1.3926	2.421	765.2	1.3857	2.295	764.5	1.3791
320	2.798	778.3	1.4153	2.637	777.7	1.4081	2.493	777.1	1.4012	2.364	776.5	1.3947
340	2.878	790.1	1.4303	2.713	789.6	1.4231	2.565	789.0	1.4163	2.432	788.5	1.4099

Temperature, degrees Fahrenheit	210 99.43°			220 102.42°			230 105.30°			240 108.09°		
Saturation	1.431	633.0	1.1713	1.367	633.2	1.1671	1.307	633.4	1.1631	1.253	633.6	1.1592
110	1.480	641.5	1.1863	1.400	639.4	1.1781	1.328	637.4	1.1700	1.261	635.3	1.1621
120	1.524	649.1	1.1996	1.443	647.3	1.1917	1.370	645.4	1.1840	1.302	643.5	1.1764
130	1.566	656.4	1.2121	1.485	654.8	1.2045	1.410	653.1	1.1971	1.342	651.3	1.1898
140	1.608	663.5	1.2240	1.525	662.0	1.2167	1.449	660.4	1.2095	1.380	658.8	1.2025
150	1.648	670.4	1.2354	1.564	669.0	1.2281	1.487	667.6	1.2213	1.416	666.1	1.2145
160	1.687	677.1	1.2464	1.601	675.8	1.2394	1.524	674.5	1.2325	1.452	673.1	1.2259
170	1.725	683.7	1.2569	1.638	682.5	1.2501	1.559	681.3	1.2434	1.487	680.0	1.2369
180	1.762	690.2	1.2672	1.675	689.1	1.2604	1.594	687.9	1.2538	1.521	686.7	1.2475
190	1.799	696.6	1.2771	1.710	695.5	1.2704	1.629	694.4	1.2640	1.554	693.3	1.2577
200	1.836	702.9	1.2867	1.745	701.9	1.2801	1.663	700.9	1.2738	1.587	699.8	1.2677
210	1.872	709.2	1.2961	1.780	708.2	1.2896	1.696	707.2	1.2834	1.619	706.2	1.2773
220	1.907	715.3	1.3053	1.814	714.4	1.2989	1.729	713.5	1.2927	1.651	712.6	1.2867
230	1.942	721.5	1.3143	1.848	720.6	1.3079	1.762	719.8	1.3018	1.683	718.9	1.2959
240	1.977	727.6	1.3231	1.881	726.8	1.3168	1.794	726.0	1.3107	1.714	725.1	1.3049
250	2.011	733.7	1.3317	1.914	732.9	1.3255	1.826	732.1	1.3195	1.745	731.3	1.3137
260	2.046	739.8	1.3402	1.947	739.0	1.3340	1.857	738.3	1.3281	1.775	737.5	1.3224
270	2.080	745.8	1.3486	1.980	745.1	1.3424	1.889	744.4	1.3365	1.805	743.6	1.3308
280	2.113	751.8	1.3568	2.012	751.1	1.3507	1.920	750.5	1.3448	1.835	749.8	1.3392
290	2.147	757.9	1.3649	2.044	757.2	1.3588	1.951	756.5	1.3530	1.865	755.9	1.3474
300	2.180	763.9	1.3728	2.076	763.2	1.3668	1.982	762.6	1.3610	1.895	762.0	1.3554
320	2.246	775.9	1.3884	2.140	775.3	1.3825	2.043	774.7	1.3767	1.954	774.1	1.3712
340	2.312	787.9	1.4037	2.203	787.4	1.3978	2.103	786.8	1.3921	2.012	786.3	1.3866
360	2.377	800.0	1.4186	2.265	799.5	1.4127	2.163	798.9	1.4070	2.069	798.4	1.4016
380	2.442	812.0	1.4331	2.327	811.6	1.4273	2.222	811.1	1.4217	2.126	810.6	1.4163

TABLE VI.—PROPERTIES OF SATURATED CARBON DIOXIDE (CO_2)

Temperature, degrees Fahrenheit	Pressure, absolute pounds per square inch	Volume of vapor, cubic feet per pound	Density of vapor, pounds per cubic foot	Heat content above 32° F.		Total latent heat, B.t.u. per pound	Entropy, B.t.u. per pound per degree Fahrenheit absolute		
				Liquid	Vapor		Liquid	Vapor	Evaporation
− 58	98.995	0.900234	1.110	− 48.222	99.162	147.384	− 0.1057	0.2613	0.3670
− 49	120.899	0.740050	1.352	− 43.416	99.720	143.136	− 0.0940	0.2546	0.3486
− 40	146.217	0.611903	1.635	− 38.718	100.170	138.888	− 0.0828	0.2482	0.3310
− 31	175.090	0.509385	1.963	− 34.056	100.512	134.568	− 0.0719	0.2421	0.3140
− 22	207.662	0.427050	2.341	− 29.430	100.746	130.176	− 0.0613	0.2362	0.2975
− 13	244.500	0.360895	2.77	− 24.822	100.854	125.676	− 0.0590	0.2305	0.2814
− 4	284.650	0.307393	3.254	− 20.124	100.836	120.960	− 0.0406	0.2249	0.2655
+ 5	331.832	0.263663	3.794	− 15.336	100.674	116.010	− 0.0304	0.2193	0.2497
14	383.178	0.226821	4.412	− 10.404	100.368	110.772	− 0.0203	0.2136	0.2339
23	440.214	0.194882	5.133	− 5.292	99.864	105.156	− 0.0102	0.2077	0.2179
32	503.366	0.167072	5.980	0	99.054	99.054	0	0.2015	0.2015
41	573.061	0.141923	7.045	+ 5.436	97.740	92.304	0.0104	0.1948	0.1844
50	650.009	0.119497	8.370	+ 11.142	95.832	84.690	0.0212	0.1874	0.1662
59	734.354	0.099955	10.015	+ 17.478	93.294	75.816	0.0328	0.1790	0.1462
68	827.091	0.082655	12.100	+ 24.696	89.856	65.160	0.0457	0.1692	0.1235
77	927.133	0.066957	14.940	+ 32.346	84.078	51.732	0.0598	0.1562	0.0964
86	1,039.59	0.048055	20.800	+ 45.396	73.008	27.612	0.0830	0.1336	0.0506
87.8	1,062.91	0.040847	24.48	+ 51.588	66.150	14.562	0.0940	0.1206	0.0266
88.43	1,071.16	0.034600	28.90	+ 58.050	58.050	0	0.1058	0.1058	0

TABLE VII.—PROPERTIES OF SATURATED SULPHUR DIOXIDE (SO_2)

Temperature, degrees Fahrenheit	Pressure, pounds per square inch absolute	Volume of vapor, cubic feet per pound	Density of vapor, pounds per cubic foot	Heat content above 32° F., B.t.u. per pound		Total latent heat, B.t.u. per pound	Entropy, B.t.u. per pound per degree Fahrenheit absolute		
				Liquid	Vapor		Liquid	Vapor	Evaporation
− 22	5.575	12.75	0.0786	− 16.326	169.218	185.544	− 0.0352	0.3890	0.4242
− 13	7.277	9.89	0.1013	− 13.734	168.534	182.268	− 0.0293	0.3790	0.4083
− 4	9.34	7.825	0.128	− 11.106	167.832	178.938	− 0.0234	0.3695	0.3929
+ 5	11.82	6.27	0.1598	− 8.406	167.184	175.590	− 0.0175	0.3606	0.3781
+ 14	14.78	5.085	0.1972	− 5.616	166.608	172.224	− 0.0117	0.3521	0.3638
+ 23	18.3	4.15	0.241	− 2.862	165.942	168.804	− 0.0059	0.3440	0.3499
+ 32	22.42	3.415	0.293	0	165.366	165.366	0	0.3365	0.3365
+ 41	27.32	2.837	0.3528	+ 2.898	164.790	161.892	+ 0.0059	0.3294	0.3235
+ 50	33.05	2.371	0.422	+ 5.868	164.268	158.40	+ 0.0117	0.3227	0.110
+ 59	39.6	1.989	0.5035	+ 8.874	163.728	154.854	+ 0.0175	0.3161	0.2986
+ 68	47.21	1.683	0.594	+ 11.934	163.224	151.290	+ 0.0234	0.3103	0.2869
+ 77	56.0	1.428	0.702	+ 15.066	162.774	147.708	+ 0.0293	0.3047	0.2754
+ 86	65.9	1.220	0.820	+ 18.234	162.306	144.072	+ 0.0352	0.2994	0.2642
+ 95	77.25	1.043	0.960	+ 21.456	161.874	140.418	+ 0.0410	0.2943	0.2533
104	90.1	0.898	1.114	+ 24.732	161.478	136.746	+ 0.0469	0.2896	0.2427

TABLE VIII.*—PROPERTIES OF SATURATED VAPOR OF METHYL CHLORIDE (CH_3Cl)

Temperature, degrees Fahrenheit	Pressure, pounds per square inch absolute	Volume of vapor, cubic feet per pound	Density of vapor, pounds per cubic foot	Heat content above 32° F, B.t.u. per pound		Total latent heat, B.t.u. per pound			Entropy, B.t.u. per pound per degrees Fahrenheit absolute		
				Liquid	Vapor	Total r	Inner r_1 Apu.	Outer Apu.	Liquid	Vapor	Evaporation
−40	6.96	12.57	0.079	−34.0	149.3	183.3	167.1	16.17	−0.075	0.361	0.436
−31	8.84	10.07	0.099	−29.7	152.9	182.6	166.2	16.43	−0.065	0.360	0.425
−22	11.11	8.16	0.123	−25.5	156.2	181.7	165.0	16.70	−0.055	0.359	0.414
−13	13.82	6.66	0.150	−21.2	159.6	180.8	163.8	16.97	−0.045	0.359	0.404
−4	17.07	5.47	0.183	−17.0	162.9	179.9	162.7	17.20	−0.036	0.358	0.394
+5	20.89	4.53	0.221	−12.7	165.8	178.5	161.1	17.44	−0.027	0.357	0.384
14	25.38	3.78	0.265	−8.5	168.8	177.3	159.7	17.65	−0.018	0.356	0.374
23	30.60	3.17	0.315	−4.2	171.9	176.1	158.3	17.84	−0.009	0.355	0.364
32	36.63	2.68	0.373	0.0	174.6	174.6	156.6	18.02	0.000	0.354	0.354
41	43.60	2.27	0.440	4.2	177.1	172.9	154.7	18.19	0.009	0.354	0.345
50	51.60	1.94	0.516	8.5	179.6	171.1	152.7	18.43	0.017	0.352	0.335
59	60.50	1.66	0.601	12.7	182.0	169.3	150.8	18.47	0.025	0.351	0.326
68	71.00	1.43	0.698	17.0	184.3	167.3	148.8	18.55	0.033	0.349	0.316
77	82.53	1.24	0.807	21.2	186.4	165.2	146.6	18.62	0.041	0.348	0.307
86	95.53	1.07	0.930	25.5	188.4	162.9	144.2	18.69	0.049	0.347	0.298
95	110.10	0.94	1.067	29.7	190.2	160.5	141.8	18.70	0.057	0.346	0.289
104	126.26	0.82	1.222	34.0	191.8	157.8	139.1	18.70	0.064	0.343	0.279

TABLE IX.—Physical Properties of Refrigerants

Refrigerant	Ammonia	Butane	Carbon dioxide	Ethane	Ethyl chloride	Methyl chloride	Propane	Sulphur dioxide
Chemical symbol	NH_3	C_4H_{10}	CO_2	C_2H_6	C_2H_5Cl	CH_3Cl	C_3H_8	SO_2
Molecular weight	17.032	58.10	44.005	30.058	64.51	50.489	44.079	64.06
Color of liquid	colorless	colorless	colorless	colorless	colorless	colorless	colorless	colorless
Odor	pungent and aromatic	slight, like illuminating gas	odorless	slight, like illuminating gas	pungent and ethereal odor	similar to chloroform	slight, like illuminating gas	pungent
Density of liquid (water = 1)	0.6818	0.60	See Note X	0.5459	0.9232	0.998	0.5853	1.4601
at temperature in degrees Centigrade	−33.35	0.0	....	−88.3	0.0	−24.09	−44.5	−10.0
Density of gas, grams 1 liter (see Note Y)	0.7708	2.6726	1.9768	1.3565	....	2.3045	2.0200	2.9267
(air = 1)	0.5962	2.0671	1.5290	1.0492	2.31	1.7824	1.5624	2.2636
Boiling point at 1 atmosphere, degrees Centigrade	−33.35	0.6	See Note X	−88.3	13.1	−24.09	−44.5	−10.0
at temperature in degrees Fahrenheit	−28.03	33.1	....	−126.9	55.6	−11.36	−48.1	14.0
Melting point, degrees Centigrade	−77.70	−135.0	−78.52	−172.0	−138.7	−91.5	−189.9	−75.2
degrees Fahrenheit	−107.86	−211.0	−109.34	−277.6	−217.7	−132.7	−309.8	−103.4
Critical temperature, degrees Centigrade	132.9	150.8	31.00	32.1	182.8	143.12	95.6	157.12
degrees Fahrenheit	271.2	303.4	87.80	89.8	361.0	289.6	204.1	314.82
Critical pressure, atmosphere absolute	112.3	37.5	72.85	48.85	53.3	65.93	45	77.65
pounds per square inch absolute	1,651	551.3	1,071	718.0	784	969.2	661.5	1,141.5
Specific heat of constant pressure (C_p)	0.5202	0.351	0.2025	0.397	0.273	0.24	0.365	0.1511
Specific heat of constant volume (C_v)	0.4011	....	0.1558	....	....	0.20	....	....
Ratio of specific heats (C_p/C_v)	1.2969	1.108	1.3003	1.224	1.1257	1.1991	1.153	1.256
at degrees Centigrade			0.0	10	73	66–68		16–34
Latent heat of vaporization at 1 atmosphere, B.t.u. per pound	589.4	165.4	256.3 See Note X	225	168.6	180.6	180.4	172.3
Suction pressure at 5° F., pounds per square inch absolute	34.5	8.7	331.8	235	4.65	20.89	43.5	11.82
Head pressure at 86° F., pounds per square inch absolute	168.5	42.7	1,039.6	677	27.1	95.53	159	65.9

NOTE X—Carbon dioxide not a liquid at atmospheric pressure.
NOTE Y—Density of gas at 0° C. (32° F.) and 760 millimeters (1 atmosphere), except for ethyl chloride, in which no temperature has been given.
For detailed data and references, see following tables.

TABLE X.—FUNDAMENTAL CONSTANTS OF AMMONIA

	Dry compression with aftercooling and superheating	Dry compression with liquid cooled to 60° F.	Dry compression with vapor superheated to 40° F.	Dry compression with liquid aftercooled to 60° and vapor heated to 40° F.	Wet compression with no aftercooling or superheating
Temperature in evaporator....	5°	5°	5°	5°	5°
Pressure in evaporator........	34.3	34.3	34.3	34.3	34.3
Specific volume of vapor, to compressor................	8.2	8.2	8.9	8.9	7.24
Temperature in condenser....	86°	86°	86°	86°	86°
Pressure in condenser........	169	169	169	169	169
Temperature after compression.....................	210°	210°	259°	259°	86°
Specific volume of gas after compression, cubic feet.....	2.36	2.36	2.58	2.58	1.77
Heat content of superheated vapor, B.t.u. per pound.....	712.9	712.9	742.5	742.5	631.5
Heat content of vapor from evaporator, B.t.u..........	613.4	613.4	634.0	634.0	550.5
Heat equivalent of work of compression B.t.u..........	99.5	99.5	108.5	108.5	81.0
Heat content of liquid in condenser, B.t.u..............	138.9	109.3	138.9	109.3	138.9
Heat rejected in condenser (item 8– item 11), B.t.u....	574	603.6	603.6	633.2	492.6
Refrigerating effect (item 9– item 11), B.t.u...........	474.5	504.1	495.1	524.7	411.6
Quality of mixture after expansion..................	0.160	0.108	0.160	0.108	0.160
Pounds of ammonia per minute per ton of refrigeration.....	0.4216	0.3970	0.4040	0.3811	0.4862
Theoretical volume of ammonia per ton per minute, cubic feet................	3.457	3.257	3.596	3.392	3.52
Theoretical horsepower per ton......................	0.988	0.931	1.033	0.974	0.928
Coefficients of performance....	4.768	5.070	4.563	4.841	5.080
Quality of mixture before compression.................	....	....	....	....	0.890

TABLE XI.—COLD STORAGE DATA*

Name	Percentage water	Storage temperature		Specific heat		Latent heat of fusion
		Low, degrees Fahrenheit	Normal, degrees Fahrenheit	After freezing	Before freezing	
Apples.....................	83	29	31	....	0.92	
Asparagus..................	94	33	34			
Bacon, smoked...............	..	30	32			
Bananas....................	..	35	40			
Beans, green.................	89	32	33			
Beans, dried.................	..	....	40			
Beef, lean..................	72	30	32	0.41	0.77	102
Beef, fat...................	51	30	32	0.34	0.60	72
Beef, fresh, chilled...........	..	30	32			
Beef, freezing...............	..	5	10			
Beef, frozen................	..	15	20			
Beef, storage................	..	....	33			
Beef, dried.................	..	....	40			
Berries....................	..	31	40	....	0.42	
Butter, tubs................	..	0	15	....	0.55	
Butter, cartons..............	..	0	15			
Cabbage...................	91	25	31	0.43	0.93	129
Cantaloupes................	..	33	36			
Carrots....................	83	30	36	0.45	0.87	113
Cauliflower.................	93	22				
Celery.....................	95	10	33			
Cheese, cream...............	..	30	32	....	0.64	
Cheese, brick...............	..	30	32			
Cherries, fresh..............	82	....	40			
Cider.....................	..	30	32			
Corn, green.................	75	....	38			
Cranberries.................	..	28	33			
Cream, fresh................	59	32	34	0.38	0.90	84
Cucumbers.................	95	32	38			
Eggs, freezing...............	70	−10	0	0.40	0.76	100
Eggs, storage...............	70	28	29	0.40	0.76	100
Fruits, dried................	..	40				
Fruits, canned...............	..	40				
Fish, dried.................	..	35				
Fish, freezing...............	73	−15	..	0.43	0.82	111
Fish, storage................	..	....	26			
Fish, frozen.................	..	5	18			
Flour and meal..............	..	....	40			
Furs......................	..	25	35			
Furs, undressed.............	..	....	35			
Flowers, cut................	..	....	36			
Game, freezing..............	..	5	10			
Game, storage...............	..	15	25			
Grapes, fresh................	..	26	32			
Grapefruit..................	..	32	36			
Ice cream..................	67	0	15	0.45	0.78	90

* From tables prepared by W. H. Motz.

TABLE XII.—COLD-STORAGE DATA (*Continued*)

Name	Percentage water	Storage temperature		Specific heat		Latent heat of fusion
		Low, degrees Fahrenheit	Normal, degrees Fahrenheit	After freezing	Before freezing	
Lard........................	..	32	38	0.31	0.54	
Lemons.....................	..	36	38			
Lettuce.....................	94	26	42			
Lobsters....................	77	....	25	0.42	0.81	108
Melons.....................	..	33	40			
Milk, fresh.................	88	32	36	0.47	0.90	124
Mutton, chilling...............	..	30	32	0.67	0.81	100
Onions......................	88	32	35			
Oranges.....................	..	32	35			
Oysters, shell................	80	30	35	0.44	0.84	114
Parsnips....................	83	32	33			
Peaches, fresh...............	87	30	30			
Pears, fresh..................	83	30	32			
Peas, fresh..................	75	32	36			
Pineapple...................	..	32	40			
Plums, fresh.................	..	28	32			
Pork, salt...................	..	....	42			
Pork, chill..................	39	30	32	0.30	0.51	55
Pork, storage................	..	....	32			
Pork, freeze.................	..	5	10			
Potatoes....................	73	30	33			
Potatoes, sweet..............	69	50	55			
Poultry, freeze..............	74	0	10	0.42	0.80	105
Poultry, storage.............	..	28	30			
Poultry, frozen..............	..	10	15	....	0.377	
Strawberries.................	90	33	40			
Tomatoes...................	94	33	34			
Veal........................	63	....	34	0.39	0.70	90

TABLE XIII.—PROPERTIES OF CALCIUM-CHLORIDE BRINE

Bureau of standards

Temperature, degrees Fahrenheit	Specific gravity									
	0.999	1.05	1.10	1.15	1.18	1.20	1.22	1.24	1.26	1.28
	Pounds per gallon									
70	8.33	8.75	9.17	9.58	9.83	10.00	10.16	10.33	10.49	10.66
60	8.34	8.76	9.18	9.60	9.85	10.01	10.18	10.35	10.52	10.68
50	8.34	8.77	9.19	9.61	9.86	10.03	10.20	10.37	10.54	10.70
40	8.35	8.78	9.21	9.63	9.88	10.05	10.22	10.39	10.56	10.73
30	.....	8.79	9.22	9.64	9.90	10.07	10.24	10.41	10.58	10.75
20	.....	.....	9.23	9.66	9.92	10.09	10.26	10.43	10.60	10.77
10	.....	.....	.....	9.68	9.93	10.11	10.28	10.45	10.62	10.79
0	.....	.....	.....	.....	9.95	10.13	10.30	10.47	10.64	10.81
−10	.....	.....	.....	.....	.....	.....	10.32	10.49	10.66	10.84
−20	.....	.....	.....	.....	.....	.....	.....	.....	10.68	10.86
−30	.....	.....	.....	.....	.....	.....	.....	.....	10.70	10.88
	Pounds per cubic foot									
70	62.3	65.5	68.6	71.7	73.5	74.8	76.0	77.3	78.5	79.7
60	62.4	65.6	68.7	71.8	73.7	74.9	76.2	77.4	78.7	79.9
50	62.4	65.6	68.8	71.9	73.8	75.0	76.3	77.6	78.8	80.1
40	62.4	65.7	68.9	72.0	73.9	75.2	76.4	77.7	79.0	80.3
30	.....	64.8	69.0	72.1	74.0	75.3	76.6	77.9	79.2	80.4
20	.....	.....	69.1	72.3	74.2	75.4	76.7	78.0	79.3	80.6
10	.....	.....	.....	72.4	74.3	75.6	76.9	78.2	79.5	80.8
0	.....	.....	.....	.....	74.4	75.7	77.0	78.3	79.6	80.9
−10	.....	.....	.....	.....	.....	.....	77.2	78.5	79.8	81.1
−20	.....	.....	.....	.....	.....	.....	.....	.....	80.0	81.3
−30	.....	.....	.....	.....	.....	.....	.....	.....	80.1	81.4

TABLE XIV.—SPECIFIC HEATS OF CALCIUM-CHLORIDE SOLUTIONS*

Temperature, degrees Fahrenheit	Densities (pounds per cubic foot)			
	1.175	1.200	1.225	1.250
−10	.....	.....	0.670	0.654
0	0.722	0.697	0.676	0.659
+10	0.728	0.703	0.681	0.663
+20	0.733	0.708	0.685	0.667
+30	0.736	0.711	0.689	0.670
+40	0.740	0.715	0.693	0.674
+50	0.743	0.719	0.697	0.677
+60	0.746	0.722	0.700	0.680
+70	0.750	0.726	0.704	0.684

* DICKINSON, H. C., E. F. MUELLER, and E. B. GEORGE, "Specific Heat of Some Calcium Chloride Solutions," *Bur. Standards Bull.* 6, pp. 379–408, 1910 (*Sci. Paper* S-135).

The results of a series of observations on a sample of calcium chloride give the following formulas for the specific heat:

Density, 1.260, $s = 0.666 + 0.00064t$ (from -35 to $+15°$ C.)
Density, 1.200, $s = 0.708 + 0.00064t$ (from -20 to $+15°$ C.)
Density, 1.140, $s = 0.772 + 0.00064t$ (from -10 to $+15°$ C.)
Density, 1.070, $s = 0.869 + 0.00057t$ (from   0 to $+15°$ C.)

where s is the specific heat and t is the temperature. All densities are referred to a temperature of 20° C. in terms of water at 4° C.

In using the specific-heat values for the desired temperature, it is noted that for a given density the equation is linear; because of this, the mean specific heat must be used for the range of temperature.

The following freezing points for chemically pure calcium chloride were obtained by test:

Density	Freezing Temperatures, Degrees Centigrade
1.12	$-$ 9
1.14	-13
1.16	-16
1.18	-20
1.20	-24
1.22	-29
1.24	-34
1.26	-40

TABLE XV.—DATA OF TYPICAL DOUBLE-ACTING MEDIUM-SPEED AMMONIA COMPRESSORS

Size of compressor	Speed, revolutions per minute	Displacement at listed speed
5 $\times$ 8	125	38,580
6½ $\times$ 10	120	78,000
7¾ $\times$ 11	110	112,500
9 $\times$ 12	100	149,140
10 $\times$ 18	85	236,000
12 $\times$ 20	85	376,500
12 $\times$ 24	82	436,000
13½ $\times$ 24	80	536,080
15 $\times$ 30	70	726,000
16½ $\times$ 30	70	884,000
18 $\times$ 30	70	1,040,000
19 $\times$ 36	70	1,396,000

TABLE XVI.—VARIOUS VALUES OF COEFFICIENTS OF CONDUCTION FOR REFRIGERATING APPARATUS

B.t.u. per square foot per hour per degree Fahrenheit

Freezing tank:
  Old-style feed, 12 to 15
  Flooded, 20 to 30

Ammonia condensers:
  Submerged, 30 to 40, old style (obsolete)
  Atmospheric, 60 to 65
  Flooded, 140; bleeder type, 125 to 150

Baudalot coolers:
  (Counter-atmospheric)
  Milk cooler, 75
  Cream coolers, 60
  Oil coolers, 10

Brine coolers:
  Shell and tube, 90 to 100

Cooling coils:
  Brine to unagitated air, 2 to $2\frac{1}{4}$; direct expansion to unagitated air, $1\frac{1}{2}$ to 2

The coefficient of heat conduction will be reduced to 70 to 80 per cent of the above values by 1 inch of ice on the pipes.

TABLE XVII.—SURFACE COEFFICIENTS FOR VARIOUS MATERIALS

Kind of material	Coefficient for still air, B.t.u. per square foot per hour per degree Fahrenheit
Brick wall......................	1.4
Concrete, 1-2-4 mixture.........	1.50
Wood (fir, one side finished).....	1.40
Cork board....................	1.25
Magnesia board...............	1.45
Tile, plaster on both sides.......	1.10

For moving air having a velocity of about 15 miles per hour, take the value of the surface coefficient to be equal to three times the above coefficient for still air.

TABLE XVIII.—HEAT-TRANSMISSION COEFFICIENTS OF CORK BOARD, GRANULATED CORK, AND MILL SHAVINGS

B.t.u. per 24 hour per square foot per degree Fahrenheit	Thickness of cork board, inches	Thickness of granulated cork, inches	Thickness of mill shavings, inches
10	1	2	2¾
5	2	4	5½
3½	3	6	8
3	4	8	10¾
2½	5	10	13½
2	6	12	16
1¼	8	16	21½

TABLE XIX.—HEAT TRANSMISSION THROUGH PIPES UNDER VARIOUS CONDITIONS

2½ B.t.u. per square foot per hour per degree Fahrenheit.............. Direct expansion to still air

3 B.t.u. per square foot per hour per degree Fahrenheit.............. Direct expansion to forced air

3 B.t.u. per square foot per hour per degree Fahrenheit.............. Flooded system to still air

3½ B.t.u. per square foot per hour per degree Fahrenheit.............. Flooded system to forced air

4½ B.t.u. per square foot per hour per degree Fahrenheit.............. Brine piping to still air

5½ B.t.u. per square foot per hour per degree Fahrenheit.............. Brine piping to forced air

12 B.t.u. per square foot per hour per degree Fahrenheit. Direct expansion to liquid (submerged)

20 B.t.u. per square foot per hour per degree Fahrenheit. Flooded system to liquid (submerged)

Table XX.—Conductivity and Density of Various Insulating Materials

U. S. Bureau of Standards

Material	Thermal conductivity B.t.u. per square foot, per inch, per hour, per degree Fahrenheit	Density pounds per cubic foot	Description of material
Air	0.175	0.08	Ideal air space.
Air cell, ½ inch	0.458	8.80	Asbestos paper and air spaces.
Air cell, 1 inch	0.500	8.80	Asbestos paper and air spaces.
Asbestos mill board	0.830	61.0	Pressed asbestos.
Asbestos wood	3.700	123.0	Asbestos and cement.
Balsa wood	0.350	7.5	Light and soft across grain.
Calorax	0.221	4.0	Fluffy, finely divided mineral matter.
Cork	0.337	5.3	Granulated ⅛–³⁄₁₆ inch.
Cork	0.330	10.0	Regranulated ¹⁄₁₆–⅛ inch.
Corkboard	0.279	6.9	No artificial binder-low density.
Corkboard	0.308	11.3	No artificial binder-high density.
Cotton wool	0.292	.....	Loosely packed.
Fibrofelt	0.329	11.3	Felted vegetable fibers.
Fire felt wool	0.625	43.0	Asbestos sheet coated with cement.
Fire felt sheet	0.583	26.0	Soft, flexible asbestos sheet.
Flaxlinum	0.329	11.3	Felted vegetable fibers.
Hair felt	0.246	17.0	
Hard maple wood	1.125	44.0	Across grain.
Infusorial earth	0.583	43.0	Natural blocks.
Insulite	0.296	11.9	Pressed wool pulp-rigid.
Kapok	0.238	0.88	Vegetable fiber-loosely packed.
Keystone hair	0.271	19.0	Hair felt combined with building paper.
Linofelt	0.300	11.3	Vegetable fiber combined with paper.
Lithboard	0.379	12.5	Mineral wool and vegetable fibers.
Mineral wool	0.275	12.5	Medium packed.
Mineral wool	0.288	18.0	Felted in blocks.
Oak wood	1.000	38.0	Across grain.
Planer shavings	0.417	8.8	Various.
Pulp board	0.458	.....	Stiff pasteboard.
Pure wool	0.263	5.0	
Rock cork	0.346	21.0	Mineral wool and binder—rigid. .
Slag wool	0.750	15.0	
Tar roofing	0.707	55	
Virginia pine wood	0.958	34	Across grain.
White pine wood	0.791	32	Across grain.
Wool felt	0.363	21	Flexible paper stock.

TABLE XXI.—COEFFICIENT OF CONDUCTIVITY OF BUILDING MATERIALS

	Coefficient
Brickwork	5.0
Concrete	5.3 (average)
Wood (fir, ⅞ inch thick)	1.0
Asbestos (sheets or boards)	0.3 to 0.5
Glass (0.085 inch thick)	24.3
Double window (½ inch air space)	1.10
2-inch hollow tile (plastered)	1.0
4-inch hollow tile (plastered)	0.6
Mortar	8.0

The figures are the B.t.u. per square foot, per inch thick (unless the thickness is mentioned) per degree difference of temperature per hour.

TABLE XXII.—THERMAL CONDUCTIVITY OF EARTHY MATERIALS
Tests made by the Food Investigation Board, 1921*

Material	Gram-calories per square centimeter per second, for 1 centimeter thickness and for 1° C. difference in temperature	B.t.us. per square foot per hour for 1 inch thickness and for 1° F. difference in temperature	Temperature range	Mean temperature of the insulating material
Diatomaceous earth	0.000193	0.560	9 to 49° F.	30° F.
Diatomaceous brick	0.000223	0.647	4 to 80° F.	42° F.
Concrete block (used for construction work)	0.0028	8.2	60 to 115° F.	88° F.

* *Special Rept.* 5, H.M. Stationery Office, London.

TABLE XXIII.—STANDARD DIMENSIONS EXTRA HEAVY PIPE

Nominal, inches	Diameter		Thickness, inches	Circumference		Length of pipe per square foot		Transverse areas			Nominal weight, pounds per foot	Number of threads, per inch
	External, inches	Internal, inches		External, inches	Internal, inches	External surface, square inches	Internal surface, square inches	External, square inches	Internal, square inches	Metal, square inches		
⅛	0.405	0.205	0.100	1.272	0.644	9.44	18.63	0.129	0.033	0.096	0.29	27
¼	0.540	0.294	0.123	1.696	0.924	7.07	12.99	0.229	0.068	0.161	0.54	18
⅜	0.675	0.421	0.127	2.121	1.323	5.66	9.07	0.358	0.139	0.219	0.74	18
½	0.840	0.542	0.149	2.639	1.703	4.55	7.05	0.554	0.231	0.323	1.09	14
¾	1.050	0.736	0.157	3.299	2.312	3.64	5.11	0.866	0.425	0.441	1.39	14
1	1.315	0.951	0.182	4.131	2.988	2.90	4.02	1.358	0.710	0.648	2.17	11½
1¼	1.660	1.272	0.194	5.215	3.996	2.30	3.00	2.164	1.271	0.893	3.00	11½
1½	1.900	1.494	0.203	5.969	4.694	2.01	2.56	2.835	1.753	1.082	3.63	11½
2	2.375	1.933	0.221	7.461	6.073	1.61	1.97	4.430	2.935	1.495	5.02	11½
2½	2.875	2.315	0.280	9.032	7.273	1.33	1.65	6.492	4.209	2.283	7.67	8
3	3.500	2.892	0.304	10.996	9.086	1.09	1.33	9.621	6.569	3.052	10.25	8
3½	4.000	3.358	0.321	12.566	10.549	0.955	1.14	12.566	8.856	3.710	12.47	8
4	4.500	3.818	0.341	14.137	11.995	0.849	1.00	15.904	11.449	4.455	14.97	8
4½	5.000	4.280	0.360	15.708	13.446	0.764	0.893	19.635	14.387	5.248	18.22	8
5	5.563	4.813	0.375	17.477	15.120	0.687	0.793	24.306	18.193	6.113	20.54	8
6	6.625	5.751	0.437	20.813	18.067	0.577	0.664	34.472	25.976	8.496	28.58	8
7	7.625	6.625	0.500	23.955	20.813	0.501	0.598	45.664	34.472	11.192	37.67	8
8	8.625	7.625	0.500	27.096	23.955	0.443	0.502	58.426	45.664	12.762	43.00	8
9	9.625	8.625	0.500	30.238	27.096	0.397	0.443	72.760	58.426	14.334	48.25	8
10	10.750	9.750	0.500	33.772	30.631	0.355	0.399	90.763	74.662	16.101	54.25	8
12	12.750	11.750	0.500	40.055	36.914	0.299	0.325	127.68	108.43	19.25	65.00	8

TABLE XXIV.—COMPARATIVE CAPACITIES OF PIPES OF STANDARD SIZES, SHOWING THE NUMBER OF TIMES THE AREA OF ONE PIPE IS CONTAINED IN THAT OF A LARGER SIZE

	⅛	¼	⅜	½	¾	1	1¼	1½	2	2½	3	3½	4	5	6	7	8	9	10
⅛	1																		
¼	1 9	1																	
⅜	3 3	1 8	1																
½	5 3	2 9	1 5	1															
¾	9 3	5 2	2 7	1 7	1														
1	14 7	7 7	4 1	2 6	1 6	1													
1¼	26 2	14 3	7 8	4 9	2 8	1 6	1												
1½	35.6	19 5	10 6	6 6	3 8	2 4	1 3	1											
2	58 6	32 2	17 5	11 0	6 9	3 9	2 2	1 6	1										
2½	83.6	44 6	25 0	15 7	9 0	5 5	3 2	2 3	1 4	1									
3	129 1	71 0	38 5	24 2	13 8	8 5	5 0	3 6	2 2	1 5	1								
3½	172 8	95 0	51 6	32 4	18 5	11 4	6 6	4 8	2 9	2 0	1 3	1							
4	222 5	122 3	66 4	41 7	23 8	14 7	8 5	6 2	3 8	2 6	1 7	1 3	1						
5	349 4	192 0	104 3	65 6	37 4	23 1	13 3	9 8	5 9	4 1	2 7	2 0	1 5	1					
6	505 0	277 5	150 7	94 7	54 1	33 4	19 3	14 1	8 6	6 0	3 9	2 9	2 2	1 4	1				
7	677 2	372 1	202.2	127 0	71 3	44 9	25 9	19 0	11 5	8 1	5 2	3 9	3 0	1 9	1 3	1			
8	878 3	480 7	261 2	164 1	93 8	58 0	34 5	24 5	14 9	10 4	6 7	5 0	3 9	2 5	1 7	1 3	1		
9	1112 4	611 2	332 1	208 7	179 3	73 4	42 7	31 2	19 0	13 3	8 7	6 4	5 0	3 1	2 2	1 6	1 2	1	
10	1378.3	757 3	411 5	258 6	147 8	91 3	52 7	38 6	23 5	16 5	10 6	7 9	6 2	3 9	2 7	2 0	1 5	1 2	1

TABLE XXV.—WROUGHT IRON WELDED STEAM, GAS, AND WATER PIPE
Table of Standard Dimensions

Nom. Inter'l In.	Diameter Actual External Inches	Diameter Actual Internal Inches	Thickness Inches	Circumference External Inches	Circumference Internal Inches	Transverse Areas External Sq. Inch	Transverse Areas Internal Sq. Inch	Transverse Areas Metal Sq. Inch	Length of Pipe per Sq. Foot of External Surface Feet	Length of Pipe per Sq. Foot of Internal Surface Feet	Length of Pipe Cont'g One Cu. Foot	Weight per Ft. of Lgth. Pounds	No. of Threads per Inch of Screw	Contents in Gals. per Foot of Lgth.	Weight of Water per Foot of Lgth. Pounds
⅛	.405	.27	.068	1.272	.848	.129	.0573	.0717	9.44	14.15	2513.	.241	27	.0006	.005
¼	.54	.364	.088	1.696	1 144	.229	.1041	.1249	7.075	10 49	1383.3	.42	18	.0026	021
⅜	.675	494	.091	2.121	1.552	.358	.1917	.1663	5.657	7.73	751 2	.559	18	.0057	047
½	.84	.623	.109	2.639	1.957	.554	.3048	.2492	4.547	6.13	472.4	.837	14	.0102	.085
¾	1.05	.824	.113	3.299	2.589	.866	.5333	.3327	3 637	4 635	270	1 115	14	.0230	.190
1	1.315	1.048	.134	4.131	3.292	1.358	.8626	.4954	2.904	3.645	166.9	1 668	11½	.0408	349
1¼	1.66	1.38	.14	5.215	4.335	2.164	1 496	.668	2.301	2 768	96 25	2 244	11½	.0638	.527
1½	1.9	1.611	.145	5 969	5 061	2.835	2.038	797	2 01	2.371	70.66	2 678	11½	.0918	.760
2	2.375	2.067	.154	7.461	6.494	4.43	3.356	1.074	1.608	1.848	42 91	3 609	11½	1632	1.356
2½	2.875	2.468	.204	9.032	7.753	6.492	4.784	1 708	1 328	1.547	30 1	5 739	8	.2550	2.116
3	3.5	3.067	.217	10 996	9 636	9.621	7 388	2 243	1.091	1 245	19.5	7 536	8	.3673	3 049
3½	4.	3.548	.226	12 566	11 146	12 566	9 887	2.679	.955	1 077	14.57	9 001	8	4998	4 155
4	4.5	4.026	.237	14 137	12 648	15 904	12.73	8 174	.849	949	11 31	10 665	8	6528	5 405
4½	5.	4.508	.246	15.708	14.162	19 635	15 961	3 674	.764	848	9 02	12.34	8	8263	6.851
5	5 563	5.045	.259	17.477	15.849	24 306	19 99	4.316	.687	757	7.2	14.502	8	1 020	8 500
6	6.625	6.065	.28	20.813	19.054	34 472	28.888	5.584	.577	63	4.98	18.762	8	1.469	12.312
7	7.625	7 023	.301	23 955	22.063	45.664	38.738	6.926	.501	.544	3 72	23.271	8	1.999	16.662
8	8.625	7.982	.322	27 096	25.076	58 426	50.04	8.386	.443	.478	2 88	28.177	8	2 611	21.750
9	9.625	8.937	.344	30 238	28.076	72 76	62 73	10 03	397	427	2.29	33 701	8	3 300	27 500
10	10.75	10.019	.366	33.772	31 477	90 763	78.839	11 924	.355	.382	1 82	40.065	8	4 081	34 000
11	12.	11.25	.375	37.699	35 343	113.098	99 402	13.696	318	339	1 456	45 95	8	5 163	43 000
12	12.75	12.	.375	40 055	37 7	127 677	113 098	14 579	299	319	1 27	48.985	8	5.875	48 930

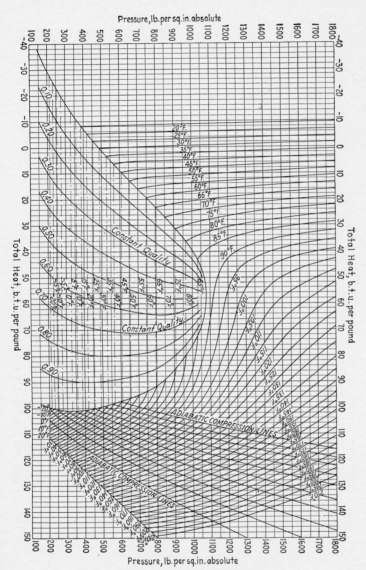

Fig. 186.—Total heat chart of carbon dioxide.

INDEX

A

Absolute pressure, 243, 245
  temperature, 2
Absorber, 20, 21, 32, 158
Absorption system of refrigeration,
  10, 18, 114, 157, 166, 233
  aqua pump for, 21. 27
  charging, 194
  operation of, 189
  vapor pressure of aqua
  ammonia, 233
Accumulator for flooded system, 51,
  59, 62, 64
Adiabatic compression, 113, 218, 245
Aftercooling, 228, 252
Agitators for brine, 303
Air agitation for can ice, 304
  high-pressure, 311
  power for, 307
  refrigeration for, 307
  as refrigerant, 11, 215
  circulation for cold storage, 345
  closed system, 216
  dense, refrigeration, 11, 216
Air-cooled compressor, 130, 134
  condenser, 117, 130, 134
Air cooling and conditioning, 55, 374
  for blast furnaces, 6
  for theaters, 55, 374
  dehumidifying, 55, 307
  in refrigerating system, 198
  piping for ice cans, 305
  psychrometric chart for, 375
  refrigerating machines, 11
  removal in refrigerating systems, 151
  saturated, 345
  spaces in insulation, 340
  system of refrigeration, 10, 216
  washers, 374
Alternating-current motors, 316

Alum pot, 294
Ammonia, 67, 70
  compressors, high-speed, 103, 105,
  107
  medium-speed, 108, 414
  diagram, 72 and Fig. 185
  fundamental constants, 410
  leakage, 181, 183
  physical properties of, 242,
  386–406
  solutions, 233, 240
  density of, 240
  superheated, properties of, 400
  system of refrigeration, 10
  vapor precooler, 50
  weight of in system, 178
  of evaporated, 178, 251
Ammonium bichromate, 161
Analyzer, 26, 28
Anhydrous ammonia, 23, 70
Apartment refrigeration, 114, 166
Aqua ammonia, 10, 18, 67, 233, 237,
  240, Fig. 148
Arctic-Pownall system, 303
Audiffren refrigerating device, 51,
  156
Audiffren-Singrun compressor, 51,
  156
Automatic can dump, 310
  expansion valve, 117, 122, 140
  refrigeration systems, 114, 121,
  135, 157
  temperature control, 116
  valves in cylinder, 104

B

Bacteria, 114
Baudelot chamber, 374
  cooler, 415
Baumé scale, 195
Bellows, sylphon, 119, 124, 140

423

Valves, compressor, 98, 108, 129
  feather, 99, 100
  float, 117, 122, 141, 142
  plate type, 129
  pressure-regulating, 118
  ring-plate, 99, 100
  strip-plate, 99, 100, 108
  suction, 98, 99, 129
Vap-air system of refrigeration, 31
Vapor pressure, 82
  heat of liquid of, 82
  latent heat of, 82
  superheated, 86
Venturi tube, 194
Vertical compressor, 96, 103
Volume delivered, 112
Volumetric efficiency, 110, 221, 223, 278
V-type belt, 131

W

Wall, composite, heat transfer, 334, 336
  construction, 341
Water, analysis of, 293
  box, 44
  coolers, 135

Water, drinking, 135
  cooling systems, 48
  distilled, 296
  filter, 294, 295
  hardness of, 293
  jacket, 104
  shut-off, 129
  softening, 294
  sprays, 49
  temperature, 181
  use of as refrigerant, 166
  vapor refrigerating machine, 4
Weight of ammonia evaporated, 178, 251
  in system, 178
Welsbach automatic refrigerating unit, 145
  compressor, 145
  cooling unit, 145
Wet compression, 86, 95, 228, 253
Wet-and-dry bulb thermometer, 375
Withdrawing charge, 178
Work of compression, 219
Working temperatures in ammonia plants, 213
Workmen, heat from, 339
Wool, mineral, 331